# COTTON
## AND
# COLD BLOOD

JOHN A CLAYTON

£7.99

In the period between the last gasps of a largely agricultural economy and the Victorian technological age one of the major influences upon the working population of Britain was that of migration. It was not uncommon for whole families to move around the country, following their trade in a form of demographic ballet as one district became more affluent at the expense of another.

Sarah Ann Davis was born into a Black Country iron-working family in 1865 and her life reflects that of the later Victorian era where many girls of working age found themselves tied into domestic service - often living and working far away from their family homes and loved ones.

A great number of girls and young women migrated from the heavily industrialised districts of the English Midlands to work as domestic servants within the burgeoning cotton manufacturing towns and villages of Lancashire - such was the fate of young Sarah Ann Davis.

These were the days when a six-chambered revolver could be purchased without question from the local cycle shop for the sum of ten shillings. The Welfare State as we know it was but a distant dream - the quality of life for a young woman in service was dependant on the nature of her employer and could be lonely - and sometimes downright dangerous.

*Cotton and Cold Blood* follows the true story of Sarah Ann whose own life in service played out against the tragedy and humour of life within the East Lancashire village of Barrowford.

Published By
Barrowford Press

First Published 2008
This Imprint 2014

*Cover design; Barrowford Press*

*www.barrowfordpress.co.uk*
*claytonj@talk21.com*

## ISBN 978-0-9553821-4-7

© John A Clayton

Printed in the UK by 4edge Limited

## OTHER TITLES BY THE SAME AUTHOR

**Valley of the Drawn Sword**
*Early History of Burnley, Pendle and West Craven*
ISBN 978-0-9553821-0-9  2006

**The Lancashire Witch Conspiracy**
(1ST and 2nd editions)
*A History of Pendle Forest
and the Lancashire Witch Trials*
ISBN 978-0-9553821-2-3  2007

**Rolling Out the Days** (editor)
*From a Barrowford childhood to wartime Burma*
ISBN 978-0-9553821-3-0  2007

**Admergill with Blacko and Brogden**
*History and Archaeology of an Ancient Pennine Estate*
ISBN 978-0-9553821-6-1  2009

*Barrowford Press Pocket History Series:*
**Lower and Central Barrowford**
ISBN 978-1499670806    2009
**Higher Barrowford**
ISBN 978-0-9553821-8-5   2010
**Blacko**
ISBN 978-0-9570043-0-6   2011

**The Pendle Witch Fourth Centenary Handbook**
*History and Archaeology of a 1612 Social Landscape*
ISBN 978-0-9553821-9-2   2012

**The Boy Witchfinder of Pendle Forest:**
**The Other Pendle Witches (1634)**
ISBN 978-0-9570043-2-0    2012

**The Annals and Stories of Barrowford**
*(Republication of Blakey, J. 1929)*
ISBN 978-0-9570043-1-3    2013

**Burnley and Pendle Archaeology - Part One**
*Ice Age to the Early Bronze Age*
ISBN 978-0-9570043-3-7    2014

**Burnley and Pendle Archaeology - Part Two**
*Middle Bronze Age to Iron Age*
ISBN 978-0-9570043-4-4    2014

# COTTON
### AND
# COLD BLOOD

# Contents

# Prologue

All roads from the village of Barrowford led to the Wheatley Lane chapel on that cold morning in March 1897. Even the fields had been full of people as they picked their way across the narrow, muddy footpaths. Now, at last, almost everyone had arrived and the graveyard was teeming with men and women from the village. The fact that they were dressed in their Sunday best on a Saturday morning showed the importance that they attached to the unfolding ceremony.

The better-off from the local towns and hamlets had arrived in their carriages, traps and gigs and these lined the chapel lane. There had been no tramping through the mud for these people but, nevertheless, they were as subdued as the shuffling, slightly uncomfortable crowd.

Silence descended on the already hushed onlookers as the solitary chapel bell began its mournful toll; a crescendo of hooves clattered ever nearer until the gleaming coachwork of the closed hearse appeared. Turning from the lane into the chapel yard the two shining ebony stallions kicked up small clouds of gritty dust as the carriage wheels crunched across the gravel, finally halting in front of the small, neat chapel building.

The undertaker in charge of the day's grim proceedings climbed down from his position alongside the driver and made his way to the head of the carriage. As he did so the nearside horse jinked sharply, setting his coal-black ostrich-feather plume swaying. The undertaker was quick to pat the stallion's shoulder reassuringly as the driver joined him and took charge of the reins.

Four men gathered solemnly at the rear of the gleaming black carriage. They had all been friends and neighbours of the deceased and were only too willing to carry out this final act of respect for her. They expertly hoisted the polished mahogany casket onto their shoulders and, perfectly in step with the

11

resonant hammer of the tolling bell, slowly processed into the chapel for the first of the funeral obsequies.

Three more carriages entered the yard but these mourning coaches carried no blood relatives of the deceased young woman. The seats that should have been occupied by her husband and family were conspicuously empty as was that of her closest friend who lay, instead, in a hospital bed.

The chapel quickly filled to the point where the century-old walls were almost buckling. At exactly eleven o'clock Mr Henry Holt entered the pulpit and the chapel fell silent. Many tears were shed within that congregation and, as the casket was borne solemnly to the waiting grave, the crowd respectfully parted to allow the chief mourners through.

Thankfully, the grave plots of Section *E* were within a short distance of the chapel and here, beneath the thorn hedge that separated the graveyard from an open windswept meadow, the procession halted.

The mourners gathered around the graveside as Henry Holt looked around; as he took in the familiar scenery he thought to himself that this must be one of the finest views from any chapel in the whole of East Lancashire. To the south, east and west grassy meadows reached across the face of the landscape, connecting all things therein. Half-a-mile below, the River Calder swept quietly through its shallow valley determined to keep an age-old appointment with the River Ribble.

Wherever the observer stood in this land the rounded, almost sensuous green hills formed themselves into protective ranks as if some unspoken understanding existed between man and landscape. In the far distance the horizon was dominated by a ridge of higher, darker and more dominant hills. Looking westward, across the intermittent groups of towering cotton mill chimneys, the moorland heights above Blackburn could be made out.

Much closer were the Hameldon Hills, rising imperiously above the town of Burnley, and far across the valley stood the massive bulk of Boulsworth Hill. Below this the experienced eye could make out the Iron Age mounds of the Castercliffe hillfort, standing, as it had always done, silent sentinel over the small town of Nelson. To the east, the tower of Saint Bartholomew's parish church rose proudly above the town of Colne and beyond rose the green hills of Yorkshire.

And always, wherever the eye might rest, there were the settled outlines of a thousand farmsteads; some reflected the weary sun from the distant heights but most were pinned to the lower verdant slopes where the undulating horizon swept down to slake its thirst in the valleys. Here, on the southern edge of the ancient Forest of Pendle, was beauty enough for anyone with the eyes to see.

As Henry Holt opened his Book of Methodist Service a repectful stillness moved among the mourners, disturbed only by the daytime song of a blackbird as she struggled to compete with the rising swell of a hoarse breeze high in the beech trees.

"And so we commit the body of Sarah Ann Nowell to the ground. . ."

The four bearers respectfully lowered the gleaming casket and each one of the silent graveside assembly cast a handful of earth into the void. A girl of around fourteen stepped forward. From her pocket she carefully took a large brooch, expertly carved from the finest Whitby jet into the shape of a rose, and dropped it onto the casket. The object settled into the sandy soil and as it did so a struggling shaft of late winter sunlight glinted across its midnight-black face. Those at the graveside exchanged knowing glances and an unspoken finality of proceedings saw the gathering make their way, heads bowed, to their waiting carriages.

A stranger quietly mingled with the other bystanders but now that the official mourning party had made their sorrowful exit he stepped up to the grave. Dressed in a new suit, new shoes and a bowler hat, the man had the appearance of a clerk but his large, calloused hands, and the blue-black scar above his right eye betrayed him. The new clothes covered a slim, yet powerful frame and his ruggedly handsome face was set firm.

Clutching the bowler hat to his chest there was but a single clue to the grief of this man; his coral-green eyes swam with the tears that he could not hold back.

As his gaze settled on the carved jet rose he saw how vividly the midnight shade contrasted with the sandy soil and his hands began to shake almost imperceptibly. Unable to take his eyes from the rose he stood motionless as if he himself had been cast from the same brittle jet. Finally he took out a piece of paper from his breast pocket and held it for a few moments before releasing it. Every fibre of his being longed to cry out, to shout, to curse a world that had brought him to this; but he held his composure as he watched the white paper flutter slowly down to settle at the head of the casket. Turning swiftly on his heels the stranger replaced his hat and walked determinedly towards the lane.

A single group of people remained in the graveyard as the church and chapel bells of Pendle Forest joined in their clamorous strike of midday. The sexton and his labourer busily refilled the void that they had painstakingly created on the previous day while whispered conversations echoed between the lettered, upright stones. The words 'tragic' and 'terrible' played on the lips of those who still could not quite take in the events of the past week - events that had shaken the village community to its core . . .

# 1

# Setting Out

The long summer of 1883 was turning to autumn and the smoky damp morning held a chill. The young woman closed the heavy wooden door behind her and shivered slightly as she stepped onto the pavement. Buttoning up her proudest possession, the heavy tweed overcoat that had taken many long months to save for, Sarah Ann Davis picked up the small cloth bag that easily held her worldly goods and looked back at the Royal Oak Inn. With a lump in her throat Sarah returned the waves from the group who were gathered at the main window; they had already said their final farewells so the traveller composed herself and took the first step of a long journey.

Sarah had woken up especially early that morning; after all, she had been waiting for this day for many weeks and did not want to miss the 07.45 train that was to carry her into an uncertain future. Enquiries of the previous week had shown that she could catch any one of the six trains running this line every day but a connecting service northwards from Birmingham meant that the 07.45 would be the most convenient. The clock on the High Street tower was showing 06.50, no problem here as Sarah had allowed a good fifteen minutes for the walk.

Long before she turned the corner from High Street the sounds and smells of the railway echoed between the blackened stone and brick buildings. The hissing, clanking and hooting of steam engines filled the sulphur-laden air as they went about their daily business. Sarah's pace quickened slightly when she saw the large sign proudly proclaiming; *The Harborne Railway Company: Harborne Station.*

Along the road a number of heavy cart horses strained at their harness, jets of vapour escaping their nostrils as they struggled with their heavy loads. Some of these carts carried the railway company name but most were owned by private carriers. Sarah loved these old workhorses, she saw a dignity in the way that they went about their daily struggle, never complaining, always willing. She often took a carrot to treat any horse that might be standing at the roadside, perhaps delivering to a shop or waiting for its master to emerge from one of the many roadside inns.

These gentle giants, however, were not always predictable as Sarah had learned one October day; she had been feeding one of William Price's delivery horses when it whipped round and grabbed the bonnet from her head. The chin-strap snapped but not before leaving an angry red whorl around her neck; this had shaken her and, hoping that nobody had noticed, she quietly left the old horse chomping on her headwear.

That morning, however, Sarah had too much on her mind to be concerned about the horses as she dodged the traffic on Station Road. A glance at the large platform clock told her that she had a full fifteen minutes before the departure of her train. Having paid a few coppers for the ticket that would take her on the first leg of her journey she stood on the platform and immediately an industrial symphony assaulted her senses. Coal wagons squealed into the goods sidings to unload their precious cargo while heavy iron castings and wrought iron bars were loaded for the sixteen-minute journey up to Birmingham and onwards to the four corners of the world. Choking smoke and steam from the labouring engines mingled with the damp air and engulfed everyone on the platform.

Sarah covered her mouth with the handkerchief that she always kept tucked in her sleeve and decided that she needed shelter from the stinging, swirling smoke. As she closed the door of the ladies waiting room behind her she was thankful that the station noise fell to a muffled background rumble. A roaring coal fire was, if anything, overheating the small room as Sarah sat on the long, polished wooden seat beneath the waiting room window. She was careful to take a position as far away from the blaze as possible.

Within a few minutes three other young women had entered the stuffy room. Two of the new arrivals were obviously of the same social standing as Sarah; in fact the casual observer would have difficulty in finding any real difference in their style of dress. The third young woman was of a higher status within society; it soon became apparent that she taught music privately and was going into Birmingham to pick up the new violin that she had ordered almost two months previously. Although the teacher had no reservations about speaking to the others she noted their appearance; stout leather shoes, woollen stockings, black linen dresses with starched white collars and lace edging, 'sensible' swept-back hair topped with plain bonnets. This mode of dress clearly marked them out as being working girls - more specifically they were of the servant class.

At precisely 07.35 the portly figure of the platform guard appeared at the waiting room door and announced that the 07.45 to Birmingham New Street Station was now ready to board. Stepping out onto the platform Sarah and her fellow passengers again felt the airborne assault upon their senses; they stood for a moment and, peering through the smoke, watched as the engine that would haul their carriages steamed gently onto a massive turntable at the side of the goods yard. With a grace befitting a squealing mechanical ballerina the engine swivelled through ninety degrees and was ready to be manoeuvred into position at the head of the two passenger carriages waiting at the platform.

The guard opened the door of the rear carriage and, as the three women stepped in, they noticed that the music teacher had made her way to the front carriage. They did not bother to stow their small travelling bags in the overhead netting as their journey to New Street would not take long. They sat uncomfortably on the hard carriage seats and felt the momentary jolt as the engine was reversed into its coupling on the lead carriage.

Walking past the carriage window the guard checked that the doors were securely closed and, satisfied that all was well, ceremoniously raised his flag. After a final glance along the platform the guard's whistle sounded and immediately the engine began to spit laboured clouds of soot and steam. Slowly but surely the train pulled away from the platform allowing the passengers to look down into the passing streets of Harborne. Sarah felt a strange mixture of apprehension and excitement as she left the area that had been home for all of her eighteen years. Although she did not realise, and perhaps it was just as well, Sarah was destined never to see her native Black Country again.

The train had now settled into a steady swaying rhythm as it left Harborne and passed over the railway bridge at Park Hill Road. This stretch of line, from Harborne to the main line, had only been operational for nine years and Sarah clearly recalled the brass bands and the pompous dignitaries who attended the grand opening of the Harborne Branch Station.

The 07.45 steamed across the high embankment of the Chad Valley and Sarah soon found that both her companions were in much the same position as herself. The two young ladies were undergoing enforced changes within their lives as they set out on their individual adventures. One had worked as a domestic help for a doctor and his family but the doctor had been offered a partnership in America, leaving her without home and work. Fortunately she had an aunt in London who had been able to secure her a position there with a chemist and his family.

The other young woman told of her move to Harborne, from Leeds, only a few months ago; she had been offered a five-year contract with the family of a local iron foundry owner. However, she soon found that all was not well; the head of the household was constantly at loggerheads with his wife and he soon turned to his domestic help for 'understanding' or, as she quaintly put it, 'he had more hands than a deck of cards.' She quickly arranged to return home to her widowed mother but her employer threatened to take action for breach of contract. Being of stout Yorkshire stock she was not easily intimidated and told him to go ahead and 'let's see what the court will make of your private life.' Needless to say she was released from her contract but there had been no fond farewells as she left for home that morning.

Sarah found comfort in the fact that she was not alone in seeking work far away from home. When she told the others that she was *en route* to a new job as a domestic servant they asked where this was to be;

"A Lancashire village called Barrowford."

The blank looks of her companions told her that they had no idea where in the world this was. The Yorkshire lass said that she had once, as a child, been taken into Lancashire (somewhere near Manchester she thought) to visit a distant relative of her mother. Other than that she said that Yorkshire folk did not have much to do with the neighbouring county unless it was really necessary!

# 2

# Irontown

It was not long before the 07.45 had almost reached the end of the Harborne branch line. In fact the steam from the departing engine had hardly cleared from beneath the previous station canopy before the train carrying Sarah and her two companions crossed the Birmingham and Wolverhampton Canal. Leaving the junction with the main London and North West Railway line the train headed northwards with little over a mile remaining of the journey to Birmingham New Street. This left just enough time for Sarah and her companions to wind up their conversation, gather up their few belongings and wish each other luck for the future.

The small Harborne train slowed on its approach into the station and, as it finally squealed to a halt, the guard quickly moved along the train turning the stout brass handles to open the carriage doors. The three young women stepped out onto the stone-flagged platform and, with a final wave, set off to find their respective trains for their onward journey.

Sarah was momentarily overcome by the echoing clamour within the glass-roofed industrial cathedral that was New Street Station. People of every description hurried and bustled along the platforms, hither and thither with no apparent pattern to their movements. Family groups hugged as one or other of them took their leave to goodness knows where; individuals lugged their baggage with faces set, lost in their own thoughts. A cacophony of iron squealing upon iron, hissing steam and slamming carriage doors formed a solid background to the megaphonic voices stridently announcing the destination of this or that train. The frantic whistles of the guards accompanied the rattling of the parcel trolleys as their iron wheels bounced and grated along the sandstone paving.

Even though Sarah had been here before she had never had need to change trains and she began to look around for help. She knew that her onward journey would be from one of the northbound platforms, but which one? With a certain apprehension she quickly walked along to the end of the central passenger building and entered the booking hall. The clerk behind the glass screen was helpful, if somewhat sullen, and Sarah was soon leaving the building clutching a second-class ticket for the 08.40 train to Crewe.

"Excuse me, I'm looking for this platform," Sarah showed her ticket to a young man of about her own age whose uniform suggested that he was junior platform staff.

"Right Miss, this way." He picked up Sarah's small bag,

"This the only baggage you have Miss?"

Having been assured that it was, Sarah's guide realised that he did not need a trolley and immediately set off walking; his rapid pace meant that Sarah had to hurry in order to keep up. Across the platform and over the iron walkway they went, the guide expertly dodging the melee of humanity as it criss-crossed in all directions at once. Onto the next platform and over another walkway; Sarah was not used to being amongst crowds of people and her head was spinning. Finally the young man pointed at a train whose engine was gently simmering at the head of a long line of carriages.

"There we go Madam, 08.40 to Crewe."

He looked up at the massive station clock and told Sarah that she could board now if she liked although departure would not be for another twenty minutes. On the other hand he suggested that she might like a cup of tea in the station refreshment room and pointed to the large glass-fronted building beneath the clock.

Sarah thanked him, slid the strap of her handbag from her arm and began to search for her purse. She had seen her dad give a few coppers to people in these situations and it seemed to be the correct thing to do now. The young man waved a dismissive hand,

"S'alright Madam, glad to help a lady. Have a good journey," with this he turned and was immediately swallowed up by the crowd.

Sarah found a seat in the crowded refreshment hall and gulped down a pot of tea before making her way to the waiting train. The first thing to strike her as she looked up and down, deciding which carriage to board, was the size of the train compared to the one that had brought her from Harborne. The engine was twice as big as those used on the branch line and the carriages filled the platform from one end to the other.

Having decided upon the third carriage from the rear, Sarah put her travel bag on the overhead shelf and carefully unpinned the carved jet brooch from her overcoat. She always did this as the brooch was far too precious to her to risk it being damaged; folding the coat and placing it on her lap she made herself as comfortable as possible on the hard seat. Within minutes the carriage had filled and the co-passengers smiled and nodded at each other as they went through the same motions of settling in for the journey north. Two guards walked the line of carriages and, as soon as the slamming of doors had ceased, Sarah heard the final announcement;

"Stoke-on-Trent for Crewe and the Western Line."

Within minutes the train was labouring out of the shelter of the station and accelerating past a wide expanse of shining rails on which trundled passenger and goods traffic alike. Soon the monotonous rat-a-ta-tat of the carriage wheels passing over the rail joints was lulling the passengers into a soporific silence. The carriage was too full for a relaxed conversation so the occupants watched sleepily as the buildings of north Birmingham slipped by and gave way to an expanse of open countryside.

The forty or so miles to the first major station of Stoke-on-Trent were interspersed with the industrial faces of Walsall, Cannock and Stafford but Sarah did not really notice the fleeting scenery. The early morning start, and the pent-up anxiety of her journey was beginning to tell on the traveller and she began to doze.

Unable to sleep because of her awareness of the others in the carriage Sarah found herself in that limbo between wakefulness and slumber where the mind leaps from one image to another without obvious reason. She found herself thinking of the life she was leaving behind and the reasons for her journey.

As her head lolled against the back of her seat Sarah recalled with a twinge of sadness how three years earlier her younger sister, Fran, had taken exactly the same journey as she herself was now taking. Fran had been thirteen years of age when she ventured north and it had almost broken Sarah's heart to see her younger sister board the train, clutching her little hold-all and looking so lost. They both realised that Fran's new job would mean security for the future but this did not make their parting any the easier.

Sarah had tried to reassure Fran with a cheerfulness that she herself did not feel,

"Don't worry Fran, perhaps in a year or two I'll have found a rich husband and I'll send for you to live with us in our new villa up Lordswood Road!"

Even though Fran was almost two years younger than Sarah she was now decidedly taller. At five foot three Sarah had never felt particularly short as most of the women she knew were around this height. Fran, however, was different; their father always said that she was a 'throwback' to their Welsh ancestry and teased her constantly about her flowing locks of fiery red hair. Fran never liked this, she was teased enough at school without the family joining in.

Now, as Fran was about to take her leave, Sarah was aware of something in her sister that she had not noticed before. She recalled the words of Aunt Mary as she brought the brown paper parcel to their house yesterday;

"We dunna want to make the Lancashire folk think we're poor down here now, do we?"

In the new dress that Aunt Mary had made, and her hair swept back into a bun beneath her best bonnet, Fran looked nothing less than elegant. Her pale, pretty features were set off by the dark linen dress and Sarah, fighting back the tears, could not help but think how proud of Fran their mother would have been.

With a half-smile Fran hugged Sarah and quickly stepped into the waiting carriage; within a couple of minutes the guard signalled to the engine driver and the train pulled away. Sarah stood motionless, watching long after the grey trail of smoke from the engine had melted into the air; at that point she wondered if she would ever see her sister and best friend again.

Things in South Staffordshire had been quiet over the Easter of 1880 but this was nothing out of the ordinary. Sarah and Fran lived with their father, John, on a Wednesbury street known as The Lyndon and it was always quiet here on the outskirts of town.

On the evening of Good Friday the gas lights were burning and John sat quietly catching up on his Thursday newspaper as the two girls finished the last of the day's housework.

"Now," John lowered his paper,

"This is interesting our Fran, there's an advert here that might suit."

He read on,

"Wanted: live-in young woman or girl to act as domestic help to chapel-going family. Apply in first inst. to Mr A Duckett, 28 Accrington Road, Burnley, Lancashire."

Fran put down the plate she was wiping with the tea cloth and turned to face her father. She knew that this was a serious matter as the family had been searching for a position for her for months with little success. Fran's age of thirteen was proving to be against her when it came to finding employment, few people were willing to take on a girl of such little experience and her previous applications had come to nothing.

Money was tight on The Lyndon in early 1880. John Davis had been ill for eighteen months and did not appear to be improving. Sarah looked after her father and ran the household; she also earned a few vital shillings by running work for her Aunt Mary. As a home-based dressmaker Mary found Sarah to be invaluable in collecting work from her customers around the Wednesbury district of West Bromwich. Sarah also returned the finished work and collected the payment, when things were a little quiet she even knocked on doors to advertise her aunt's services.

Fran also earned a little money by helping out their local grocer. First thing in the morning she would unload the delivery cart, trim cauliflowers, boil beetroot, set out the pavement display and generally clean for a few hours per week. She had done this as a 'part-time' scholar during the previous year but now she was looking for full-time employment. The meagre wages earned by the girls were all well and good but they did not compensate for the loss of their father's skilled income. The family had enough money to survive when John's parish money was added to the girl's contributions but living was hard. It had been decided that the best thing all round would be for young Fran to take up a live-in job if they could find one, this would mean one less mouth to feed and she could send part of her wages home. Sarah would stay and look after John and do the best she could.

John had never wanted his girls to go into factory work; he knew how hard was the day-to-day grind of the bench girls who turned out thousands of small metal items every day. The work was arduous, monotonous, dirty and low-paid and there were few prospects for the factory girls.

This was a reflection of the times in the Black Country. In the first half of the nineteenth century the area had seen a rapid expansion of industry on the back of unlimited coal and iron-stone production. Over one-third of the population worked within the coal and iron industries and employment was readily available.

25

However, the Black Country was no different to other districts of Britain where particular types of industry were subject to outside forces. The turning point for much of South Staffordshire came in 1876 when the dwindling coal and iron-stone reserves of the 'ten-yard seam' finally began to give out. The following decade saw an exhaustion of the life-blood of the district and many mines were neglected leading to flooding and subsequent abandonment. On top of this major blow another problem had become all too apparent. Advances in the production of steel meant that the material had become a serious rival and the world-wide engineering industry now began to favour it over wrought iron.

The traditional Black Country industries dwindled and this proved to be an advantage to the town of Birmingham. Skilled iron workers flooded into the expanding metropolis where they turned out almost every type of metal product imaginable.

This, then, was the situation of the Davis family; there was little work locally, the only real prospect for Fran would be for her to travel to a Birmingham factory. In Lancashire things were different; the cotton industry was again booming following a period of gloom and workers of every kind were welcomed into the villages, towns and cities of the county. Iron workers were in demand to run the foundries that were building steam engines and loom parts for the cotton mills while miners found ready work in the new coal pits. The workers from Staffordshire and Birmingham were recognised as being industrious and an asset to the workforce. This led to prospective Lancashire employers advertising for workers in the Staffordshire newspapers as, indeed, had Mr A Duckett.

Fran looked puzzled,

"Where the heck's Burnley?"

John thought for a minute, he knew of the Burnley and Wigan coalfields and he also knew that his sister-in-law bought bolts of 'Burnley Fancy' cloth. He also knew that some of the canal barge lads who worked for Clayton and Company carried goods up into Yorkshire and then across to East Lancashire.

"Well lass, it wunna be more than a couple of hundred miles up north."

"What, like Scotland?"

Fran was clearly unhappy with the prospect of moving to the far ends of the earth, living amongst strangers away from her father and sister. John could say little to allay the girl's fears but nevertheless he decided to reply to Mr Duckett's advertisement. His main consideration here was the fact that the Burnley family were 'chapel-goers' and this gave a clue to their religious preferences. They would be Methodist in all probability, as were the Davis family.

After chapel on the following Sunday Sarah drew Reverend Tillotson to one side and told him about the situation. The Reverend thought for a moment and recalled that he had heard the local manufacturers speak of the high volume of trade in the water and gas pipe sector of their industry and Lancashire was at the forefront of this demand. He was aware that certain parts of Lancashire were undergoing rapid growth and work was plentiful for those willing to seek it out.

With the Reverend promising to look into the matter the pair took their leave. Arriving home Sarah told John of the Reverend's comments, and his promise to help if he could. John put a few precious strands of his favourite Balkan Sobranie tobacco into his old pipe (he had allowed the carbon to build up on the inside of the bowl to such an extent that it hardly held any tobacco at all). This pleased Sarah because she had never liked the smell of her dad's pipe, she likened it to the pungent whiff of the glue factory down the road. John took great exception to this as he considered that his tobacco had the aroma of fresh rain falling upon pine forests. Lighting up, he peered at Sarah through a thin column of blue smoke.

"Hope he doesn't take long, otherwise the job'll have gone."

There was no need to worry; on the following morning Reverend Tillotson called at the house and, over a cup of tea, told John that he had been speaking to a chap who had worked for a number of years as a bricklayer in the small Lancashire town of Blackburn. The builder told the Reverend that there were hundreds of Staffordshire workers around Blackburn; there was great demand up there for the skills of Black Country iron workers, miners and builders as the place was booming.

His building work had taken him to Burnley on a number of occasions and he knew the area quite well. Burnley was a small but rapidly expanding town; the cotton industry there ruled everything and everyone; there were cotton mills 'on every street corner' the same as there were pits and ironworks on every corner of West Bromwich. Despite the industrial spread, however, the district of East Lancashire was attractive; there was a great deal of open green countryside around the towns and the air was somewhat cleaner than the Black Country. The people were a mixture of all the British countries and counties and the builder had always found them to be fair,

"Lancashire folk are a bit rough but if you find your way into their hearts they'll keep you there," was how he put it.

Methodism had a strong foothold in the mill towns of Lancashire and, as far as possible, those with money liked to employ people of their own persuasion. This would be why the Duckett family said that they were 'chapel,' they would want a girl of the same religious background to look after their children.

In all probability young Fran would be treated well in such a family. Reverend Tillotson also pointed out that there would be no tying contract due to Fran's young age and, after all, she could come home if things didn't work out. This all sounded reasonable to John and he asked the Reverend if he would be good enough to supply a reference for Fran.

"I'll do better than that, John."

He was only too pleased to help such a respected and stalwart member of his church.

"I'll draft a letter this evening and we can get it off in the morning."

John thanked the Reverend and, after showing him out, waited for Fran to return from her work at the grocery shop to update her on the situation.

The letter was duly despatched and the family went about their normal business. In the middle of the following week John answered a knock on the door. Reverend Tillotson stood on the step and, with a smile and a wink he waved the letter of reply in front of John's face.

"There John, just shows you what the power of the church can do!"

The pair sat themselves down and the letter bearer read the contents out loud; the essence of the reply was that Mr Duckett would be pleased to offer the position to Miss Fanny Davis, on a trial basis of three months, and could she start on the Monday two weeks from now? John always smiled when he saw Fran's 'Sunday' name of Fanny; it reminded him of Sarah's attempts to pronounce the name of her new little sister when she was no more than eighteen months old. 'Franty' was the best she could do and the name stuck, Fanny became Fran thereafter.

That, then, was that; Fran's future now lay in a faraway place. However, the Reverend and her father seemed assured that she would be safe in Burnley, after all, the new people up there were Methodists like herself.

All too quickly the days flew by and, before she had truly come to terms with the move, Fran found herself hugging Sarah goodbye. The Harborne Station platform slipped away and she caught a final glimpse of the tears rolling down her big sister's cheeks - and then she was gone. As the train passed over the Park Hill Road Fran could contain her feelings no longer and a flood of pent-up emotion creased her delicate features.

She had wanted to show her big sister that she was grown-up enough now to take her place in the world but this was far from the truth. Luckily she was alone in the carriage and she felt no shame in sobbing her young heart out. The past few years had not been easy for the family but at least they had been together - now that she was leaving she knew that even that was being taken away.

Fran saw that her falling tears were staining the new dress and she suddenly sat bolt upright. She had never been one to allow feelings of hopelessness to overtake her and she was not about to start now.

"Right," she told herself firmly, "This is how it is and I can't change it. I'm going to be good at my new job, I'll show 'em what us West Brom girls can do!"

# 3

# The Royal Oak

Sarah could not say that she had been truly happy at her work in Harborne. Life as a live-in domestic help at the Royal Oak was monotonous but on the other hand she did feel reasonably secure and that was important. The family had made her welcome when she arrived on a cold, rainy morning in October 1880. Joseph Johnson was the landlord of the public house; he was a big man but his intimidating bulk was offset by a playful twinkle in his eyes as he ushered the dripping new arrival into the kitchen.

Sarah immediately felt the spreading warmth from the cast iron range as it roared contentedly on the far side of the large room. The high ceiling of the kitchen, and the stone-flagged floor, gave an echo to the room as Joseph invited Sarah to sit at the heavy, bleached-pine table where his wife, Margaret, was already seated. Margaret, or Mrs Johnson as she was to be addressed, noticed Sarah's wet coat and bonnet and these were quickly draped over the wooden ceiling rack to dry.

The newcomer looked around the hub of her new workplace, the long tables around three of the walls held all the tools required in a busy hostelry. Pots and pans were neatly stacked on the tops while bowls of dough and other foodstuffs were hidden on the lower shelves behind netting that slid along lengths of wire. A large pantry held the cleaning materials that Sarah would need, along with a meat safe for the daily intake of fresh pork and cheap cuts of beef.

The kitchen window allowed a view of the bustling street and beneath it sat a massive slop-stone sink, carved from a single slab of sandstone. It was here that Sarah would come to pass many hours over the next three years washing the domestic dishes along with the glasses and bottles from the public bars.

Sarah had been alerted to the fact that the Johnson's would need a domestic help by her father's cousin, James Davis, who lived next door to the Royal Oak. He had called into the pub on his way home from work, as he did on most weekday evenings, and ordered his usual 'gill of Mitchell's best chucking-ale.' The barmaid hadn't found this funny the first time she heard it and it was certainly no funnier now. As she served him with his second gill she happened to mention that the Johnson's domestic help was leaving in two weeks to return home to her family as her mother had been taken ill. James immediately thought of his cousin's daughter as he knew that she was desperate to find work. He had a word with the landlady and it was arranged for Sarah to come along for an interview.

Something about the upright way in which Sarah held herself impressed Mrs Johnson. The girl's plain, honest face often broke into a wide, if slightly self-conscious smile and the respectful manner in which she addressed her seniors did not go unnoticed. Sarah was hired and arrangements were made for her to move from her home in Wednesbury to the Royal Oak in three weeks time.

And here she was; having yet to turn sixteen, and on her first day in service, the new recruit sat at the kitchen table sipping the hot sweet tea that had appeared as if from nowhere.

As Mrs Johnson rose from the table to refresh the huge teapot she ran a hand over her bulging stomach and let out a groan. Sarah's new mistress was heavily pregnant, the baby being due around Christmas time. It appeared to Sarah that in the three weeks since she had last seen Mrs Johnson she had almost doubled in size and she wondered how anyone could function with such a pronounced load.

As Sarah's coat and bonnet began to gently steam another figure bustled into the room clutching a cleaning cloth and a slightly bent bottle-brush. This was Joseph Johnson's sister, Ann, who, at twenty-five, was almost ten years senior to Sarah.

In all honesty the tousled jet-black hair, pretty but lived-in face, and slightly overweight figure gave the impression that Ann could have been five years older.

In the spring of 1875, less than a year after her brother Joseph had moved his family into the Royal Oak, he had offered Ann the job of live-in barmaid and she had no hesitation in taking him up on the offer. She liked her new home in Harborne, a town that was actually little more than a village. The district appeared somewhat genteel after the smoke and grime of the iron foundries and collieries surrounding her native town of Bilston.

Harborne formed the quiet end of a chain of settlements stretching eastwards between the large conurbations of Wolverhampton and Birmingham. Heading from Bilston at two mile intervals were the districts of Wednesbury, West Bromwich, Smethwick, North Harborne and then Harborne town. After this the eastward road took the traveller into Edgbaston and the town of Birmingham proper.

On seeing Sarah for the first time Ann noticed that the new arrival appeared to be slightly ill at ease, nervous in fact. Ann made an attempt to make the girl feel welcome,

"Ah, the new lass! We'll soon have you running round here as if you owned the place."

Far from placating Sarah the brash manner in which Ann had delivered this statement made her even more uneasy, she had not been used to such outward self-confidence from a young woman and she wondered if they were going to get along. As it would turn out Sarah need not have worried; she quickly realised that beneath the brusque exterior Ann had a heart of gold. Indeed, the two were to become firm friends as the elder took the younger under her protective wing; over the following three years Ann would take on the role of surrogate big sister to the somewhat naive girl.

Seeing that Sarah had drained her mug of tea down to the leaves Mrs Johnson said that, as it was her first day, she would show her around the place and run through the daily list of chores that the domestic help was expected to carry out. The

33

work was not over-demanding; Sarah would rise at 06.30 and set the fires in the family living quarters and, this done, the range was to be stoked up from its slumber and the water boiler to the side of the main oven checked. The water from this was never to be used for tea making as it usually had a rust-tinged quality. This water was for filling the tin trough used by the family for their occasional baths; the kettle and pans standing on the hob were for tea-making and cooking.

Next on the list was Emily, the Johnson's eleven year old daughter. As Mrs Johnson slowly gathered herself for the day ahead, and her husband busied himself in the pub cellar, Sarah was to see that young Emily was up, washed and had her breakfast before being despatched to school on time.

The family breakfast being finished there was washing-up to contend with before bed-making and general cleaning duties both in the house and the public bar areas. On Fridays the kitchen range, along with all the other fire surrounds in the house, had to be black-leaded. This was a job that Sarah had hated doing at home, the oily blacking paste seemed to get everywhere and was the devil to remove from aprons and sleeves. She noticed the six-penny tins of *Zebo Blacking* in the kitchen pantry and this, at least, was something. She never bought the other major brand, *Zebra Paste Grate Polish;* this was manufactured by Reckitt and Sons in one and two-penny tins but she had found it to be too liquid or 'runny.'

There were gas lighting mantles to be replaced on a regular basis but this was no problem as Sarah's father had taught her how to do this task years ago. The trick, she had learned, was not to touch the fine mantle gauze as the concentration of grease from fingers caused the lit gauze to flare and burn out almost immediately. Another reason for the early demise of a new mantle was a delay in lighting it when the gas had been turned on. Some gas lights had fancy glass globes with a permanent pilot light where the pull of a chain automatically lit the mantle. The wall lamps in Royal Oak public bars had this arrangement but the lights in the house were operated by means of a gas tap. Once the tap was turned on the flame from a wax taper was applied to the mantle but if this was not done quickly the resulting 'pop' of igniting gas blew a hole in the gauze and raised many derisive comments from the rest of the household.

Sarah was to be on duty from rising until her daily work was done, or Emily was put to bed, whichever happened to be the last in the evening. She then had time to sit in the kitchen and darn or sew any clothes that were found to be in need of repair. There were always shoes to be polished in the evening and her own washing was done before retiring for the night, usually at around 9.30pm. Sarah was not expected to have any connection with the public house side of the property other than the daily chore of helping Ann to dust and polish the saloon and the tap room.

This was one of the few daily tasks that Sarah actually enjoyed and Ann was only too pleased to let her take charge of polishing the bars. The saloon bar was a grand affair constructed of beautiful rich Cuban mahogany whose surface gratefully soaked in each application of *Silas Hardacre's Patent Beeswax Preparation*. Sarah would spare no effort in buffing up the polished wood and was always rewarded by the rich blood-red depths from which her reflection shone. Having polished the bar to her satisfaction she would watch as the incoming shafts of daylight caught the newly bright wood and marvel at how different it looked each time.

Occasionally a clumsy customer would leave a new bruise or chip in the mahogany and when Sarah saw this on her morning rounds she took it as a personal affront. This became a standing joke among the family; Ann, of course, thought that Sarah was 'potty' for caring so much about such a trivial matter. Having said that, when Ann had finished polishing the large brass hand-pump handles mounted on 'Sarah's' bar, and buffed the ceiling-high mirrors that formed the backdrop of this drinking theatre, she grudgingly admitted that the renewed glow created by their efforts had been worthwhile.

During opening hours the pub was strictly the domain of the adults within the household. Although the Royal Oak was not considered to be a 'rough' establishment there were times, nevertheless, when Mr Johnson had need to exercise his large bulk in ejecting some rowdy collier or foundry man who had 'taken one over the odds.' Fortunately these occasions were now much less frequent than when the Johnsons had first arrived at the Royal Oak.

Joseph had taken the tenancy with money loaned for the 'incoming' by his father, a small manufacturer of weighing scales who also ran a public house in Bilston. Joseph had been thirty-four when he took the Royal Oak and he immediately began to stamp his authority on the place. The previous landlord had run a decent house where rowdy customers were banned from the premises but, when Joseph had taken over the licence this rowdy element returned to the pub and were soon up to their old tricks. Furthermore, others among the regulars were quick to ask for a slate; knowing full well that credit would not be allowed they were trying Joseph's patience to see how far he could be pushed.

It did not take long for Joseph to get the measure of the Royal Oak regulars; within a week he had ejected three of the formerly barred troublemakers by the seat of their trousers, depositing them unceremoniously into the street. He also stated that anyone else who thought that he was a soft touch would rapidly follow them and the word spread around Harborne that you did not mess with Joe Johnson.

Mrs Johnson was to allow one official afternoon off every Sunday but in reality Sarah would also have a few additional hours to herself on the quieter days when her workload proved to be lighter than usual. She was also allowed to attend chapel for the early Sunday service. Tuesdays were traditionally Ann's afternoon off but she managed to persuade Joseph to change this to Sunday so that she and Sarah would be company for each other.

In the December of Sarah's first year at the Royal Oak Mrs Johnson had given birth to a healthy, bellowing baby boy. Following the birth of young John the workload had understandably increased for Sarah; the baby's mother had taken a while to recover and she found that much of her time was taken up with caring for him. Sarah now took over the shopping under strict instructions from her mistress. The meat order had to be collected from the same High Street butchers that Mrs Johnson had used since arriving at the pub. Fruit and vegetables were a different matter as Sarah had a certain amount of freedom to buy whatever produce might be good on the day. She did, however, have orders never to shop at the fruiterers near the bottom of the High Street as Mrs Johnson said that;

"They always manage to throw in a couple of rotten apples and tomatoes when you aren't looking."

In Sarah's last year with the Johnsons she had been considered to be old enough to learn the basics of bar work with a view to filling in for Ann or Mrs Johnson when necessary. At first the atmosphere of drinking and smoking grated with Sarah's somewhat sheltered upbringing, she had certainly not been prepared for some of the characters who passed through the doors of the pub. The tap room especially often rang with the bawdy banter of the hardened working men who were its staple customers.

On one of Sarah's early forays into the tap room a married man, who lived around the corner on Stoney Street, had all but propositioned her and she was at a loss as to how to deal with this. Ann lost no time in coming to the rescue and firmly escorted the chap from the premises with the promise that his wife would hear about this. Sarah did not see him again for a few weeks and when he did finally show his face he sheepishly avoided her. It was not long before the pupil barmaid had learned from her mentor to give the customers as good as she got and they came to respect her for it; they knew not to cross the line of decency.

# 4

# A Chance Meeting

Ann Johnson did not have any particular friends in Harborne. Since her move to the Royal Oak she only ever met people of her own age through her work as a barmaid. The men here were all either married, about to be married or downright unsuitable as friendship material. She was glad to have a companion with whom she could while away the all too short leisure hours and, in return, Sarah enjoyed Ann's company.

The Sunday lunch would be cleared and the washing up done and every week Mrs Johnson would wink at Sarah,

"Right you young'ns, off you go and don't do anything I wunna do."

Taking their cue the two would set off arm-in-arm, sometimes for a stroll along High Street to watch the local people parading in their Sunday best or to chat with other domestic helps that they vaguely knew. At other times they would take the train into Birmingham where they would window shop and treat themselves to coffee and fancy cakes. Very occasionally, when Ann had to cover for Joseph Johnson, Sarah would set out alone and take the coach to visit her Uncle Reuben.

Both Reuben and Sarah's father, John, had been born in Bilston between Sarah's native Wednesbury and Wolverhampton. Reuben married Mary, who was also a native of Bilston, and they had stayed in the town, Reuben having secured work there at a foundry in the Bradley district. In fact, the couple were considered to be quite posh in Queen Street; they were purchasing their small terraced back-to-back home at number four and when the house to the rear became vacant they bought that too. Reuben had been fortunate to secure a rental-purchase agreement with the elderly lady who owned the whole row. Her father had built the houses but she was now frail and, having no children to inherit her estate, she was pleased to sell to Reuben on favourable terms. Nevertheless, it would be many years before the couple would be able to call the properties their own.

On almost every other Wednesday Mrs Johnson would announce to Sarah that things were quiet and she could finish work by mid-afternoon. Sarah took full advantage of these precious hours of freedom to catch the omnibus into Wednesbury and call in on her father.

John lived alone now and he looked forward to his daughter's visits when she would make a fuss of him, tidy around the house and make his tea. All too soon it would be time for Sarah to catch the last bus back to Harborne and John watched with a sigh of resignation as his visitor walked away down The Lyndon.

Sarah would always return from the Sunday outings feeling invigorated but tired; Ann said that this was due to breathing fresh air when they weren't accustomed to it! Ann would usually return to her bar work while Sarah, after seeing that young Emily Johnson had clean clothes ready for the morning, would relax in her room at the top of the house.

It was always good to spend time with Ann, there was never a dull moment and their outings took Sarah's mind off her work. Left to reflect in the evening, however, Sarah could not help but feel a strong sense of loss. Only a few years before she had been part of a loving, chattering, laughing family with everything to look forward to. Now, however, she often felt that she was trapped in a life over which she had no control. She appreciated that the Johnsons had made her as welcome as possible, they were certainly fair people to work for, but she could see nothing ahead but a soul-destroying daily grind.

The gloom of the late evenings caught Sarah out more often than she cared to admit. Even as a child she had been subject to bouts of what the family doctor called 'melancholy.' For some reason she had a very real aversion to the massive winding-gear wheels that marked many of the coal pit heads. As the massive silhouettes slowly turned against the smoky sky she saw them as both living entities and the portents of doom. This, of course, was unfortunate for Sarah given the large number of collieries in the West Bromwich area.

Sarah's dad said that she was 'highly-strung, but never mind - she would grow out of it.' This was partly true as Sarah managed to control her phobia as she grew older. Nevertheless, she would hear of some colliery accident, or a disaster on the railways, or at sea, and she became inconsolable for days. Her parents quickly stopped talking about the tragic events in the newspapers so as not to alert her to the sadness so often contained within the headlines.

Things did improve as time passed but Sarah could never shake off a deep inclination to expect the worst from situations. If something good happened then there would be an equally negative occurrence to balance it out. John called this, 'our Sarah's gloom.' He had lost count of the number of times that he had tried to lift his daughter's spirits by telling her to, 'snap out of it lass, it'll probably never happen!' This did not help whatsoever and John finally realised that a reassuring arm around Sarah's shoulder was far better than any amount of good intentioned hectoring.

Sarah learned to live with her 'doubting side' and she hardly ever gave the outward impression that she was not happy. This was because a steadfast nature, and a quiet sense of humour, saw her through her daily life. Every day was a balancing act, some days were happier than others but on the whole life seemed to even itself out. The times when Sarah was only too pleased to dim the candle on a day were thankfully rare.

For a short period the Sunday outings took an unusual turn for the girls from the Royal Oak. One sunny afternoon, in the spring of 1882, they had decided to walk out to the Hilly Fields and take in the views over Smethwick way. Leaving the dust of the Harborne lanes behind the pair found themselves treading the footpath that led over the Chad Brook. Standing for a few moments on the rickety old wooden bridge they watched the bubbling rafts of yellow foam as they swirled and pirouetted downstream, as if waltzing with the current. Mesmerised by this performance Sarah had been startled by the aerobatics of a low-flying swallow as he dipped his forked tail in the stream before soaring upwards, almost skimming her head; she hoped that this early spring arrival would be the harbinger of a nice summer to come.

The Hilly Fields was an area of agricultural land above and beyond the town and a latticework of footpaths around the fields and scattered woodland led many of the townspeople up here. Sarah and Ann only ever ventured up here when the paths were dry as this made for a pleasant meander among the welcome openness.

The unseasonably warm days brought large numbers of bumble bees and their hovering drone intermingled with the dull background hum from within the distant industrial haze. Out of the shimmering distance a thousand earth-bound stars twinkled where the sunlight reflected from the glass windows of countless factories.

In the Black Country people were fond of the standing joke of how the sparrows always flew backwards in order to avoid choking on the mucky air. Today, somehow, the birds on the Hilly Fields seemed to be more active and free than their bedraggled town cousins. A lark soared and chattered with joy, before fluttering down somewhere in the distance and lapwings busied themselves noisily among the tussocks of thorny ground cover.

Sarah and Ann sat on a dry grassy banking and quietly took in the smells and the sounds around them. Half lost in their daydreams the approach of the two young men went unheeded until they were only a matter of feet away.

"Hiya girls, how you doin' then?"

The loud, cheery greeting startled the pair from their thoughts and they looked round in unison at the cause of this intrusion.

"I'm Bill Cox and this is Luke Harris."

Waving a large hand at his friend the more forthright of the two young men grinned,

"Dunna say much, Luke, but he thinks a lot!" Bill winked at his mate who returned a shy, awkward smile.

Sarah and Ann weighed up the two in the twinkling of an eye. Bill was tall, muscular and outgoing with a grin that lit up his heavily-freckled face. Both men wore their Sunday clothes, three-piece serge suits with the open-neck of their collarless shirts filled by tightly wound white silk mufflers. The slightly shiny jacket sleeves betrayed the age of the suits as they were an inch or so too short and out of the sleeves protruded large hands whose calloused skin betrayed years of physical labour. Their heavy boots, with worn heels and countless scuff-marks, were nevertheless highly polished while rather tatty caps sat jauntily on their heads.

Sarah saw the ginger hair protruding from the sides of Bill's cap and she noticed that it was almost the same colour as that of her sister; she thought that the freckles and red hair made Bill look younger than the twenty-one years that he told them he was. Luke, on the other hand, had mousy hair and an effort of a moustache that would win no hirsute prizes. He was shorter than his friend but something about him attracted Sarah, perhaps it was his coral-green eyes, or was it his lazy lop-sided smile?

"You're right," Ann addressed Bill,

"He dunna talk much you're friend," turning to the slightly pink-faced Luke she asked his age.

"I'll be eighteen this September," with that he looked awkwardly at the floor and, jamming his hands into his pockets, kicked idly at a stone embedded in the footpath.

Luke was hardly much older than Sarah. Having no brothers she was not used to speaking with young men of her own age; a reddish bloom began to colour her cheeks and this intensified noticeably as she caught Luke looking at her off the side. Turning away to hide her embarrassment Sarah picked a tall stalk of grass and began to twine it tightly around her middle fingers.

The awkwardness of the two youngsters did not go unnoticed by either Ann of Bill who caught each other's eye and laughed out loud. Ann was a good judge of character, a skill born out of years behind a public bar, and she saw in Bill a big, gangling lad who would be fun to be around although he was certainly not her 'type.' If the truth be known Ann would prefer an older man than herself who would be able to take her out of service and support her in the manner to which she would like to become accustomed.

The four of them chatted easily for the next hour or so but all too quickly Bill's silver pocket watch told Ann that it was time to be heading back. The men accompanied Sarah and Ann into Harborne from where they intended to catch the five o'clock coach home to Wednesbury. Arriving in town they all agreed that it had been a pleasant afternoon and Bill wondered if they would like to do it again the following Sunday. Sarah glanced at Ann who gave a slight wink and said that they would like that, on condition that the fine weather kept up. A provisional appointment having been made they parted company, Sarah and Luke somewhat demurely and the older pair with grins and waves.

The lads had not told Sarah and Ann the reason for their being on the heath that afternoon. The truth of the matter was that they had heard of a hare-coursing event that was to take place on open land near to Norfolk Farm that day and so they had travelled over from Wednesbury hoping for an afternoon's sport – only to find that the event had been cancelled. Seeing that it was such a nice day they decided to have a walk on the heath before returning home for tea, after which a couple of hours at the Malt Shovel would be called for. They had not mentioned this to the girls as, in their admittedly limited experience, the fairer sex were decidedly unimpressed by such things as dog sports.

Whereas Luke and Bill formerly had no reason to visit Harborne, other than for the odd bout of coursing, they now had the following Sunday to look forward to. That day dawned clear and as bright as the mustard tinged industrial air would allow; the lads were scrubbed, dressed in their Sunday suits, and ready to catch their coach into Harborne by midday.

The week passed slowly for Sarah. Although she would certainly not admit it to Ann she was looking forward to the Sunday outing more than she had ever done before. She wondered if the two young men would turn up as promised and, if they did, what would they talk about? She also went over and over their last meeting in her mind, especially as she lay in bed waiting for sleep to overtake her. The more she thought about it the more she felt that she could really get to like Luke. His quiet manner and bashful smile had left an impression on Sarah and she could not shake it off.

Ann, on the other hand, appeared to be quite blasé about the matter.

"Aw, they probably won't turn up. It's a bit of a long hike to see the likes of us."

She was sceptical that the lads would take the trouble just to spend an hour or two with them, in fact she did not really care if they turned up or not; she was only going because she knew that Sarah liked young Luke.

Mrs Johnson had noticed a renewed vigour in the way that Sarah went about her daily chores; the mahogany bar especially had been the subject of extra attention and glowed like a pit-head beacon. When Mrs Johnson mentioned this to Ann she was amused to be told with a wry smile that Sarah;

"Had got a feller."

# 5

# Luke Harris

Stepping out into the Sunday bustle the newly-free girls linked arms and headed off to keep their appointment. Sure enough, as they turned the corner into Oldbury Road they saw Luke and Bill outside the Fiveways Inn where the coach had dropped them fifteen minutes earlier. Bill was leaning in his easy manner against a gas standard while Luke, hands thrust deep into his pockets, shuffled a little nervously. Their faces lit up when the girls appeared and, after an initial moment of awkwardness they were walking towards the open countryside.

By the time they had reached the brook the four had split into two couples, not through any particular intention but more because of the fact that Bill was larking around and teasing Ann with a length of grass. He had stripped the seeds from the top of the stalk and, pushing it into Ann's dark curls, twisted it between his thumb and forefinger. This had the effect of knotting the grass in Ann's hair and she did a little dance of pretend annoyance as she struggled to remove it.

The older pair lagged behind as Sarah and Luke climbed the slope of Hilly Fields. Being deep in conversation about who knew who in their native district around Wednesbury they had not noticed that the others were some distance away. Luke lived near to the Monway Colliery but he did not know the Davis family from The Lyndon. In actual fact Sarah had lived less than half a mile from the centre of town but considered herself to be first and foremost a 'Lyndonian.' West Bromwich people lived in relatively isolated pockets within its many parishes and it was typical of them to be more loyal to their local district than the town itself.

As it turned out Sarah and Luke knew of each other's area but they had few acquaintances in common. In fact the only name that they were both familiar with was Mr Hudson, the soap manufacturer. He had started in a small way on the High Street and made his fortune by setting up a factory in Liverpool from where he supplied the world with his *Hudson's Soap* products.

As they chatted a bead of sweat ran down Luke's temple, the slow climb up the hill had been warm in his serge suit. Having taken off his jacket he rolled up his Union shirt sleeves and lounged back against the spongy grass of the banking. Sarah saw the blue-black scars on Luke's arms and knew them for what they were; almost all of the colliers she had ever seen carried these tattoo-like marks. Deep underground there was no escaping the coal dust and any slight cut or abrasion picked up by the miners would quickly be impregnated with the oily black powder. Once the dust was under the skin then the scar healed over and left the miner with yet another souvenir of his coal-winning days.

Both Luke and Bill worked at the Patent Shaft and Axletree Company Colliery in Wednesbury; the elder as a 'pikeman' and the younger as a 'carrier.' The two often had heated, if good natured, debates about each other's wages. Luke said that Bill was privileged because he was a pikeman and, to a certain extent, this was true. The girls had noticed that Bill often carried more money than his friend but Luke put this down to the fact that he had not yet been paid.

The fact of the matter was that most of the South Staffordshire colliers were paid on the 'long pay' system. This was a long standing method of wage payment that had probably been instigated when navvies were digging the new tunnels for the Birmingham canal network. The pay system had been carried forward into the burgeoning mining industry of South Staffordshire and had proven difficult for the miners to shake off.

Luke attempted to explain the basis of the 'long pay' system.

"You've heard of the 'Truck' shops?"

"Course I have."

Sarah had not lived amongst miners all her life without knowing something about the 'Truck.' She had also heard people speak of the 'long pay' on many occasions but she had never really understood just what this meant.

"Well, the Truck shops wouldn't be there but for the 'long pay'."

Luke went on to tell Sarah of the way in which most miners were paid in arrears, in some pits the workers were paid every fortnight, in some it was every month and in yet others it might be six or even every eight weeks. The colliers who could last until payday received the full money owing to them. The problem was that many men had debts of varying kinds; some colliers gambled too much and many spent the housekeeping money on beer. Very soon after the 'long pay' day these men were again in the position of having no cash.

This was where the Truck shops came into their own. A miner could ask for a sub on his wages at any time and he would then receive a Truck shop ticket. This was useless anywhere other than the shop belonging to the particular colliery where the man worked. The normal way in which the tickets were used was for the collier's wife to take it into the Truck shop and hand it to the counter clerk. When she had ordered the goods required to feed her family for a few days the clerk entered the amount owing in cash in an 'advance book.' The shopper then took the book to a cashier who gave her the amount in cash and this was then handed over to the counter clerk in exchange for the ordered goods.

"So far, so good," Luke was warming to his subject now. Like most colliers he had an intense dislike of the 'long pay' and Truck systems.

"But there's one major problem and that's the cost of the stuff on the Truck. My mam says that everything's so pricey that it costs a week's wages to live for two days. She said last week that the last pound of bacon she got from the Truck had cost her three times the corner shop price!"

Sarah could sympathise with this as the high prices charged by the colliery owners were well known. Of course the owners excused their extortionate Truck shop prices by pointing out that they had to stock the goods and pay the clerk's wages.

Luke laughed to himself and told Sarah about Mrs Griffith, a neighbour of his from three doors along the road. Two weeks ago she had need to cash in a Truck ticket but after collecting the money from the cashier she 'legged' it out of the shop without picking up her order.

"Old Ma Griffith's bin sloping again," Luke's father, Ben, guffawed as he told Luke and the rest of the family. He had seen the counter man from the Truck shop banging on Mrs Griffith's door on the evening of her 'slope.' She answered the door to be met by the red-faced clerk, sweating and tugging at his collar as if he was desperate for air.

"Mrs Griffith, I'm disappointed. This isn't the first time you've left the store without picking up your order. It means endless trouble for me, my stock won't tally and my books will be out at the end of the week. Oh dear, this is no good at all. And it's not the first time Mrs Griffith."

By now he was almost beside himself and was probably rescued from some kind of terminal infarction by Mrs Griffith slowly closing the door on him as he reached full flow. Ben watched this little scene with great delight; after the door had been closed the clerk still carried on dancing from one foot to the other before flouncing off down the street mopping his brow with one hand and clutching his collar with the other.

Of course the mine would not be out of pocket because of the slopers as the money was deducted, with costs, from the miner's next long pay. The usual consequences of this were that a miner could fall increasingly further behind until all of his 'long pay' was required to settle his Truck debts.

Sarah looked thoughtful for a minute.

"I suppose that's where 'sloping off' comes from when someone leaves without saying anything?"

"Suppose so," Luke had never considered this.

"So why does Bill always seem to have more money than you?"

"Ah, the pikemen are treated different to the rest of us, Bill's not on the 'long pay' like me."

As a pikeman Bill was a member of the team responsible for freeing the coal from the seams and, because the rest of the colliers depended on the 'pikeys' to make progress through the coal face, they had certain privileges. The job of the pikey was hard and dangerous, injuries, not to mention fatalities, ran at a high level in this occupation.

As they pushed the coal face the pikeys burrowed with their picks beneath a seam of coal that could be as high as a man. The skilled men knew how to leave sufficient standing coal to form pillars that would support the gallery. When enough material had been removed from beneath the coal face the whole mass would collapse into the cleared space below, breaking up into large shiny black lumps. The loaders and carriers then transported the newly-won coal to the bottom of the main pit shaft ready to be hoisted into the daylight.

Because of their skill, and the dangerous nature of the job, the pikemen enjoyed a certain freedom in the hours they worked - on condition that they progressed at the rate required by the pit owners. Furthermore they were paid on regular piecework called a 'measurement stint' and this meant that Bill normally collected his wages on a weekly basis. Unfortunately the young man was in the habit of spending most of his wages in the Malt Shovel and this was a practice that Luke didn't agree with.

Luke pointed out to Sarah that he was not much of a drinker; in fact he considered that anything over a couple of glasses of beer was a waste of money. Like Sarah, he had been brought up as 'chapel' and had attended the Spring Head Wesleyan church for most of his life. He had seen the damage that drinking did to families when the wage earner spent most of his money on beer and this was not the life for him.

"That's what Mr Johnson said," Sarah recalled,

"He wunna serve more than two pints to the iron and pit men 'till they've been home to their wives."

Sarah was pleased that Luke was also chapel, this was important to her and she felt a surge in the growing affection that she held for her new friend.

"I was taken to the Lyndon Street Wesleyan church from being two years old, living so near we'd go to both Sunday services."

Sarah and Luke realised that their paths must have crossed at some point in the past as their chapel congregations each visited the other on a number of occasions. The local congregations were always staging musical concerts of one kind or another and the small productions would tour within the local area.

Sarah chuckled to herself,

"Did you see the Amazing African Mission Brothers when they were here last year? I went with my dad to see them when they were at the High Street church hall."

With a knowing smile Luke replied that the act hadn't been in his area but he had heard about them. The Mission Brothers had caused quite a stir among the West Bromwich folk. They were billed as a family of natives discovered in the African jungle by the famous Scottish explorer, Doctor David Livingstone. The brothers were said to be from a tribe previously unknown to the civilised world. Livingstone brought the brothers into the missionary camp from whence they were subsequently introduced to England where astonished audiences could witness the 'miracles wrought by good works.'

Everyone assumed that the brothers would be illustrating their exotic far-off land through the medium of the magic lantern, just as intrepid explorers did when giving lectures at the local Mechanics Institutes and theatres.

As the heavy curtain was raised to reveal the impressive church hall stage Sarah, along with her father, John, settled into the front row of an expectant audience. The band struck up their introduction with a supposedly African tune;

unfortunately this sounded more like a strangled Irish jig and set the tone for the rest of the performance.

Out of the wings emerged the Amazing African Mission Brothers and a rather strange spectacle ensued. Shuffling along one behind the other were three men of distinct appearance, each with an outstretched arm resting on the shoulder of the Brother in front. At the head of the line was a tall individual with a wild shock of bright-red hair and an even redder beard that was all the more vivid against the ghostly pallor of his face. Standing over six feet five tall his scrawny frame was clad in a tight-fitting single-piece woollen swimsuit into which false buttocks and knobbly knees had been stuffed

Following on behind came an individual of less stature, in fact he was shorter than his colleague in front by a full thirteen inches. On his head he wore a pith helmet three sizes too big and his huge protruding belly was draped in the gaudiest kilt imaginable. From his short-sleeved tunic dangled a pair of puny, chalk-white arms. This outfit was, presumably, intended to represent Doctor Livingstone but the reason for his carrying a stuffed goose under his arm was somewhat of a mystery.

Last, but by no means least among the line-up was a very short man. He was bald on top with lanky hair at the sides reaching to his shoulders; he also had the most unfortunate features seen upon any stage in many a long year. Beetling eyebrows rose and fell independently and, when raised, they disappeared into the deep folds of a permanently frowning forehead. The poor fellow was cross-eyed and his heavy, drooping jowls gave the impression of a jaundiced bulldog with toothache. The short frame was set off by the uniform of a missionary excepting for a pair of knee-length khaki shorts and a pair of massive pit clogs.

In conga fashion the three performers shuffled around the stage to some obscure tune that the conductor was forcing out of the band; all the while the trio glared at their bewildered audience. After a couple of minutes they left the stage and almost immediately reappeared teetering ungainly on monocycles. As they jerked around the stage the lanky red-

51

haired Brother began to juggle the three clubs that he had produced from down the front of his costume.

All went well for a full thirty seconds until he dropped one of the clubs and the short one with the unfortunate face rode over it. This twisted the wheel of his cycle and threw him flat on his face. It was too late for the kilted one to avoid his stricken friend and he also was unceremoniously dumped on the polished boards of the stage. Unfortunately for the audience he landed on his back, with his legs waving in the air, and this meant that the kilt of many colours rode up around his waist. As a consequence of this the first three rows of the audience were treated to a sight that no church-going person should ever have to witness.

Seeing this, the failed juggler carried on cycling around the melee of arms, legs and monocycles. By now he was down to a single club, having dropped a second one, and was half-heartedly passing it from one hand to the other whilst still glaring venomously at the audience. This debacle only came to an end when the two fallen heroes disentangled themselves from their machines; deciding that discretion was the better part of valour the troupe left the stage with a final grimace at the front row of the unfortunate audience.

The curtain came swiftly down on proceedings and there was a moment's stunned silence. The audience did not know how to react; a smattering of polite applause, intermingled with muffled laughter, broke out. This was quickly drowned out by a chorus of boos and the stamping of feet - this had not been what they had paid their money for and the crowd were not best pleased.

In an attempt to stave off a riot the Chairman of events sent on Miss Greenwood, a well known local contralto who could belt out Music Hall songs and hymns with equal gusto. Along with Miss Greenwood's dulcet tones the promise of a refund of half the entry ticket price did the trick and the audience were reasonably satisfied. There was still a great deal of muttering on the way out, however.

"There's some strange beggars in them African jungles," the man sat next to John said as they made their way towards the exit.

"They didn't even look like proper brothers to me!" his wife added.

No one knew where the 'Brothers' had come from but they never appeared on the Black Country Methodist circuit again. Luke wished that he had seen the performance but he had to content with Sarah's first-hand account. The pair fell into a thoughtful silence as Sarah mulled over the many problems that drink could cause amongst the working families.

In the summer of 1872 her parents had put her name forward, through the Lyndon Street church, to join the district Methodist Children's Committee. The senior committee members voted for the five children considered to have been worthy of the honour and, in the January of 1873, the Birmingham Daily Post carried a paragraph stating that Miss Sarah Ann Davis had received 146 votes. This was only three less than the highest vote and therefore Sarah was duly elected to the local branch of the Protestant Dissenting Charity Committee.

In the time that she served on the Committee Sarah had seen true poverty in the homes of the unemployed and the near destitute. Despite her youth she sometimes accompanied the Reverends Clarke and Tillotson on their welfare rounds and she realised now, as she worked her daily routine at the Royal Oak, that she was relatively lucky.

True, she had no money and no real prospects but she did have her health and a constitution that, God willing, would always allow her to work. This was vital in keeping the Poor House at bay and for this she was grateful; there was a very fine line between the working poor and grasping poverty and this worried her.

# 6

# Happy Sundays

The Royal Oak girls continued their liaisons with Luke and Bill over the following weeks. The weather remained kind; the perfumed blossoms of spring had now fallen and the hedgerows were filling with their summer foliage. The four of them returned to Hilly Fields again but they also varied their outings by heading south to an open area known as The Park.

As the weeks progressed Sarah became increasingly comfortable in Luke's company. Gone was the awkwardness of their earlier meetings, this had been replaced by an ease between them born of mutual respect. Sarah admired Luke for his maturity and sincerity while Luke had been overtaken by an attraction to Sarah's unassuming and selfless nature.

On the other hand there was no developing bond between Ann and Bill. The first couple of weeks had been fun as far as Ann was concerned. Bill's clowning around had amused her but things were different now. As Sarah and Luke became closer they would leave their friends and find a quiet spot where they could hold hands and talk without interruption. This left Ann alone with Bill and she was becoming bored with the situation; Bill too felt as though he was now a mere travelling companion for his friend. In all honesty he would rather spend his afternoons in the Malt Shovel; it had become quite obvious that Luke had eyes only for Sarah these days and Bill felt isolated.

On their fifth outing the situation had become too much for Ann and she felt that she had to say something. As usual the other couple had been whispering and laughing together while

Ann and Bill made inane small talk. Before they met the young men Sarah and Ann had enjoyed each other's company and Ann had never felt left out as she did now.

As the four walked back to Harborne the niggle that was bothering Ann grew; finally she could stand it no longer and, before any arrangements could be made for a meeting the following week, she spoke out.

"I'm sorry but I won't be coming next week."

Sarah's raised eyebrows showed that she had been taken aback at this and the young men looked at each other.

"Why?" asked Sarah, "What's the matter?"

"I'm fed up with just standing around every week. It's no fun anymore, I might as well work Sundays than do this - at least I'd get paid for it."

Sarah was clearly hurt by Ann's unexpected outburst.

"Come on Ann, there's no need to be like that."

"Well I think there is, let's face it, me and him," Ann waved a hand in Bill's general direction, "have to stand round like lemons while you two soppy love-birds are giggling and whispering."

"I didn't know that's how you felt."

Sarah turned to Luke, who was looking decidedly uncomfortable, and told him that she and Ann would have to sort things out.

"Perhaps it'll be better if you don't come over next week." With that Sarah gave Luke a quick peck on the cheek and the lads took their leave.

As the girls walked home to the Royal Oak there was a decided tension in the air and hardly a word passed between them. Ann held the back door open as Sarah stepped through into the kitchen; taking off her bonnet and coat she quickly disappeared up the stairs to change for her evening shift in the bar. Sarah put the kettle on the range and sank into the worn old armchair in the corner to mull over the events of the afternoon.

Realising that there was now a real doubt over her Sunday afternoons with Luke there was not much that Sarah could really do other than talk to Mrs Johnson. She was not so naive as to think that her employer was unaware of the situation - and she was right.

Early the following morning, after Sarah had set the fires and prepared breakfast, Ann flounced somewhat haughtily into the kitchen.

"Mornin'."

"Morning," Sarah returned the muffled greeting.

The frosty atmosphere over breakfast did not go unnoticed and, when Sarah had gone off to see to her duties upstairs Mrs Johnson turned to Ann.

"Now, what on earth's going on between you two? You've been like cat an' dog ever since you came in yesterday tea time."

It was in Mrs Johnson's best interests to keep her staff happy.

"After all," as she was fond of saying, "a tight ship is a happy ship."

Ann explained the situation, she really had no gripe with Sarah, it was the situation that she did not like rather than something that her young friend had deliberately done. However, Ann was not prepared to put up with it any longer.

"I see," Mrs Johnson understood immediately.

"I can see the problem. And just how serious are things between the lass and her fancy man?"

"Well, it looks serious enough to me, you wunna fit a sixpenny piece between 'em when they're out these days!"

Mrs Johnson had not realised that things had progressed between Sarah and Luke just as far as Ann was suggesting they had. As Sarah's employer Mrs Johnson knew that she held a certain responsibility for the girl but this was all the more serious because Sarah was under-age and living beneath her roof.

"Right, leave it with me and I'll try to sort this out."

Ann busied herself setting up the bar areas while her sister-in-law mulled over the situation. She had known about the two young men since the beginning as Sarah had spoken about

Luke whenever the opportunity arose. Mrs Johnson could see no problem with the weekly meetings as she trusted Ann to keep an eye on young Sarah. Unfortunately things seemed to have got out of hand and Ann now felt that she was nothing more than a chaperone to her friend.

It was the mid-afternoon and Sarah knew by the manner in which her employer approached her that she was to be 'spoken to.'

"Sit down lass, I'll fetch the tea."

The massive iron kettle filled the equally massive Burslem teapot and as the infusion brewed Mrs Johnson set about her task.

"There's a problem with your Sunday outings I hear. I think you know how Ann feels about it?"

"Well I didn't until yesterday but I can see her point."

Mrs Johnson cut straight to the chase.

"Are you for giving this young feller up then? I mean, it puts me in a tight spot, what with you being under-age and all."

This came as no surprise to Sarah, she knew that there was no way that she would be allowed to see Luke unaccompanied. Mrs Johnson had promised Sarah's father that she would look after her as long as she lived in the Johnson household and she was not the kind of woman to break her promises.

"I mean to say lass, you're young and heaven knows you wunna want to make a mistake and be tied down with a family in your position, what with no money or house of your own."

Sarah's cheeks flushed at the inference of her having a family; the mere mention of anything related to sex always made her feel uncomfortable. Although her parents had never been what could be called over-prudish there had been an atmosphere in the Davis household where relationships were not openly discussed. The people that Sarah had mixed with all her life were largely of the church congregation and there was little sex education to be had in these circles.

It was fair to say that Sarah was aware of the basic physical machinations involved between men and women as no youngster in West Bromwich could escape the coarse talk of some of the rougher children from the tenements. However, the fact that Mrs Johnson could even think that she had been doing such unspeakable things with Luke upset her. What she found even more hurtful was the fact that anyone could think that her Luke would actually want to do them with her – surely he respected her too much for that?

"You see, lass, you're not exactly worldly-wise now are you? These things happen in the twinkling of an eye and you are stuck with the consequences for the rest of your life. Look at Poor Rosie Malone!"

Mrs Johnson rested her case with this final statement, she had every confidence that this would put her point over to Sarah by holding up Poor Rosie as an example of fallen morals.

Sarah recalled a night, perhaps two months ago, when the family at the Royal Oak had turned into bed and the candles were being extinguished one-by-one throughout the house. At around eleven-thirty there was the resounding crash of breaking glass followed by a moment of silence. Soon the neighbourhood dogs were barking and voices could be heard echoing along the street, the loudest voice of all turned out to belong to Poor Rosie Malone.

Rosie had once been a respectable young West Bromwich woman; she had been apprenticed to Price Milliners at a young age and had showed great promise in the trade. Mr Price always held her up to the other youngsters in his small factory as the ideal employee and suggested that she would be managing their High Street shop one day.

"Ooh, things are lookin' rosy for Rosie," was the usual banter from the other girls in the factory. They were slightly resentful of what they saw as favouritism towards Rosie but she didn't care; she was not the sensitive type.

Rosie's bright career ended in the third week of July; on her fifteenth birthday in fact. It was the annual summer visit of the travelling fairground and the girls from Price Milliners had gone down there in the early evening so that Rosie could enjoy spending her birthday money. It soon became clear that one of the fairground lads had his eye on Rosie; he was a handsome individual whose long dark hair set of a flashing smile that dazzled the youngster.

She was flattered when the lad asked her if she wanted a drink or something and offered to show her behind the scenes of the bustling, clammering fairground. Rosie and her friend thought this would be nice and were soon alone with the lad in his caravan.

"Here you are girls, have a sup of this lemonade, it's grand stuff."

The girls, in their naivety, took him at his word not realising that this 'grand stuff' was a gin-laced mixture prepared by some of the fairground lads for exactly this situation. Rosie drank her tumbler straight down but her friend screwed up her nose and said that it tasted funny.

"Aw, it's alright, can I have another?"

By the time she had finished her third drink Rosie was acting a little strangely, lolling about and slurring her words. Her friend by this time had become uneasy, she said that she was leaving and pressed Rosie to leave with her.

"I'll jush 'ave another."

This was the point at which Rosie's quick slide into desperation began. Her friend left with an anxious backward glance and in the following spring Rosie's child was born.

The whole episode of her pregnancy had been a disaster for Rosie's family who, as soon as the problem had become apparent, had sent her to relatives in Shropshire. The alternative of Rosie having the baby at home had been unthinkable; the disgrace would have killed her mother. As it was, a healthy son was safely delivered in Shropshire and immediately adopted there. Rosie returned home only to find that she was no longer welcome, her mother could not stand being reminded of her daughter's infidelity and her hen-pecked father dare not go against his wife's wishes.

Rosie was now an official inmate of the West Bromwich Hallam Street workhouse. From here the story of Poor Rosie Malone was that of many other young women; she had no job, no home and nobody to look out for her. Realising that she was destined for a life of drudgery in the workhouse she left the institution for the city streets.

It was not long before Rosie found herself in bad company; she filtered rapidly downwards through society and was soon a part of the Birmingham underworld. It was here, amongst the unfortunate dregs of humanity, that she learned how to make money without working.

By now Rosie was addicted to the powerful gin much favoured by those who had good reason to forget and she needed a steady supply of money. Within months she had been in the police courts for soliciting and served a two-month sentence in prison with hard labour.

A year after her descent into the dark underworld of the city, passers-by often found themselves stepping over a filthy bundle of rags on the pavement from which a gruff voice incessantly repeated the pitiful phrase that gave rise to Rosie's nickname,

"Spare tuppence for poor Rosie Malone."

A few doors above the Royal Oak stood the Georgian-style gentleman's residence of a local carrying agent. The central door of this imposing building was flanked by grand, multi-paned windows - that is until Poor Rosie Malone heaved a brick through one of them.

The resounding crash brought Joseph Johnson thundering down the pub stairs at full pelt. Thinking that there were intruders he brandished the cavalry sword that he kept under his bed and it would be God-help anyone he might find. He checked the downstairs windows before venturing out onto the street where he saw the cause of the commotion. The local police constable had hold of Poor Rosie by the sleeve of her tattered dress and she was shouting ill fit to burst.

"Gerroff you big bugger, unhand Poor Roshie at onesh."

Rosie had returned to West Bromwich a few months earlier as things had been getting increasingly difficult in Birmingham. The city police knew her only too well and she was the first to be questioned when thefts were reported on their patch. Furthermore, there were rumours that Rosie had been involved in running bets for some shadowy bookmaker in the city and she owed him money.

Understandably Rosie had moved out to the sticks to allow things to cool down but she did not stay long in her home town. Rosie had been living rough in Harborne for the past month and public disorder complaints had quadrupled since her arrival. The Harborne Constable had come to know Rosie well in her short sojourn in the town.

"Come on Rosie, what the 'ell are you playing at now?"

With a feigned air of injured dignity Rosie attempted to shake herself free of the Constable's secure grasp.

"Well it's like thish, you've locked me up often enough for nowt sho I thought I'd give you shummat to lock me up fer."

The truth of the matter, of course, was that Poor Rosie was reaching the end of her resilience to the cold and damp of the streets and merely wanted somewhere warm to sleep - things had not turned out so rosy for Rosie Malone after all.

As Sarah sipped at her tea she remembered the salutary tale of Poor Rosie. Not long ago she and Ann had come across the destitute woman in the High Street when a dishevelled figure emerged at speed from the doorway of the New Inn. Rosie had all but knocked Sarah flying as the landlord forcibly evicted her onto the street.

"Gerrout of it you old shod, thersh no need ter treat a lady like that."

Rosie spat at the landlord and gave a grimace that reminded Sarah of the cart horses when they impatiently stamped the ground and whinnied, showing their huge yellow teeth. In Rosie's case her facial expression was even more unedifying as she only had three teeth left in her head, each a different colour.

Sarah and Ann had been stopped in their tracks and looked on open-mouthed.

"'Ere, wot the 'ell you gawpin' at you nosey buggers?"

Sarah learned a few new words from Poor Rosie that day.

Mrs Johnson was correct in that if Sarah had been contemplating a physical relationship with Luke then the story of Poor Rosie would have acted as a truly sobering lesson. This was the one thing that Sarah had always feared; the threat of the workhouse was like a slumbering monster that constantly stalked the poorer working people. Sarah had seen just how close this unspoken threat could be when unemployment was followed by debt or a drinking habit; illness or accident could so quickly lead to true poverty.

Sarah attempted to explain her relationship with Luke.

"I want to keep on seeing him, I think a lot about him and we don't get up to anything we shouldn't. I'm sure Ann will tell you that."

"I'm sure you don't lass," Mrs Johnson was being as diplomatic as possible, "But one thing can soon lead to another and it puts me in a bit of a pickle. I can't agree to you seeing the lad on your own as I owe it to your dad to look after you."

Sarah's employer felt for her as, after all, she had been young herself. She knew that the youngster was at that difficult age in the limbo between childhood and maturity and she did not want her to feel that she was being heavy handed. She was also aware that Sarah was a little 'highly strung' and a tactful compromise was called for whereby the youngsters could still see each other while Mrs Johnson could be satisfied that they 'behaved.'

"What if the lad came here on Sunday afternoons?"

Sarah looked at her employer and rubbed her chin in thought. Mrs Johnson went on;

"You can entertain him in the parlour, nobody'll bother you."

Sarah realised that Mrs Johnson was making an effort to keep her happy. The downstairs parlour was never used except on special occasions, such as birthday teas and Christmas, and Sarah appreciated the gesture.

"That's good of you, I'll ask him if he wants to do that."

"Right lass, that's settled then."

When Ann was told of the new arrangement she was naturally disappointed that she would be on her own on Sunday afternoons but at least she would not have to play the gooseberry any longer.

The trouble now was that Sarah and Luke had parted on the previous Sunday without having made further arrangements to meet. Sarah wondered about catching the omnibus through to Wednesbury and calling on Luke at his home. She quickly decided against this as it was not the done thing for young women to call on young men. She might send her new friend a letter to explain the situation, though.

As it turned out there was no reason for Sarah to contact Luke; he was waiting outside the Royal Oak on the following Sunday morning as she left for church.

"Hiya Sarah, I had to come and see where we stood after last week. I didn't know if you would want to see me anymore."

Sarah's face lit up and she threw her arms around the smiling young man.

"'Course I do. I'm sorry if Ann seemed a bit stroppy but she's alright now. I was thinking of sending you a letter."

The pair set off to walk to the church and Sarah invited Luke to accompany her to the service. She felt so proud to have the handsome young man sitting beside her and she noticed the others in the congregation nudging each other and winking as they looked in the young couple's direction.

Sarah told Luke of her conversation with Mrs Johnson and he fully understood the position that Sarah's employer found herself in.

"I don't care what I have to do as long as I can see you. I'll come over next Sunday at half-past one if that's alright?"

The appointment having been agreed the two parted company, but not before they embraced. Luke gave Sarah a lingering kiss, his first real physical show of affection since the pair had met; a feeling of warmth engulfed Sarah and she felt decidedly light-headed on the walk home. This was a new sensation for the young woman and the feeling of elation stayed with her through most of the following week.

Luke was true to his word and over the coming months the couple found themselves holding hands, kissing and giggling like school children in the comfort of the Johnson's parlour. Luke became a popular Sunday visitor in the household and he was always careful to bring Mrs Johnson a small gift; his host seemed to really appreciate a posy of violets or a block of fudge from Mother Hanson's sweet shop on the High Street. Even Joseph Johnson warmed to Luke; if he was not too busy in the pub he would come through to the parlour with a jug of Mitchell's ale.

"Now then lad, I know how thirsty you collier lads are, get this down."

Although Sarah had no previous experience in these matters she realised that what she felt for Luke must be nothing short of love. She thought about him every waking hour and her dreams were filled with the flash of his green eyes as his laughter echoed around her mind. She had no doubt that these were the happiest days of her life.

# 7

# Bombshell

The days and weeks melted into each other and Luke found that his work at the pit was not as tedious as it used to be; his thoughts were constantly with Sarah and their Sundays came in quick succession. However, in Luke's short experience of life things were never fully stable and his relationship with Sarah was no exception; there was a cloud on the horizon.

His father, Ben, was also a collier and he had been made redundant when the pit in which he worked had closed the previous year. Although he tried for numerous jobs in other local pits he found that his age was against him, there were more colliers than jobs nowadays and employers wanted the youngsters.

A few of Ben's former workmates had been in the same position and had managed to find work by moving out of Staffordshire. Some had gone to Lancashire, to work in the new coalfields of the district while others were now employed in the busy mining industry of Newcastle. Ben was contemplating a move if he could find work but Luke put this to the back of his mind; he was in love and things such as this tended to take a back seat when a young man's emotions were riding high.

Nothing much had been said at home, the possible uprooting of the Harris family was somewhat of an 'elephant in the room' when they were gathered together. It was obvious to all that Ben was not happy; he had been a working collier all of his life and he felt the stigma of unemployment deeply. He and Luke's mother discussed the possibility of working elsewhere but they kept the details from Luke and his brother. That is until one Friday evening in late summer.

As usual Luke had returned from his shift at the pit and, sitting in the tin bath in front of the iron range, he tried his best to scrub the coal dust from his pores. Dressed and ready for the evening meal Luke sat down with the others, his face shining from the carbolic buffing that it had recently received.

"Right lads, me and your mother have some news."

Ben took a letter from behind the large pottery dog on the mantelpiece and sat down.

"I didn't want to say anything until it was confirmed, and now it is. I've been offered a job up north and I've accepted it."

Luke and his brother exchanged quizzical looks and, seeing this, Ben pushed the letter across the table for their inspection. The crux of the letter was that Ben had been offered work in the Cumbrian town of Whitehaven; a new shaft had been sunk to connect to the Wellington Pit there and the company were in need of skilled men to mine the high quality coal and ironstone seams.

The consequences of Ben's news slowly dawned on Luke. He was now faced with the reality that he had tried to suppress for the past months. He knew that he and his brother would be unable to stay in the family home as it was rented from the Wesleyan Mission and a stipulation of the tenancy was that the house was for married couples and families only. Besides which he and his brother would struggle to run a house; his sibling was only fifteen and not yet on full wages. Luke voiced his reservations,

"What'll happen to us then?"

"Dunna think I haven't thought about that son. There's plenty of work up there for us all. I've been promised that you and the lad will have jobs with me."

Luke did not mention it to his family but his first thought was for Sarah. If he were to up sticks and leave he might never see her again and that would be unbearable. Why did this have to come up now? A few months ago he would have had no qualms about moving to pastures new; he was young with no ties and he would be with his family. Now, however, things were very different.

Having slept fitfully Luke rose on the Saturday morning but the move to Whitehaven did not appear to be any more attractive than it had been the previous evening. In his mind he had gone over and over again what he was going to do - if he did go with the family what was he going to tell Sarah? It had been confirmed the night before that Luke's younger brother would definitely be going north and this would obviously leave the elder of the two alone should he refuse to go.

It was not as though Luke had any relatives to stay with; his closest family were grandparents on his mother's side but they lived in Leicester and were too elderly to cope with a lodger. Besides which there was the problem that Luke had not yet come of age and he was still firmly under his parent's wing. By the time that the family sat down for their Saturday tea Luke had come to realise that he had little choice.

"When do we go?" he asked of Ben.

"Well, there's a few formalities to be gone through but the job's good from the end of October."

That, then, was the matter settled. Ben would confirm with the mining company that his two sons would require jobs and they, in turn, would allocate a cottage for the family to be ready to move into on the first day of November.

Sarah knew that something was wrong. Luke turned up as usual, half-past one on the dot, but their first hour together was not the same; Luke was subdued and there were no funny stories of the antics of his workmates during the past week.

Finally the hapless young man summoned up the courage he had been hoping for and told Sarah his unwelcome news; for a minute she did not fully take in what he was saying but, as he went on, Sarah began to realise that in actual fact he was telling her the last thing she wanted to hear. The young man who had filled Sarah's days and nights - the one person who had changed her life - was leaving?

67

"I don't really follow what you mean," Sarah was desperate to have misheard the news.

"If your dad's found a new job then that's good – but why should it mean that you have to leave as well?"

Luke explained that the whole family were to make a new start.

"After all, Cumbria's only a few hours train journey from here, I can come back to see you regular away."

Sarah heard this but she could not take it in. This day had started out with all the promise of the other Sundays she had spent with Luke and now it had turned into a disaster. Whether he could come back every so often or not did not detract from the fact that Luke was leaving her – possibly for good.

"It's alright you saying that, Luke, but I know that it wunna work like that. Our Fran went up north a couple of years ago but I haven't seen her since."

Luke saw the desperate disappointment welling in Sarah's eyes and this almost brought him to tears.

"Aw, come on Duck, it's not the end of the world. I promise I'll be back in no time. Another year or two and I'll be of age and I'll have money saved, I'll be able to afford to send for you. How would that be?"

Sarah was inconsolable; she wasn't stupid, she knew full well that no relationship could flourish when the couple were hundreds of miles apart, trains or no trains.

When the time came for Luke to take his leave he felt more depressed than he could ever remember in his life. He and Sarah were hardly on the brink of marriage, after all they only saw each other for a few short hours every week; but he knew that something important was ebbing away and it was through no fault of his own.

Both Mrs Johnson and Ann tried their best to comfort their young friend. Ann in particular sympathised; she had come to terms with the loss of Sarah's companionship on their free afternoons and had seen that the young couple were serious. Ann wished her friend well; she knew how lonely life could be 'on the shelf' as unattached women approaching thirty were deemed to be. If Sarah had found herself a nice lad to settle down with, and she was sure that Luke would be good to her, then the best of luck to her.

During her precious months with Luke there had been a marked change in Sarah's demeanour whereby the doubting side rapidly gave way to a positive, light-filled world in which Sarah now realised she had been a stranger. The dark unknowable form that inhabited her deepest thoughts had lifted as surely as if someone had physically grasped it and locked it securely in the heavy wooden chest at the bottom of her bed.

The night that she learned of Luke's leaving Sarah heard the ominous rasp of rusty hinges as the lid of the wooden chest slowly opened. The old familiar companion was once again free and scrabbling at her brain - back again, trying to penetrate deep into its comfortable home within her thoughts - and this time it was to take up residence for good.

# 8

# Messrs. Duckett and Atkins

Fran's move to East Lancashire had gone well. Although she missed her older sister she quickly settled with the Duckett family in Burnley; they had made her as welcome as if she had been a part of the family and she soon made new friends in the area. As it turned out there were a number of young women in Accrington Road who were from Fran's neck of the woods. A junior doctor lived at number twenty-six and his domestic help originated in Shropshire. Number twenty-four was occupied by a surgeon and both of his domestic servants had also moved up from Shropshire. At number thirty-two a Northamptonshire girl worked as a domestic to a solicitor and further along the road lived a Glossop girl.

The high number of immigrants in the immediate neighbourhood provided an idea of the scale involved where workers were flooding into Lancashire from other counties. In particular demand by the flourishing business class were domestic servants, as Fran well knew. This meant that there was a sense of camaraderie amongst the domestic girls wherever they lived, be it village, town or city. Fran had been worried that she would stand out as an outsider following her move north but this had proved to be far from the case. She had new friends with similar accents to her own and the easy, humorous manner of the local people made her feel at home

Sarah and Fran exchanged regular letters through which they kept each other informed of their comings and goings. Fran was sad to hear that her sister's young man was leaving the district; she could tell from her letter that Sarah felt her loss deeply. She knew that, out of the pair of them, Sarah had always been the more intense; whereas she herself could quickly shake things off, Sarah tended to dwell on them. This, Fran recalled, had never been more evident than when the family dog had died; although he had led a long and happy life Sarah mourned his passing for weeks while Fran was more practical.

"We can just get another dog if that's how you feel."

Sarah was more emotional and couldn't see how a new dog could possibly replace old Jed.

Sensing from Sarah's letters that she might be descending into a similar period of melancholy Fran thought long and hard as to how she might lift her spirits. She mentioned to her sister that she might be able to get a weekend off and come down to see her but Sarah didn't want to put her out, besides which there was the expense of the train fare.

The solution to the problem came from an unlikely quarter. Alfred Duckett was a director of the much respected Burnley building firm of James Duckett and Sons, a company that had been founded by Alfred's father, James; as a youngster James had followed his father into the cotton mill but he soon found that he was not suited to this life. He then joined his brother as an apprentice stone mason and they worked together on the erection of Saint Thomas' church in Barrowford, a village some five miles to the east of Burnley, between 1837 and 1841.

Shortly afterwards, while still in his teens, James was made a partner of the Duckett building firm and he never looked back. His reputation for quality building work meant that numerous large contracts for church buildings and houses in Lancashire towns were soon forthcoming.

James branched out into brick-making and was at the forefront of the new technology in this industry. Soon he was also manufacturing earthenware products for the sanitary-ware market and built a factory which occupied both sides of Blannel Street in Burnley. The new firm of James Duckett Sanitary Pipe Manufacturers went on to become one of the largest producers of its kind in the world. There was a

71

particularly strong market for their *'Duckett Underground Tippler Flush Toilet System'* and the aptly-named *'Duckett Clencher'* toilet bowl.

On one particular Saturday afternoon Fran was sitting by the kitchen range, lost deep in thought, when a strident clanging almost caused her to spill her tea. Scurrying to answer the front entrance bell Fran opened the door to reveal the impressive figure of a smartly dressed man whose bowler hat and expensive suit added to a general demeanour that radiated wealth.

Fran put on her best Sunday voice,

"Good hafternoon Sir, are you hexpected?"

She knew very well that the visitor was expected because Mrs Duckett had warned her that they were entertaining that evening. Nevertheless it gave Fran a feeling of satisfaction to follow this ritual of pretence.

"Ah, good afternoon my dear; Atkins - Mr Duckett is expecting me I believe."

Mr Atkins left his gloves and hat with Fran as she ushered him into the drawing room where her employers were waiting. Alfred Duckett rose to his feet and shook hands with his guest; physically the host was very different from his guest as became apparent when he stood up. The former was a short stocky man with a rotund waist while the visitor stood tall and erect. Both men sported a fashionable, bristling walrus moustache.

"Good afternoon James, glad you could make it. All's well with the family I hope?"

James Atkins nodded;

"Afternoon Alfred, aye, all's well – and you?"

Alfred Duckett and his wife, Rachel, ushered their guest into one of the large leather armchairs by the roaring fire that Fran had set earlier. Mrs Duckett always hired a cook when they were to entertain and it was Fran's job to help serve dinner. It turned out that the reason for James Atkins' visit was that Alfred Duckett was supplying the building materials for James' new venture in the neighbouring town of Nelson. Because this small cotton manufacturing town was only a couple of miles along the road from Burnley many of the builders there used the services of Alfred Duckett's firm. He also had a contract with the Nelson Borough Council to supply lime and mortar for the erection of their municipal buildings and the new town-gas works.

James Atkins owned a farm but his main business was that of supplying coal from his canal wharf at Reedyford, in Nelson. Like his father before him James had made a very good living from the increasing demand for coal and trade had gone from strength to strength. He was now branching out into the manufacture of town-gas, the fuel of the future as he saw it. To this end James was busy erecting a gasometer at Reedyford in order for him to supply gas to the town council.

There was another reason why the two business men were friends; they found this to be a mutual advantage in that both counted members of the Nelson Council as their friends. Alfred Duckett had many business dealings with Nelson mill owners as he had supplied a number of them with the materials to erect their mills. James Atkins knew many other factory owners through his coal business and he was particularly keen to expand his gas manufacturing enterprise. Between them the pair could count on a decent level of support within the various Council Committees and these business contacts were invaluable.

As dinner progressed Fran bustled in and out of the dining room keeping glasses filled and removing empty plates. Over port the two gentlemen lit up a pair of Alfred Duckett's finest cigars and the conversation turned to staff.

"That's a good lass you have there, Alfred, I wish we could find a reliable girl. Martha, my wife, has been looking for help for a while now. My mother-in-law and my aunt Betty live with us and do the house-keeping but Betty is nearly eighty now and it's getting too much for her. Trouble is there are so many people wanting domestics nowadays that we're struggling to find anyone suitable."

At this point Fran came in to check if the port and sherry decanters were in need of a refill.

73

"Now then Fran, Mr Atkins here was just singing your praises."

Fran coloured slightly but carried on undaunted.

"Oh, thank you Sir. You alright for port?"

"Yes lass, I think so. You could kindle the fire for us though."

As Fran busied herself with raking the dying embers and banking up new coals on the fire her employer went on to tell his guest that he and Rachel had been in the same position. He told him of his advertisement in the Birmingham newspaper that had led to Fran becoming a part of the Duckett household.

Fran heard this and quickly picked up from the gist of the conversation that Mr Atkins was looking for a domestic help. An idea immediately sparked in her head and before she had realised what she was doing she was speaking out loud.

"I don't mean to be forward, Sir, but I cunna help overhearing that you're in need of a help. If you are, Sir, then might you consider Sarah Ann, my sister? She's looking for a new position and she has good references and everything."

The two men looked at each other and the host pursed his lips.

"Now old chap, there's food for thought."

"Mmm, that's very interesting lass. We certainly need help. Just let me have a word with Mr Duckett will you?"

Fran left them to their port and cigars. Within the hour the parlour bell rang and Fran hurried through to answer her employer's call. Atkins was taking his leave and, as Fran brought him his hat and gloves, he told her that Mr Duckett assured him that he thought any sister of Fran's would surely be an asset to his household. The single clinching fact had been that the Davis sisters had been raised in the Wesleyan tradition and James Atkins happened to be a Wesleyan lay preacher.

"Here's my card, lass. Ask your sister to write if she might be interested in working for me and we'll see what we can do."

Fran returned to her kitchen duties and, when she had finished for the evening, took the introductory card from her apron pocket and read the address - *Spring Hill, Upper Park*

74

*Hill, Barrowford.* She had never been to the place but she knew that Barrowford was reasonably local.

After her Sunday chores were completed Fran sat down and excitedly wrote a letter to Sarah. It would be wonderful if her sister came to live nearby, they could spend time together and she was sure that Sarah would benefit from a new start.

Mrs Johnson handed Sarah the letter and she knew immediately that it was her sister's handwriting. She always liked to save her letters until her spare evening hours when she could read them at leisure so the envelope was carefully placed behind the mantle clock until the waiting day's chores were despatched.

That evening Sarah sat on her bed and read Fran's news. Having read the letter through twice the matter slowly began to take hold in Sarah's mind; it would appear that Fran had found her a job near to her new home in Lancashire. Putting the letter down on the bed Sarah began to consider this turn of events.

It had been almost a full year since Luke had taken his leave but she still missed him. True, they had corresponded and Luke had kept his promise to visit. He had returned last Easter, staying at his friend Bill's house overnight; Mrs Johnson gave Sarah the Saturday off and they had been overjoyed to spend a precious day together. The pair took the train into Birmingham and wandered the streets, hand-in-hand, looking every inch the happy couple.

Luke took Sarah into a restaurant with tablecloths for a meal and afterwards, as they walked along the main street, Sarah stopped short outside a jeweller's shop window. There, nestling in a small box lined with white silk was the most beautiful brooch she had ever seen. The midnight lustre of finest Whitby jet shone from the surface of the carved rose and Sarah could not take her eyes off it. Luke could see that she was taken by the object and within five minutes he had spent half of his weekly wage. Sarah was delighted with her gift and vowed that she would never part with it. The pair had high tea

75

in the town before returning to the Royal Oak for the evening but all too soon it was time for Luke to leave.

When Sarah pulled the bedclothes close around her that night her doubting side climbed into her thoughts, it knew that she had enjoyed a wonderful day and so it was time to redress the balance. The problem was that this long distance relationship held little satisfaction for a young woman and Sarah now faced long months before she might see her Luke again. They were trying to build a relationship through snatched visits and occasional letters and she felt that she was very much back in the same dull routine of daily life that had been her lot before she had met her young man.

There was also another thing to consider in life at the Royal Oak and that was the fact that business had been quiet lately. Mr Johnson said that it was because the old industries were moving out of the area and Harborne was becoming 'gentrified.' Most of the new influx of middle class residents did not drink in pubs and the few that did were no substitute for thirsty iron workers and miners. Sarah realised that the Johnson's would not require her services for very much longer.

John Davis was pleased, as always, to see his daughter on the following Sunday afternoon and he became thoughtful when she broached the matter of her having been offered a new position.

"Dunna you worry about me lass. You go to your sister. I'm fitter now and, besides which, your Aunt Mary calls in regular to see that I'm alright."

John knew that Sarah had been hurt by Luke's going and he agreed with Fran that she would benefit from a new start. That, then, was that. Sarah asked Reverend Tillotson for a reference and, of course, he was only too pleased to help. Mrs Johnson was sad to hear that Sarah would be leaving but she fully understood; she had seen the sadness in her eyes over these past months and she realised that things could not stay as they were forever. She wrote a short but glowing reference for Sarah in which she said that anyone lucky enough to employ her would not regret it.

# 9

# Hummadruz and Iron

Hurriedly fumbling in her handbag Sarah produced her ticket for the guard who tore off the top and returned the other half.

"Next stop Crewe – ten minutes."

For the first time in her life the Black Country girl found herself outside of her home county. The Cheshire town of Crewe was proud to be known as the centre of the thriving northern railway system - and it showed. The railway station here was truly overwhelming to the first time visitor; it took Sarah almost twenty minutes to book her onward journey and find the platform from which her train would leave. That said, she still found that she had fifteen minutes to spare before the 11.45 to Manchester would carry her into yet another strange county.

There was just enough time for refreshments and a quick splash of water in the ladies waiting room to clean off some of the sooty morning. The onward train had as many carriages as the previous one but Sarah found that she only had three companions on this leg of the journey. Within ten minutes the train was steaming happily through the open Cheshire grassland to the north of Crewe and again Sarah began to be lulled by the steady sway of the carriage.

Her eyes closed and almost immediately a vision of Luke appeared; his eyes were slightly mocking as he mouthed something that Sarah could not quite catch. His face seemed to loom from the darkness before it slowly melted into scenes from Sarah's past – almost as if his image was acting as a surreal Master of Ceremonies introducing a magic lantern show.

Strangely, Sarah began to visualise Queen Victoria aboard her royal train - the probable explanation for this would be a memory triggered by Sarah's journey between Birmingham and Stoke-on-Trent. Sarah recalled a conversation between her dad and Uncle Reuben when they had both read a story in the weekly newspaper. A member of Queen Victoria's staff had let it slip that whenever the Royal train made one of its frequent trips to Scotland the sovereign always ordered that the window blinds be closed as it passed through the Black Country. This was to protect her from the disquieting sight of the industrial scenery which obviously offended her Royal Highness.

"Bloody cheek," was Reuben's opinion,

"She dunna complain when we're making the guns for her armies, digging coal for her fires and making nails to build her palaces!"

John had been equally peeved with what the whole of the Black Country considered to be an insult.

"Aye, and her husband was glad of our lads when he wanted his glass house building."

This was a reference to the massive construction undertaken by the Chance glass factory, in Smethwick, for Prince Albert's Crystal Palace Exhibition of 1851. The Black Country had supplied the materials and the craftsmen to erect the acres of glass needed for the Prince Consort's design and the palace proved to be a huge success.

The general consensus was that the Queen, through an innate ignorance of the industrial heartland of her empire, had missed the fundamental essence of the Black Country. She saw the smoking chimney stacks, heaps of rusting metal, the pit heads with their skeletal winding gear framed against a sulphurous sky. She saw the grey carpet of housing criss-crossing the landscape with demonic columns of black vapour interspersing the matrix - but she saw no further.

The Queen could never have realised the humanity within this vast living entity that, in the vernacular, 'Ate coal, drank molten iron and shat liquid gold.' The genuine sense of dignity and pride of the skilled workers within the rolling scene was matched only by an open honesty that a sovereign might never see within the closed realms of power.

If Victoria were to have opened her blinds on a night journey through Staffordshire she would have seen a sight that astonished everyone who ever witnessed it. As the mustard sunset gave way to darkness a pyrotechnic display of truly Dantean proportions ensued. Innumerable forges and furnaces blasted the Black Country basin into a wonderland of exploding light. From many miles away the yellow glow of a thousand artificial suns competed with the brilliant incandescence of newly forged iron. Living, crackling, spitting, soaring sparks filled the outer darkness of the night as they rose in their short arc of life.

This was the outward show provided by the industrial landscape of the Black Country but the true heart of the place was reflected in an extract from an early nineteenth century broadside ballad that Sarah's father had learned from his father;

> *Oh, the slaves abroad in the sugar canes,*
> *Find plenty to help and pity their pains,*
> *But the slaves at home in the mine and the fire*
> *Find plenty to pity but none to admire*

In reality, then, when the Queen closed her carriage blinds she was making a very real statement; to her there was no beauty within the heart of her nation. Instead she found within the empty acres of Scotland all the space she required to indulge a self-imposed, solitary and prolonged widowhood - and the working people of Staffordshire knew it.

The carriage gave a sharp jolt as it rode a loose joint in the rails and Sarah sat up; the smartly dressed man opposite smiled.

79

"We don't want too many of those, gave me quite a start!"

Sarah smiled and nodded; she was soon drifting back into her thoughts and the vision of Luke still swam there. The lazy barking of a dog somewhere in the distance of a hot summer's day filled the dreamer's thoughts and she was back on The Lyndon.

Sarah's mother, Emma, had died when Sarah had been twelve and Fran ten; Emma was a kind and understanding mother and, naturally, her husband and children thought the world of her. She was a proud woman with an air of quiet authority that belied her position in life. An overriding memory for Sarah was of her mother's warm, all-enveloping embrace; this brought comfort to many over the years and Sarah was not the least amongst them. To all the children on The Lyndon she was Aunty Emma and they knew whose door to go to when they had fallen and grazed a knee.

Sarah remembered vividly the day that she had been given a new dress for the Whitsun parade when all the local chapels marched proudly through the streets. She had worn the dress with pride and, following the chapel service, John and Emma went home leaving the sisters to play in the Sunday school grounds.

It was time for dinner and the girls headed home; Sarah vented her high spirits by climbing onto a low wall and running along it for most of the length of Lyndon Street. Needless to say she slipped and fell, covering herself and the dress in thick black mud. Sister Fran thought this was hilarious and lost no time in predicting the reaction of their parents when she arrived home in that state!

With tears streaming down her cheeks Sarah sidled into the house and awaited the scolding that Fran had so confidently predicted. Immediately weighing up the situation Emma sat Sarah down on her knee.

"Come on child, dunna worry – nobody's been hurt have they? Let's get you cleaned up and we'll take that dress round to Aunty Mary, she'll have it good as new in no time."

Sarah's father smiled down on this happy scene and thanked God for the family with which he was blessed. John had worked all of his life in the local iron industry; he began as a furnace man and, working alongside his brother Reuben, had risen to the respected position of iron puddler. He worked for many years at the foundry of Richard Disturnal and Company, near Wednesbury Bridge, where, in the 1850s, they made coach springs and axles for the railway rolling stock.

As a puddler John was responsible for smelting crude and scrap cast iron in a specially constructed furnace. The puddler had to know his material intimately and he also needed to read the furnace temperature with exact precision. When the product of the furnace was judged to be exactly right the puddler removed the spitting fiery molten globe of iron as if he were harnessing an earth-bound meteor. The molten ball was then placed in a barrow and wheeled to the steam-hammer where constant blows served to remove impurities and consolidate the wrought iron.

In short, the puddler turned brittle cast iron into malleable wrought iron and the process ensured that a supply of the material was available to satiate the national hunger for this material. All branches of industry, from the home-based nail maker to the engineers who produced every kind of machinery, required a constantly increasing supply of good quality wrought iron. An expanding industrial world greedily consumed every pound of the material that it could get its hands on and always wanted more.

John, Emma, Sarah and Fran lived in a small worker's house on The Lyndon within a parish of some 25,000 people. Sarah had been born in this house during the first snows of 1865 and the family were well settled in the area. The Lyndon neighbourhood was largely made up of iron workers and on many occasions groups of these men would gather on the street and remember the 'old days.' The older men were fond of recalling the days of some twenty-five years ago when they worked at the local Phoenix Ironworks. A huge overseas market for corrugated iron sheeting had developed during the

Californian and Australian gold rushes of 1849 and 1851-52 and the iron workers enjoyed full employment with relatively high rates of pay.

"Aye, them were the days," a grizzled chap of around seventy puffed on his stubby old pipe as his eyes misted.

"Tin roofs, musket parts by the million and plenty o' coal."

This was a common subject among the Black Country miners and iron workers during the 1870s. Most of them remembered the heady days before the South Staffordshire coal and ironstone fields began to run out.

Coupled with this, the overseas markets were rapidly becoming adept at supplying their own iron and steel. Emigrant workers from Shropshire, Staffordshire and Warwickshire had been flooding into the New World and their skilled labour ensured a home supply of wrought and cast iron. In the earlier decades of the nineteenth century many Black Country iron workers had specialised in the production of trigger mechanisms for the Birmingham musket trade and countless numbers of these were supplied to skilled local workers who filed them with the machine-like precision. Many of the finished triggers were attached to weapons for the military and yet more were exported to the Colonies.

The plains of Western America, the Australian hinterland and the South Africa savannah were all heavily populated by ex-Europeans intent upon expanding their interests and a massive supply of reliable firearms was vital to them. Again, this greedy market for Black Country goods was not to last as, in the face of increased competition from German iron manufacturers and a cheap supply of guns from the new American armourers, the Birmingham trade suffered.

Nevertheless, things were not too bad in the early 1870s for John Davis. The great diversification of products leaving the Birmingham iron foundries ensured that the industry ticked over and, by 1874, he had secured a job at a small foundry supplying the local Patent Nut and Bolt Co. Ltd with wrought iron bars.

When Emma had fallen pregnant with her second daughter, Fran, the family were delighted, none more so than Sarah who thought it would be wonderful to have a baby sister or brother. Unfortunately Emma contracted diphtheria when she had been carrying the child for five months and Doctor Starkey had been worried for the lives of both mother and baby. With the help of his sister-in-law John made sure that Emma did not have to overdo things in her final sixteen weeks; when they had finished their day's work they cleaned the house, cooked for the family, did the washing and went to the shops.

When the day arrived the new baby weighed just two and-a-half pounds and the doctor ordered her to be washed down twice every day with olive oil. By all appearances mother and daughter were none the worse for Emma's untimely illness but little did they know that there would be tragic consequences. A week following Sarah's twelfth birthday Emma collapsed in the street and by the time Doctor Starkey arrived she was dead. The doctor stated that Emma had died from heart failure and this was almost certainly due to damage caused during her bought of diphtheria.

The happiness of the small family on The Lyndon had been shattered within the blinking of an eye. John's work at the face of the open furnace had made him hard and strong, there had been nothing that he would not take on physically but the death of his dear wife hit him like the blow from a sledge-hammer.

The family struggled to come to terms with Emma's untimely demise at the age of forty-eight. The girls drifted through their final years at school without much enthusiasm and John's health deteriorated. Friends and neighbours rallied around and did the best they could to help the family while Aunt Mary took over Emma's roll until the Lyndon household returned to as near a normal life as possible.

Sarah found that her doubting side was only too ready to surface at the smallest opportunity but she came to realise that by living each day as it came she was able to keep her darker thoughts in check. For a while Fran drifted, she lost her sparkle and was often in trouble at school; she had fallen in with a group from the rougher end of town and John was worried where this might lead. Fortunately, after she had taken up her part-time work at the grocery, things began to return to a semblance of normality.

Things would have been easier for the family if Sarah's grandparents had been living at this difficult time. The girls loved their Gran and Grandpa and Sarah had many happy memories of when her dad would take them visiting to their small house in Bilston. Grandpa Davis had been in his mid-seventies at that time and Sarah always thought that his snow-white hair and moustache made him look quite distinguished. Gran was a full ten years younger and was a small, light-framed woman who was never still, bustling here and there all day long. The elder Davis family would make a fuss of the girls; there were always treats for them and Grandpa would seat each of them on his knee in turns and tell them stories.

Both Davis grandparents had been born and raised in the village of Clun, in Shropshire; the nearby Teme Valley was a hop growing area that every autumn attracted a mass of people from the Black Country who would appear in the district to pick the crop. This was a source of income for the Staffordshire people, many of whom were struggling nail makers. The migrant workers brought with them stories of the growth in trade in the Black Country and how anyone who was willing to work the coal fields or the iron foundries would find a job with little difficulty.

Following their marriage both grandparents migrated across to Bilston where Grandpa found work as a collier. He was fond of telling the girls of his childhood and one story in particular stayed with Sarah.

On the outskirts of Clun there were forest areas which stretched over to the Teme Valley. There were also ranges of hills for a young lad to climb and he was often to be found wandering their weathered heights. One spot that he was particularly fond of was an area where an ancient stone circle, known as the Whet Stones, stood in proud isolation.

84

Sometimes, as the youngster sat day-dreaming among the upright stones, a strange deeply resonant buzzing would fill the summer air. The local people were well aware of this ethereal phenomenon and gave it the name of *'The Hummadruz.'*

Nobody ever knew where the sound originated although many people tried to get to the bottom of it. There was little industry in the area to cause such a noise and it never came from a single direction. Grandpa said that when you were on the hills you could not only hear the Hummadruz but you could actually feel a kind of vibration in your body. Whenever the girls had misbehaved in some way he would lift them up and rub his bristly chin against their face.

"Now then, if you don't watch out young'un I'll give you to the Hummadruz!"

Grandpa could remember the Black Country of the early 1800s and a major change that he had seen was the demise of the home-based nail makers. When he and Grandma had first arrived in Bilston almost every other house was occupied by a nail making family. These workers were supplied with iron bars by nail masters from the nearby towns who would later collect the finished product.

Nail making was a hard and unrewarding way of life; the work was usually carried out in nail shops about ten feet square, the only outlet for the smoke and fumes from the forge being a single doorway and small unglazed windows. Three or four families would crowd around the forge, heating the iron bar and hammering it into shape in an iron forming block.

The poverty of the nail makers was matched by the increasing wealth of the nail masters and this led to a great deal of simmering discontent in the nail districts. Unfortunately the nail makers were scattered far and wide and this prevented the formation of a viable union. The problem of low pay was further exacerbated from 1830 when new machines began to mass produce nails thus lowering the price of the finished product.

Another incident that Grandpa Davis would relate to the girls was the outbreak of cholera in Bilston in 1832. Sarah's father had been six years old at the time and his parents were worried that the child might succumb to the dreadful disease. The major expansion of population within the Bilston area led to overcrowding, poor sanitation and poor water quality and this was major factor in the rapid spread of cholera.

Fortunately the Davis family were able to avoid the disease but the deaths of one person in very twenty had hit the community hard. Everyone who survived knew friends, relatives or neighbours who had died and it would be a long time before the scars left by the visitation of cholera began to heal.

The days of being a part of an extended family were now over for Sarah and Fran, their grandparents on both sides of the family were dead and so was their mother. With a sigh Sarah opened her eyes and was once again in the reality of the swaying train carriage as it sped steadily northward.

She began to clear her thoughts as the scenery rapidly changed from rolling green fields with their lattice-work of stone walls. An increasing number of buildings now filled the view from the carriage window as the train approached its destination of Manchester and, seeing that Sarah was awake, the man in the opposite seat smiled at her.

"Well, we're almost there. Do you live in Manchester?"

Sarah explained that she was travelling on to East Lancashire.

"Ah, yes, I know it well. I travel for a Manchester cotton factor and I deal with quite a few manufacturers over that way. You'll have need to change across to Victoria Station for your onward train but it's easy enough. There's a regular tramway service now for connecting passengers, you'll find it just outside the station."

Within a matter of minutes the guard was announcing their arrival at Manchester London Road. Sarah gathered her bag, put on the tweed overcoat and made her way towards the arrow indicating the exit from the station.

Having handed her ticket to the clerk at the exit Sarah emerged onto the Manchester streets and, sure enough, outside stood a horse-drawn tram with the words *Manchester Carriage and Tramway Company* written in gold lettering along the sides. Her enquiry confirmed that this was the connecting service between Manchester's main stations and she climbed aboard. The ticket clerk at Victoria Station told Sarah that her onward journey to Burnley would require her to take the 1.30 to Accrington where a connecting service would take her onward.

This allowed for a half-hour break at Victoria and Sarah made full use of it to freshen up and have something to eat. Within the hour the Accrington train was steaming through a steady drizzle of rain as it left Manchester behind. The massive outlines of red-brick mills appeared and disappeared, dwarfing any other buildings that happened to exist within their shadow. As these textile temples became fewer a steady pattern emerged of small built-up areas interspersed by open fields. Some of the smaller stations along the way carried names that Sarah thought were quite odd, Ramsbottom and Oswaldtwistle in particular sounded distinctly foreign to a Black Country girl.

The waiting passengers at Accrington Station saw the inbound train from Manchester slowly materialise from out of the grey distance. The engine ground to a halt and Sarah was about to step down onto the platform when a great commotion erupted outside the next carriage. A woman was screaming and others were shouting for the guard to come; the cause of the drama soon became apparent when the guard arrived and plucked a young girl from where she had fallen between the platform and the stationary train. The girl's mother was beside herself, she shouted unmercifully at the shaken girl and this only served to upset the child even more. By this time a crowd had gathered and a man who had seen the girl fall said that she had been impatient to board the carriage before the other passengers had alighted and in her rush had slipped down the platform gap.

Another onlooker spoke to Sarah.

"S'not t'fst time tha'nos. T'platform wern't built reight int' f'st place, t'edg's in't wrong shop an gap's too gert."

Sarah looked askance at the chap, wondering what part of the world he was from. He certainly did not speak English as Sarah knew it but, from the style of his clothes, he didn't look any different from the men in Sarah's home town - other than he was wearing a pair of clogs. The chap waved at the large gap between the running step of the carriages and the platform edge and Sarah assumed that this was what he was talking about. If this was the way that people spoke in Lancashire then Sarah thought she was going to be in trouble.

The ticket clerk spoke in much the same way,

"Aye lass, tha's wantin' t'other platform fer B'nley." But at least she got the gist of this.

As the train built up speed Sarah knew that, at last, she was on the final part of her long journey north. The raindrops that had raced each other down the carriage windows of the 3.20 to Burnley were now scurrying horizontally and, between the tiny rivulets, the shining wet grey-slate roofs of thousands of terraced houses slid by. Built in rows of varying lengths the houses gave the impression of designed chaos; some reached out towards the moors while others followed the line of the railway and its parallel companion, the Leeds and Liverpool canal.

Everywhere she looked Sarah saw a forest of tall factory chimneys; some were billowing out black plumes of smoke to be swept westwards to the moors while others stood silent in the watery air. These were the cotton weaving mills that Sarah had heard about; from a distance she thought that they did not look as bad as people said they were. Each mill boasted a single chimney to launch the smoke from its Lancashire boilers skywards and the mill buildings were smaller than those to be seen in the Manchester and Rochdale region. To the newcomer, in actual fact, the landscape had the feeling of being a much scaled down version of the Black Country. There was a definite openness about the place once you looked beyond the boundaries of the small towns.

The monotony of the two-storied houses was broken by the larger buildings of churches and chapels and, of course, everywhere stood the monolithic mill chimneys. To Sarah the sprawling houses looked much the same as her homeland except in this part of Lancashire they were built out of honey-coloured sandstone instead of brick. Beyond the grasping reach of the streets were green fields sweeping up to distant moorlands and this gave the passing settlements the appearance of being huddled together in a long valley.

The same pattern of terraced streets passed the carriage window as the train clattered over an embankment along the edge of the town of Padiham. Within minutes the embankment gave way to a deep cutting and the passengers heard the guard call 'Burnley - Rosegrove.'

Rosegrove was the main rail station in the town of Burnley, a fact reflected in the large goods yards and sheds visible from the carriage window. Having exchanged one handful of passengers for another the engine gave a few mighty gasps and within minutes was coasting into the next station; this was the one that Sarah had been waiting for, 'Burnley - Barracks.'

Sarah had been apprehensive throughout her journey but the tension was now overtaken by a feeling of excitement; she was about to see her Fran again after all this time. Thoughts raced through her mind - would her sister have changed - would a newcomer be made welcome here and what did her future hold in this land of menhiric chimneys?

It had been arranged that Sarah was to stay with Fran for the weekend. Mr and Mrs Duckett had kindly offered to put her up and gave Fran two days off so that the sisters could spend time together. On the Monday Sarah was to travel on to her new home at Barrowford but for now the sisters were to be reunited for two whole days.

# 10

# Burnley

The iron-squeal of the braking engine echoed around Burnley Barracks station and as the final plumes of steam curled away from beneath the carriages Sarah stepped down onto the platform. The first thing that she noticed was that the drizzle had stopped but, even so, the stone platform flagstones were still shiny and looked as though they might be slippery. The second thing to strike Sarah was an overpowering smell that she could not quite identify; it was sweet but not unpleasant as it drifted heavily on the breeze. Sarah's carriage had pulled up at the far end of the station and as she looked down towards the passenger building a small crowd of people moved forward. Some were greeting passengers from the train but most were waiting to board.

The new arrival buttoned her overcoat, carefully fastened the brass pin of her jet brooch, picked up the small travel bag and began to walk towards the building. As she peered anxiously along the platform a figure emerged from the milling group and began to run towards her with both arms fully outstretched. Even before she had seen the shock of red hair spilling from the sides of her bonnet Sarah knew that the approaching figure was her Fran. With a cry of delight Fran threw her arms around Sarah's neck and almost bowled her over.

"Sarah! At last you're here, I dunna believe it."

Both the young women were crying and laughing at the same time. Sarah took a step back and looked her sister up and down.

"Well, who's this lovely young woman? She looks a bit like my little sis but she's all grown up!"

Fran had indeed grown up. Her figure had filled out and she was no longer the gangly youth that Sarah had waved goodbye to on Harborne Station.

"I swear, you're even prettier than ever. They must be feeding you well up here!"

Fran laughed and told Sarah that she too had changed; she had lost her slightly chubby face and now looked every inch a grown woman. Actually Fran thought that her sister looked pale and drawn around the eyes but she put this down to the long journey. Fran also noticed that Sarah looked quite grubby, her white collar in particular carried a black tide-mark from exposure to hours of sooty rail travel.

"Come on sister, let's get you back to the house and you can freshen up."

The two linked arms and made for the station exit where Sarah handed in the remnant of her ticket. The girls stepped out of the station and made their way chattering and laughing along Junction Street. Number twenty-eight Accrington Road was what Mr Duckett called 'nobbut a spit-and-a-stride' from the station and the pair were soon sitting before the blazing kitchen range.

"Right, I'll get you a jug of hot water and you can change into a clean collar and cuffs before you meet the family."

Sarah smiled at her sister's fussing, Fran had certainly changed in the past three years – she was quite the professional domestic now!

Having done as she was told Sarah followed Fran through to the parlour; Fran tapped on the door and popped her head into the room.

"Hello Sir, we're back. Can I introduce my sister Sarah?"

Fran beckoned her visitor into the room and there Sarah saw the stocky figure of Alfred Duckett with his head stuck inside a huge grandfather clock.

"Not be a second," came a muffled voice from inside the open clock case.

Mr Duckett extricated himself from the clock and set the large brass pendulum in motion. Standing with his head cocked slightly to one side he listened intently to the tic-toc of the movement as the pendulum went lazily about its business. A slight adjustment to the back of the clock movement made the tic-toc more even in its rhythm and he appeared satisfied. He replaced the heavy mahogany hood, closed and locked the door in the front of the case and stood back to admire his handywork. The seven-foot monster ticked away quietly now that the hood had been replaced and, with a final check of his gold pocket watch to calibrate the time, Mr Duckett turned to Sarah.

"Sorry my dear, damned thing's been hunting time lately. Better now, I think. So! You must be the sister that our Fran has told us so much about. Very pleased to meet you at last. Had a good journey?"

Sarah smiled, she could see in Mr Duckett a kindly man.

"Yes, thank you Sir. The trains have been running well, I'm just a bit tired, been a long day."

"Well I'm sure that you have plenty to catch up on the pair of you. I hope you'll be comfortable while you're with us."

Sarah thanked her host again and, on her way out of the room, mentioned that the she never seen such an impressive clock. There had been a grandfather clock in the corner of the saloon in the Royal Oak but it must have been almost two feet shorter than Mr Duckett's. Recognising the familiar depth of colour within the mahogany Sarah felt an urge to touch the clock case, to run her hands over the highly polished resonance of the glowing surface.

"Aye, lass, it's a grand piece of workmanship," he ran a finger over the intricate carving and fine Grecian columns of the case.

"It's a Manchester clock, eight-day movement, moon phase dial. . ."

At that moment Mrs Duckett swept into the parlour and smiled at the sight of her husband waxing lyrical over his daft old clock.

"Now, now Alfred, don't be boring these girls with your clock, once you start you know you can go on about it for hours!"

Her husband frowned in a feigned show of injured pride and winked at Sarah but she did not notice; she was looking around the room and taking in the heavy furniture that filled every spare inch. A heavy carved sideboard, topped grandly by a large oyster-shaped mirror, stood next to a writing desk which in turn rubbed shoulders with a piano standing by a bureau. . . Sarah noticed that every piece of furniture was of her favourite mahogany and she drooled at the thought of lovingly polishing this lot. She didn't mention to Fran how lucky she thought she was to be able to lavish attention on all that wood for fear that she would get the same negative reaction as she had from Ann at the Royal Oak!

As soon as Sarah stepped out of the house she noticed the same smell that had greeted her at the station and asked Fran what it was. Fran sniffed the air and looked at her sister as if to say 'what smell?' when the penny suddenly dropped.

"Oh that! I'm so used to it that I don't notice it anymore. That's Bridge End Brewery."

Sarah then realised why the smell had been familiar; the sweetness came from brewing malt and this was similar to the smell of the newly opened barrels of Mitchell's beer in the Royal Oak.

"Come on," Fran tugged at Sarah's arm, "We're going right past the place, I'll show you."

They walked down the hill and, sure enough, at the bottom stood the overwhelming bulk of Massey's Burnley Brewery. Carts and wagons were busily entering and leaving the yard and the overpowering aroma of the embryonic Massey's Golden Bitter from within the huge edifice almost knocked Sarah off her feet.

Within a short distance they came to the large market building and the girls made straight for the refreshment hall. Eyeing the menu Sarah pointed at the list and looked puzzled.

"What's this -Black pudding?" The bill of fare became even stranger as she looked further down the list,

"Tripe and elder, cow heel, pig's trotters, sheep's brains on oatcake, stew and hard?"

Fran remembered that this was exactly the same reaction she had when first confronted with this odd-sounding food.

"It's nowhere near as bad as it sounds. In fact I've got quite used to black puddings, they say they're good for you. The stew and hard is good too, it's like the pork brawn that mam used to make but it comes with flat oatcake and raw onions."

Sarah played safe and ordered mutton stew while Fran tucked into a plate of thinly-sliced roast beef. Sarah related the incident on Accrington Station where she couldn't understand a word the chap on the platform said and the conversation turned to the local accent. Fran sympathised with her sister as she had also experienced difficulty at first in understanding the broad local dialect.

"Narthen lass, don't thee werry, tha'al soon pick up t'local manner o' speykin'," Fran laid on the Lancashire accent with a trowel and they both burst into laughter. She explained that the broadest speakers tended to be the factory workers and country people; each rank of society had its own level of dialect, the higher levels tended to use the dialect only rarely. Sarah thought of Alfred Duckett and realised that she had understood him perfectly.

"One thing," said Fran, "You'll have no trouble understanding Mr Atkins at Barrowford, he's fairly posh."

Fran showed Sarah a little of the town before the early autumn dusk began to draw in; they walked down Saint James Street where crowds of people scurried here and there. The men wore leather clogs on the soles of which were fastened horseshoe-like 'irons'; these made a loud clattering sound as they passed over the sandstone flag pavements and granite 'sets' of the cobbled streets. Many of the women also wore clogs and all had woollen shawls which they wrapped around their heads or across their shoulders.

The people who had recently finished their day's work in the cotton mills hurried homeward, or, in some cases, to the pub, while the housewives could be distinguished by the wicker baskets that they carried. The contents of these could be a loaf of bread or a small cut of meat, a few vegetables and perhaps a couple of herring; the baskets were invariably covered by a white linen cloth to keep out the airborne soot.

Outside the theatres and hotels on Saint James Street the tourists caught a tram for the short trundle across to Brunshaw. Fran pointed out the sign saying *Turf Moor* and told Sarah that this was the new home of the Burnley Football Club. Turf Moor had been the home of Burnley Cricket Club for years but now the Football Club had moved from Calder Vale and were to be based there.

"According to Mr Duckett the football team is sponsored by Charles Massey from the brewery and he said that they had to play in the brewery livery of amber and black."

"Oh, right," to Sarah the Turf Moor appeared to be nothing more than a sloping field with a fence around it and a large mound at one end but, then again, she knew absolutely nothing about football.

Sarah had seen the massive pit head wheel and its attendant chimneys in the distance but tried her best to ignore it. This was only the second one that she had seen since coming to Burnley and she now realised why she had found the local landscape much less overbearing than that of home. Fran remembered her sister's aversion to these spinning monsters and pointed up the dusty, rutted lane leading towards it.

"Don't worry Sister, we wunna be going up there. That's Bank Hall Pit and further along is the workhouse with its infirmary and smallpox separation houses."

Sarah gave a slight shudder and gratefully followed Fran as they walked the few hundred yards back into the centre of town. Here the pair passed another brewery, this time the sign on the towering building proclaimed: *Well Hall Brewery;* although it was now operated by Mr Grimshaw this brewery had been started by the Kierby family. As they turned into Calder Vale Road, Fran turned to Sarah.

"This'll make you feel at home!"

When Sarah saw the Atlas Iron Works she realised what her tour guide had meant.

"There are foundries all over the town," the sweep of Fran's hand described a full circle.

"I've been told that they make more cotton looms here than anywhere else in the world." She considered this for a moment.

"But they're not the same size as the foundries at home."

Fran took her guest on a different route back to Accrington Road; they turned up by the large corner building of the Bull Hotel and along Manchester Road where she pointed out the impressive Mechanics Institute building and the School of Art. Higher up, as they turned towards the area known as Trafalgar, they passed a large building from which a number of cotton merchants operated. They walked along the Trafalgar where the cotton mills jostled for position along the roadside and, reaching the cross-roads, they turned down Accrington Road towards the Holy Trinity church. Having passed the General Havelock and the Angel public houses they soon came to Trinity Terrace in the middle of which stood the Duckett household.

The terrace had been built only a few years earlier and contrasted sharply with the other terraces along Accrington Road. Whereas most of the houses along here were erected as worker's dwellings Trinity Terrace was obviously of a higher status. The smooth-faced sandstone glowed amber and pink in the dying sun and the houses here were much larger than their neighbours. Trinity had been designed with the professional person in mind and every house here could, indeed, boast a middle class family.

Within minutes Sarah and Fran were taking off their coats in the kitchen; the watery autumn light was fading rapidly now and Fran pulled the chord of the ceiling gas light and the room slowly filled with a warm yellow glow. She brought out a heavy stoneware jar from the pantry and poured them each a glass of cloudy ginger beer as Sarah sank gratefully into a chair at the large table.

"I'll be glad to get these shoes off Fran, my feet are killing me!"

From the other end of the house drifted the high-pitched bell of Mr Duckett's pride and joy as it struck the hour of eight o'clock.

"You must be tired after such a long day, you just tell me when you're ready for bed."

"Well," Sarah took a drink of the sweet spicy concoction, "I wouldn't mind going up after I've finished this."

Sarah was to have her own bedroom; she had expected to share with Fran and this would have been no problem, after all they had shared a bed for most of their lives when they were on The Lyndon. A room of her own, then, was an unexpected luxury and, as Sarah's head hit the firm feather-filled bolster, she let out a deep sigh. There had not been a moment during the day when she could fully relax and the constant strain had taken its toll. Within minutes she was drifting into sleep and all the while the constant *rat-a-ta-tat, rat-a-ta-tat* of drumming train wheels filled her head. Sarah's exhaustion proved to have one distinct advantage in that her dark companion did not surface that night.

The clatter of clog-irons in the street woke Sarah early on the Saturday morning. Fran was already up and about, even though she had been given two days off she could not tear herself from breakfast duties. The bedroom door opened and Fran brought her guest a large jug of hot water, a bar of Hudson's soap and a towel.

"See you downstairs when you're ready, sleepyhead."

Sarah appeared in the kitchen fifteen minutes later and Mrs Duckett was already seated at the table with her son.

"Good morning Sarah, sleep well?"

"Like a log ma'm, thank you. I certainly feel better this morning."

"Good, good. This is George by the way." Picking up the toast that the child had dropped on the floor she took his hand.

"George, say hello to Sarah."

"Hello," the child was dressed in a head-to-toe woollen night smock out of which an intelligent chubby face smiled up at Sarah.

"It's my birthday next week – I'm three."

Sarah laughed and shook the lad's hand in mock solemnity.

"Do you know Fran?" his big brown eyes were quizzical.

"Oh yes, Fran's my sister and I've come to visit for a couple of days."

Satisfied, the youngster tucked into his boiled egg and soldiers while Fran served up the same to Sarah with a few rashers of bacon on the side.

"Where are you girls off to today, anything planned?"

"Not sure yet ma'm, we'll have to have a think." Fran had not thought beyond Sarah's arrival. As far as she was concerned they could be anywhere as long as they were spending the time together.

The girls were in no hurry to go out, it was nice just to catch up on each other's lives. Fran wanted to know about the family back home; Sarah brought her up to date with the news and Fran broached the subject of Luke.

"Well, to be honest Fran his letters have been tailing off lately. They don't arrive as often as they did at first. Anyway, I've given him my new address in Barrowford so he can still write to me."

Fran could see that this was a very sensitive subject for her sister and she pressed it no further.

"I know what we can do, the Burnley Theatre and Assembly Room Company are putting on a show this afternoon – *When Love's Embers Die* – what do you think?"

Fran immediately realised that she had put her foot in it.

"Oh I'm sorry Sarah. I never thought, both feet as usual."

"Don't be daft," Sarah hadn't even registered her sister's slight *faux pas*.

"Let's go, I haven't been to the theatre in ages."

The downstairs clock was half-way through striking eight o'clock when Sarah awoke. There had been no clatter of weaver's clogs that Sunday morning and she was glad of the lie-in. She dressed in her best clothes and, after a leisurely breakfast, set out with Fran and the Duckett family for the morning church service.

When Fran first arrived in Burnley she had been surprised to find that the Duckett family were not actually of the Methodist persuasion, as everyone back home had assumed. They were members of the Congregational church, or 'Congos' as it was more commonly known. As far as Fran was concerned this was not of any great importance; like the Wesleyan church, the 'Congos' was non-conformist and she had no qualms about attending their services.

The sisters linked arms and fell in behind Fran's employers as they took the short walk past the Mitre Hotel and down to the Westgate Congregational church. As the morning worshippers filed quietly into their pews it became obvious to Sarah that Fran was a popular member of the church. In particular, young men would make a point of speaking to her.

'Morning Miss Fran, lovely day,' and so on. Sarah looked at her sister as she conversed with yet another admirer and thought to herself that it was no surprise that the chaps had taken a shine to Fran, she looked so radiant in her Sunday outfit.

The sermon that morning was to be given by a guest minister from the nearby Anglican Church. The Reverend J M Owen was a tall, thin man with a slight stoop and he had been the vicar of the Holy Trinity church, within whose parish the Ducketts lived, for five years. The theme of his sermon was;

*'The brotherhood of man and the benefits of co-operation between religious denominations.'*

On the short walk back to Trinity Terrace Mr Duckett walked with the sisters.

"He's a good man, Reverend Owen, works hard for his parish. He only has two curates to help him run four Sunday schools, two mission rooms and the church itself. There's nearly 17,000 people in his parish."

It crossed Sarah's mind that, with all that work to do, it was little wonder the poor chap's shoulders were stooped.

In the afternoon Fran took her guest along to the Mechanics Hall where she often met up with other domestics from the neighbourhood. They would gather in the tea room and chatter about all manner of things; the news, happenings around the town and, more than any other subject, their families. The girls never actually gave away personal information about their employers – they were too loyal for that. However, the comings and goings of their masters, the antics of the children, these were things that were open for discussion and this allowed the girls to compare their position. Hearing of the lot of some of her more unfortunate colleagues Fran realised, very soon after she arrived in Burnley, that she was well-off with the Duckett family.

Sarah immediately settled in this company, these were the type of girls that she was familiar with and she felt as though she had known them for years; their quick sense of humour and easy-going manner were like a breath of fresh air.

A slight hush suddenly descended on the tea room and the girls noticed that people were looking round to where a small group had made their entrance through the large glass doors. The object of the attention was a woman whose rather short stature was compensated for by the flamboyance of her dress. She wore a tan-coloured pair of gazelle-skin boots that reached almost to the knee and, rather daringly, the hem of her pleated skirt only just reached the top of the boots. A waistcoat-like blouse was fastened by means of leather laces and the whole thing was finished off by a short coat of pale-green velveteen. There was no boring Sunday bonnet for this lady; her head was adorned by a wide brimmed, rather faded leopard-skin hat that gave her the appearance of being taller than she actually was.

Accompanying the colourful new arrival were the familiar figures of Doctor John Brown and his wife, Mary. The Browns had been in Burnley since 1879 and had made a definite impression on the people of the town. Mary, or Mrs Doctor Brown as she was known locally, carried out unstinting works with the poor and destitute and as a consequence she was highly respected.

Mary was a native of South Africa and had been a friend of the explorer, Doctor David Livingstone, who had stayed with her family near Cape Town. Mary met her husband when he was working in South Africa and, following their marriage, had returned to England with him.

The eyes of the tea room followed the trio as they sat at a table beneath the window in the far corner and ordered tea and fancies. A young man at the next table to the Davis sister's party leaned over to his friend and told him in a hushed voice that he knew who the stranger was. Although she knew that it was rude to eavesdrop on other people's conversations Sarah could not help herself as she strained to pick up the low tones of her neighbour. It became apparent that the young man was a medical student and he knew Doctor Brown. He also knew that the popular author, Ralph Iron, was a close friend of the Doctor and his family. In reality this was a pseudonym because Ralph Iron was actually a lady called Olive Schreiner. Olive lived in South Africa and, as a close friend of Mary Brown, was visiting while she was in England to promote her new publication '*The Story of an African Farm.*'

When the sisters returned to Trinity Terrace Fran mentioned the exotically dressed lady and Mr Duckett confirmed that the stranger was indeed Olive Schreiner.

"In actual fact, I've ordered her book. Should be here any day now, Brown has been recommending it."

That evening, after finishing the dishes from their evening meal, the two sisters settled down in the kitchen and Fran ran through the list of duties that Sarah would be expected to perform in the Atkins household. As Sarah suspected, the work in Barrowford would be very little different to that of the Royal Oak other than the Atkins had three children as opposed to the Johnson's only daughter.

The evening, like the whole weekend, passed only too quickly and it was time for Sarah to turn in. She had enjoyed being with Fran more than words could say; seeing her sister happily settled into a new life gave her a rare sense of optimism. Perhaps the future might not be too bad for both girls after all.

It had been arranged that Sarah would catch the 11.10 train in the morning for the eastward journey to Nelson where her new employer would meet her. Before settling down for the night Sarah opened the town directory that Mr Duckett had lent to her. The small book held details of streets and businesses in the local towns and he thought that Sarah might benefit from looking through it. In the section on Barrowford she read;

*This is a populous manufacturing township, two miles west of the market town of Colne, in the parliamentary division of Clitheroe. The acreage is 1,368 acres; and its rateable value amounts to £16,562. The population in 1851 = 2,875; 1861 = 2,880; 1871 = 3,110 and 1881 = 3,842 inclusive of Blacko.*

Sarah's eyes soon grew heavy; none of the information within the directory actually meant a great deal to her although it was interesting to see that the village population would now be around 4,000. She thought of her native West Bromwich with a headcount of some 56,000 and realised that Barrowford was indeed going to be a much smaller place than she had been accustomed to.

# 11

# Barrowford

The 11.10 train from Burnley rolled into Nelson as the massive station clock showed 11.23. Sarah picked up her bag and the guard opened the carriage door; this was the end of her long journey north. As she stepped onto the platform the familiar metallic cacophony of a busy railway goods yard assailed her and this was exactly like the Harborne Station that she had left only, what . . . three days ago? It seemed more like weeks.

Goods trains clanked along their sidings and the pervasive smell of sulphurous steam filled the station canopy. There was another familiar noise that Sarah could not quite place but, as she walked along the platform towards the passenger building, she suddenly knew; below the station was a sprawling factory with belching chimneys and from within came the sound of the Black Country. The constant thump of hammering rang out the tune of heavy iron-working and sure enough, there was the massive sign; *William Roberts & Co. Ltd. - Phoenix Foundry.*

As she approached the station buildings Sarah stopped and let the other passengers walk through to the exit. At that moment a woman, who appeared to be in her mid-twenties, stepped forward.

"Good morning, are you Sarah by any chance?"

Sarah looked at the woman and saw a thin face with a square chiselled nose that gave an air of refinement.

"Yes, I am - morning. You must be Mrs Atkins?"

The woman laughed and Sarah saw that the even white teeth complimented her features perfectly.

"Oh, thank heavens! I've already accosted two young ladies as they left the station. Never mind - third time lucky."

Sarah handed in her spent ticket and the pair of them walked down the sloping, tile-lined passenger tunnel. In the far corner of the station yard a young lad held the pony and gig that was to transport Sarah to her new home in Barrowford.

Mrs Atkins slipped the lad a few coppers for his services and helped Sarah to climb up into the gig. A sharp shake of the reins set the pony into motion and they were soon bowling along Railway Street towards the Nelson town centre. Mrs Atkins steered the pony across Leeds Road and then turned right at the Nelson Inn. This, she explained to the newcomer, had given the town its name; until recently Nelson had been known as Great Marsden but the railway company eventually named its station after the old inn. The town immediately took this name and hardly anyone used the Marsden appellation nowadays.

They were now on Scotland Road and this would take the travellers the mile or so down into Barrowford. On both sides of the road were impressive stone-built shops, interspersed by the attractive frontages of a Methodist church and the Victoria church hall. Within a short distance the gig rounded the bend at the Bulls Head Hotel and began the steady half-mile descent to the river at Reedyford. On the right of the road, amidst thick woodland, Mrs Atkins pointed out the large house of a friend of hers. This was Reedyford House, built by William Tunstill who was a great benefactor of the Wesleyan movement in Barrowford.

As they swept past the woodland the road began to deteriorate alarmingly. A few cottages stood on either side of the road at Reedyford, just a few yards from the river that marked the boundary between the town of Nelson and the village of Barrowford. The pony lined himself up with the narrow bridge and they rattled across, they were now entering the lower part of the village known as Newbridge and Sarah could not help but notice that the road here was in a dreadful state.

"Hold onto your seat, Sarah, these ruts can throw you out if you are not ready for them."

The passenger was glad that she had been forewarned; outside the Victoria Hotel the gig gave a mighty sideways jolt and she almost lost her bonnet. The deep wheel ruts were filled with water and mud from the weekend showers and there was hardly any way that anyone could have passed comfortably on foot. Mrs Atkins explained that everyone complained about the road in Newbridge but little ever seemed to be done about it.

Sarah saw that there was a great amount of house building going on in this part of Barrowford. There was a marked contrast between the older buildings, with their soot-stained stone facades, and the attractive honey colour of the new ones. This area of Newbridge had recently become known as New Town, so great in number were the shops and houses that were spreading across the once-green fields.

As the pony clipped along the straight road towards the Barrowford village proper the surface began to improve; after a quarter of a mile or so the ride became much smoother and Sarah could relax her iron grip on the seat. On the right stood Berry's Victoria Mill and alongside it a cluster of cottages, shops and small factories vied for position along the river bank. The cottages here, on Water Street, the Old Row and the Square were squat and their higgledy-piggledy appearance suggested that they had seen better days. Nevertheless, this is where a large number of Barrowford workers lived and 'Th'old Row' was a proud community of mill workers.

A few yards further along, and across the road, stood the tall buildings of the Co-operative Wholesale Society and the Fleece Inn. This latter building struck Sarah as being very odd in as much as it was shaped like a smoothing iron. This was as a result of its position at the junction of two roads; turning up by the Fleece Inn, and heading up to Wheatley Lane, was Back Lane (or Church Street to give it its Sunday name). Looking over her left shoulder Sarah saw, on a small hill above the Fleece, a house whose heavy mullioned windows suggested that it had been there for many years.

"That's Sutcliffe's Bank Hall," explained Mrs Atkins, "They say it's over two hundred years old. In fact I think it will be around the same age as the White Bear Inn."

She pointed to another old building a few yards along. The White Bear Inn stood back from the road with a small area of land to the front sweeping down the short distance to the river.

"Now that's Hargreaves' Great House but it's been the White Bear for many years now."

Looking across the river as they passed the White Bear Sarah noticed the flat fields at the far edge of which rose a long, heavily wooded embankment. The backdrop of trees gave the whole area an attractive rural setting and the lazy rippling of the river added to the effect. This embankment was known as Rye Bank and had actually given Barrowford its name. Until a century or so ago the main river crossing in this area stood a few yards down the road from the White Bear and *'bearu,'* the Old English name for *'wooded embankment,'* became coupled with the river crossing thus providing the name *Barrow-ford*.

Happily oblivious to this fact, Sarah took in her surroundings. She had noticed that from Newbridge up to the White Bear the village appeared to have been built along one side of the river only.

"Yes," Sarah's new employer answered her query, *"'Barrowford all on one side'* is a common and accurate description. Most of the land on the other side of the river has always belonged to Park Hill Farm and the owners have never allowed their lands to be built on."

Martha Atkins drove another hundred yards, past the waterfall where water was extracted to run the old water powered cotton spinning mill, and on a little further until the gig was level with the George and Dragon Inn. Taking a sharp right turn over the bridge she pointed at the old building just off to the right,

"There, that's Lower Park Hill."

As Sarah looked at the whitewashed gables and the stone mullioned windows she thought that this building was similar to the old ones further down the village. This was not

106

surprising given that most of the early Barrowford houses had been erected within a short period of each other.

The pony slowed as it began the climb from the bridge but fortunately its uphill slog was to be a short one. Within a few yards the hill began to level and on the left stood another farm, Higher Park Hill. The driver steered the pony through the open wrought iron gates of a fine Georgian-style house standing rather imperiously next to the farm. On one of the massive square stone gateposts a sign indicated that they had arrived at Spring Hill. The gig carried along the side of the house before finally drawing up outside a small coach house.

"Here we are, home."

Mrs Atkins helped Sarah to climb down and a young lad appeared from the farm buildings.

"Thank you Bill."

The lad took charge of the reins ready to back the gig into the coach house and lead the pony around to the farm stable where it lived.

Sarah picked up her bag and followed her mistress as she marched quickly back down the drive and up to the side door of the house. Before the pair had reached the door it was thrown open and a melee of waving hands and smiling faces emerged; the newcomer was instantly surrounded by three excited children, pulling at her skirt and dancing excitedly around. Two women emerged, one appeared to be in her fifties and the other was quite elderly.

Mrs Atkins began to introduce everyone, starting with the elderly lady.

"Sarah, this is Betty, my husband's aunt." She rested her hand on the arm of the other lady.

"This is Ellen, my mother. And these little terrors are my children, James, Mary and Ellen. "

Looking at the three happy, well scrubbed faces smiling up at her Sarah weighed up their ages; she thought that the youngest, James, would be about three years old, Mary around five and the eldest, Ellen, would be about eight.

"My husband is not here at the moment but he will be home later. In the meantime why don't we go through, I'm sure that Sarah must be dying for a cup of tea after her journey."

Sure enough, two hours later James Atkins strode into the parlour. Sarah noted his upright bearing and the smart riding clothes as her new master threw his crop onto the large leather armchair by the fireside.

"Very nice to meet you my dear, I trust that my family are looking after you?"

Sarah rose from the table where she had been helping young Ellen to sort her pressed flower collection.

"Good afternoon Sir, yes, very well, thank you."

Sarah knew immediately that she was going to get along well with this family. Young Mary appeared from the back garden and made a headlong dash for her father.

"Daddy, this is Sarah, our new help, and she speaks funny."

Mr Atkins scooped up his middle child and swung her round. Winking at Sarah he pointed out to Mary that no doubt Sarah found their accents funny too. Sarah laughed.

"We'll all get used to each other soon enough I expect."

When Sarah settled into her clean, comfortable bed that night she considered the events of the day and was pleased. The Atkins family were nice people and Barrowford seemed to be a place that she could be comfortable in. There would be room to breathe here amongst the green fields and hills surrounding Spring Hill. There were no overwhelming doubts to haunt her dreams that night.

# 12

# Ellen Sutherland

The day following Sarah's arrival at Spring Hill Mrs Atkins' mother, Ellen, showed Sarah her duties and told her how pleased she was to have help, especially with the children.

"I don't mind the housework so much but the youngsters drive me mad at times – I'm getting too old for all that now!"

Sarah's first impression of Ellen was that she might be a little aloof. Her pale-blue eyes flashed when she wasn't pleased and the tall figure, her grey hair platted at the sides, gave a definite air of confident authority. Sarah was slightly overawed by Ellen but as she spent time with her the two quickly became firm friends; in many ways Ellen reminded Sarah of her mother, Emma.

When the early duties had been carried out Ellen thought it might be a good idea to walk her new help into the village to show her where the family shopping was done. As they stepped out onto the front path Sarah hesitated, she took a deep breath of the farm-scented air and looked around. The garden of Spring Hill fronted onto the lane leading out of Barrowford towards the town of Colne. On the village side of the house stood the farm buildings of Higher Park Hill while the upper and rear boundaries adjoined on to open fields. Ellen saw that Sarah was trying to gather her bearings; she pointed along Colne Lane to a nearby detached house standing to the side of a hump-backed bridge.

"That's where Mr Atkins' cousin lives with his wife, Jemima. He's also called James so to avoid confusion everyone calls him James Senior. And that banking running along behind his house is the canal; they tell me that this is the highest stretch of the whole canal between Leeds and Liverpool. There are five locks here and not far towards Yorkshire is the Mile Tunnel. We'll have to go for a walk on there when we have an hour to spare."

Ellen went on to point out the surrounding landscape. The view in all directions encompassed the high ridges that Sarah had noticed from the train as she steamed into the district. From Burnley, five miles to the west, along to Tum Hills just across the shallow valley in Nelson, the rolling landscape dominated the heights.

The fields behind Spring Hill stretched all the way to the hill upon which Colne town proudly stood and, to the north of there, the sharply pointed rise of Noyna Hill made its presence known. Ellen informed Sarah that the quarry on Noyna had been a major source of millstones for the district, the gritty sandstone being particularly suited to this purpose. Further round to the north was the bulk of Weets Hill, standing guard over the Lancashire and Yorkshire border.

Carrying on around the distant landscape Sarah's guide showed her the rough slopes of Burn Moor and the rounded green crowns of Wheathead Height, Brown Hill and Stang Top. Having saved the most impressive until last Ellen pointed to a massive bulk rising whale-like above the smaller hills.

"And that's Pendle Hill, there are more legends connected to Old Pendle than you can shake a stick at."

"Ah, I'd noticed that hill. It seemed to appear as I got to Accrington but it looks to be a different shape now."

"Well, Pendle does change shape depending on where you are viewing it from. It has three faces but I always think the one we see from Barrowford is the best! They taught us at school that if the hill had been another 120 feet higher it would be high enough to be called a mountain."

Ellen then drew Sarah's attention to a large house of the Georgian period nestling in the hillside on the other side of Barrowford.

"That's Pasture House where I lived with my husband and Martha; my husband died when Martha was a child and I managed that place on my own for years. That's how James and my daughter first met, he had the tenancy of Lower Fulshaw Farm."

Ellen pointed to a group of whitewashed farm buildings a few hundred yards to the left of Pasture House.

"James was very good to us, he helped me whenever I had a problem with the property and he even supplied us with free coal. One thing led to another and James asked my permission to court our Martha when she was sixteen. I was only too pleased, after all, she liked him and James was such a nice chapel-going young man. Anyway, the two of them were married at Christmas time in 1873 and they moved in here, bringing me with them."

Ellen looked at Spring Hill, she had been happy in this house and she knew that her daughter had made a good marriage. Nevertheless, it was not the same as having her own place with her own family; turning towards the garden gate Ellen sighed.

"Right, that's enough lecturing for one day, let's get down to the shops before the best meat has all gone."

Over the following days Sarah found that Ellen was a font of knowledge on all things to do with Barrowford. She knew which families were related to other families, what the latest news in the mills happened to be and the village gossip. She was also keenly aware of the history of her village; having been born here she had always taken an interest in the events of times past.

Sarah learned that Ellen had been born in 1826 to Richard and Nanny Berry. Richard had started life as a poor cotton spinner but his determination to succeed soon led to him opening a small cotton factory. Ellen remembered clearly that, as children, she and her brother spent a great deal of time in helping their parents to inspect the handloom cloth pieces produced in their factory. She also remembered many of the old characters, most of them handloom weavers, who filled the village at that time.

"They were different times. The days of the handloomers were easier than today's power loom weavers, in a lot of ways they were better off as they were their own bosses and they got a good price for their finished cloth pieces. A lot of the families had three or four weavers in the house and they earned good money between them, my father always said that his days were the best for the weavers."

"From 1790 through to 1814 a lot of the families had three or four pounds per week coming in and their rent, food and coal were stable and cheap. That's how my father got going, he and mother worked hard and saved, he borrowed seventy pounds from another mill owner and never looked back."

By 1840 Richard had been successful enough to build his own cotton spinning mill.

"You would have seen Victoria Mill further down the village when you drove past?"

Sarah remembered Mrs Atkins pointing out Berry's Victoria Mill on the riverside.

"Well, my father built that in the late 1830s and my nephew, Thomas Berry, is extending it at the moment. He's knocking down my father's original spinning mill and extending right across to the main road, they're going over to weaving instead of spinning. Thomas tells me that there will be a new steam engine and boiler and that the new sheds will hold 1,700 looms. It's a pity to see the old mill go but that's progress I suppose."

Ellen's daughter, Martha, was born in 1856 but shortly afterwards her father died. Ellen then married John Sutherland, an Inland Revenue officer from Scotland who was six years her junior. John took Ellen and Martha to live at Pasture House but they had not been there for twelve months before John died, at the age of forty-two, again leaving Ellen a widow.

Ellen looked pensive; she remembered the heady days when her father's business was continually expanding; life was good and the family were happy. However, things did not always run smoothly after he built Victoria Mill. Barely a year went by without interruption of the cloth production but R Berry and Son always managed to ride the roller-coaster of industrial unrest.

As the nineteenth century progressed more cotton mills appeared in the village and the industry began to specialise. Some mills were still spinning but most were building large weaving sheds. Within the wider district mills tended to weave a different kind of cloth; stripes, fancies, coloureds, velveteens, sail and linen cloth were produced in Blackburn, Burnley, Nelson and Colne and the wages paid by each district for their particular product varied.

This meant that a velveteen weaver in Blackburn might be paid more per cloth length than their counterpart fifteen miles the east in Barrowford. This, of course, led to unrest and strikes ensued if the employer would not pay parity wages. Eventually it was agreed that a standard 'list' be drawn up and each district would pay that same list price to their workers. Again, the workers felt badly done-by when the employers reneged on the list wages and strikes remained commonplace.

The Lancashire textile industry operated on a knife-edge of uncertainty in both its supply of raw materials and the global market for its finished goods. Many of the ills to befall the industry were beyond the control of the manufacturers but this was not always the case; a good illustration of this was seen during the time of the American Civil war of 1861-65.

In the period of 1859-60, before the outbreak of war, the Southern American States exported more cotton than the world needed and Lancashire manufacturers overproduced. All good things must come to an end, however, and by the May of 1860 the boom ceased as quickly as it had begun. There were now over 300,000,000 pounds weight of cotton goods stored in the vast warehouses of Manchester and Liverpool; the market was saturated and the goods could not be sold at a profit.

Furthermore, to finance the boom many mill owners had borrowed heavily and the collapse of the market left them over-exposed. A period of short-time working ensued in many mills as the manufacturers gradually sold off their stocks at low prices. To a certain extent, then, the outbreak of war in America came just at the right time for some mill owners to blame their predicament on the lack of raw cotton supplies. This diverted the attention of their workers and investors from the fact that they had been blinded by the 'cotton rush' and consequently had badly misjudged their pre-war production.

In the early months of 1865 panic spread across Lancashire when it was seen that the financial institutions of the south of England were collapsing and two Liverpool banks failed. By the spring of 1866 there were many failures in the banking sector and this caused a run on the Bank of England. Fortunately reserves held out but the aftermath of this was yet higher interest rates and a long period of recession.

Many of the financiers involved in the cotton debacle of the 1860s lost money, some lost their large houses and yet others lost land. This, however, did not compare to the the the lot of the seething mass of unemployed cotton workers across Lancashire, many of whom lost their lives, or saw their loved ones die of malnourishment and disease.

The cotton famine placed an unprecedented strain on the Poor Law system, by the November of 1862 the Board of Guardians were paying relief to over a quarter of a million persons. The crowded city dwellers fared worst of all; their living conditions had been poor before the famine and they were particularly vulnerable to a cut in their food and fuel supplies. The normal Poor Rate had been one shilling per qualifying person but this had to be raised to three shillings. This compared badly with formerly high wages of weaving families and serves to illustrate the struggle of the unemployed poor at that time.

To a certain extent the village of Barrowford fared better than the larger towns and cities although this is not to say that there was no grasping poverty. Relief Committees abounded and they carried out sterling works in the distribution of charity payments. The churches also provided a great deal of relief as did the contributions sent by workers from other parts of the country.

The 'outdoor relief of the poor' was paid to those who were deemed fit to work but were unemployed through no fault of their own. The recipients of payments were put to work on a variety of schemes, usually building roads, but unfortunately a number of the mill workers had spent all of their lives in factories and they were not used to the outdoor life. The winters in particular affected them badly, especially as they did not possess the outdoor clothing necessary for the work. A number of these men suffered from cold related ailments and some of them died from pneumonia.

Where women, children, the elderly and infirm became dependant on poor relief they were split up and placed in a workhouse, often some distance away from their home district, where they were expected to weave for their keep. The 'in house' relief payments were less than those for the outdoor payments so that there was no incentive for anyone to take the 'easy' option of the workhouse over outdoor work.

It was common for working families to exist solely on a diet of thin porridge made out of a few handfuls of oatmeal and a little blue milk. This diet would sometimes be eked out by the addition of a few vegetables (if the family had a garden plot to grow them) or a rabbit or two from the local fields.

Ellen knew that even now there were a lot of people in the village whose daily food intake consisted of oatmeal and little else. Admittedly, things were better than the 1860s but strikes and lay-offs still happened on an all too regular basis - none of the workers were getting any richer.

Ellen mixed daily with the village people and was keenly aware of the social implications of being from a manufacturing family. She was quick to point out to Sarah that the Berry's were thought of as good employers in village. Sarah employed the diplomatic skills of a domestic servant and said nothing but the thought crossed her mind that the Berry's grand houses contrasted sharply with the two-room dwellings of the workers. She knew from her own experience that the line between employer and employee formed an immutable social and monetary barrier.

Sarah could see from what her new friend had told her that things were little different up here in Lancashire than they had been in the Black Country. The nailers once worked in family groups, turning the raw materials supplied by the nail masters into finished goods, and returning them for a fixed rate of pay. Similarly, the Barrowford handloom weavers took cotton warps from the 'putters out,' or merchants, and wove them up into cloth pieces of a specific length for which the merchants paid them. In both cases the advent of steam-powered machinery eventually put an end to their traditional way of life.

The irresistible force of automation had come up hard against a highly malleable workforce who were, by and large, resigned to a changing world. Just as the early lure of the seductive steam powered factories had soaked the countryside dry of labour so the onward march of progress was to bleed the life out of the formerly independent home-worker in order for it to feed a new and ever more powerful generation of industrial growth.

# 13

# The Nowell Family

It was the high-summer of 1885 and as the red sun surmounted Boulsworth Hill a celestial switch was thrown spreading burnished rays of dawn light in a billowing sheet of flame across the valley. In a heartbeat the glassy water was painted with the shadows of both man and boy; small and unimportant they sat, quietly intent, quietly satisfied, quietly in awe of the slumbering entity on whose edge they waited. Long before they felt the spreading warmth a moderate pre-dawn light had filled the sharp autumn air, light enough for the fisherman and his young companion to prepare for the hunt. As they cast their invitations into the still, dark waters the floating mists joined hands and danced in a twisting, woven layer, sheltering the lake from the searching bright invasion.

The distant sound of disturbed water drifted across to the quiet figures and they saw another world emerging from its misty bed; weary swans had been overnight guests of the generous lake but were now anxious to search for new horizons; they bade farewell to their host and lifted as one, rising wraith-like out of the violet-grey haze. As they slipped free of the lake damp fingers of mist clung to outstretched silken wings, only to recoil in the new light. The skyward forms now glittered as droplets of jewelled liquid danced across the sunlight to re-join their dank lair.

Silent and majestic the birds climbed to override the yawning willows; higher now than the stretching oak boughs the white drift graced the sky above a diamond-studded meadow; whirling once more amid the farewell beat of mighty wings the ethereal group was gathered in a billowing flame. Straight and far they flew, into the redness of a new morning as the bright air took them.

The two companions remained silent as the lake settled beneath her grey-violet shield and in that autumn memory of misty glass and flame they were together again, the fisherman and his son. Long ago the fisherman took his own journey along that red, billowing road. But the boy remembered - the day will never fade while his dreams hold the dawn.

Edison Nowell slowly awoke; his head hurt and his joints were stiff from the cold dampness of a grassy bed. He rubbed his bleary eyes and waited for the morning to focus; when it finally became clear the familiar glassy expanse of Old Ebby's lake filled his vision.

He had done it again! People had told him that it was a strange thing to do, sleeping rough by the lakeside when he had a perfectly good bed to go to. But they didn't understand, they didn't know how he felt. Here, beneath the high canopy of willow he could dream and nobody would disturb him. It did not matter that the dream was always the same; it was his dream and it brought a comfort that little else could.

Edison had been born into a farming family on Flax Moor, not a quarter of a mile from the lake and, ever since he could remember, he had harboured an impossible desire to sit on the water's edge with his dad and fish the mysterious depths. He never wished for riches, nor did he envy those who lived the good life; there was but a single issue that had burned within him throughout his twenty-four years.

Edison's story began in 1840 when his grandparents, James and Sophia Nowell, were delivered of a healthy baby girl. They named the newcomer Susannah and she was soon running around her parent's farm on the Blacko hillside with her older sister and brother. Blacko had been an area of scattered farmsteads sitting between Barrowford and the Yorkshire border but it began to form the semblance of a village when the new turnpike road to Gisburn was created in 1804.

The area was dominated by the conical Blacko Hill as it rose to a height of one thousand feet. The hill once resembled the sharp peak of an extinct volcano but a century of stone quarrying had flattened the upper slopes. To the south the hill fell gently down to the canal, to the west it tumbled sharply into Pendle Water and northwards it skirted the bulk of Weets Hill as it joined the rolling Yorkshire hills of West Craven.

Here, then, on the southern slopes of Blacko Hill, young Susannah Nowell lived the first years of her life. By the time she had turned ten Susannah had four younger brothers in Richard, Jimmy, Thomas and John to join her elder brother, Peter. The family had now moved a little further down the hill to the forty-four acres of New House Farm where father James hoped to expand his cattle dealing business.

The family worked hard at New House; James often needed to travel into Scotland to buy the long-horn cattle that he would sell to the Lancashire and Yorkshire farmers at Gisburn market. On his regular forays over the border the running of the farm fell to the thirteen year-old Peter and the farm hand who was only a year older. With the help of the rest of the family the farm ticked along nicely.

When she reached the age of twelve Susannah began to train as a dressmaker with a lady in Barrowford. Come rain, hail or shine she would walk the three mile round journey every day and work on the farm in her spare time. Life was busy and there was little time for socialising.

In the later 1850s James moved the family again when he took the tenancy of the neighbouring farm of Flax Moor. He had to let the farm hand go as the farm was not big enough to support more than his sons; Jimmy was nineteen now and able to run the farm with his younger brother John.

When Susannah turned twenty-one the family hosted a gathering in the barn and many of the local farmers came, as did the farmer's lads. The walls of the stone barn rang to the fiddler's tunes well into the early hours and the hayloft was littered with the comatose bodies of those who had over indulged in the barrels of ale laid on by the nearby Cross Gates Inn. A good time was had by all, in fact Susannah enjoyed herself a little too much and nine months later, in the March of 1861, she was delivered of a baby son.

Susannah never told anyone who the boy's father was. Both her father and brother Jimmy had stated their intention of finding the man responsible and giving him a good hiding but this did little to encourage Susannah into divulging the secret that she would carry to her grave.

In an attempt for Susannah to avoid the stigma of having had an illegitimate son it was decided that her father James would be the boy's official father. All the local people knew that the boy was illegitimate but when officialdom came calling young Edison Nowell was the son of James and Sophia Nowell. Thus his birth certificate carried the name of James Nowell as the father as did the census of 1861 when Edison was but one month old.

Growing up knowing that he had a father locally, but without knowing who that man might be, had a profound effect on young Edison. As a small child he realised that this was not a normal situation, after all everyone else knew who their fathers were.

Of course, the whole village knew the truth and as Edison grew older the other lads goaded him cruelly with taunts of 'bastard' and 'where's yer dad?' Even the adults would stop their conversations and sneer behind his back as he passed. Things grew worse when Edison was sent down to the chapel school in Higherford; by now the lad had resorted to telling everyone that his father was James Nowell. The alternative would have been to say that he didn't know who his father was and this would invite certain derision.

Susannah obviously did not feel that she wanted the boy's real father to be a part of their lives. No doubt she worried that if she told her son the truth he would contact his father and the genie would then be out of the bottle. In her own small way she was trying to protect herself and her son but in doing so she did not realise that young Edison felt it very deeply. His whole being ached for the father that he knew he was destined never to have.

In the spring of 1866 Edison's grandfather, James, passed away and it fell to Jimmy to carry on with the farm tenancy. Jimmy carried on his father's business of cattle dealing but the trade, which had never been easy in the best of times, had been particularly bad in the year that James senior died.

One of the regular outbreaks of foot and mouth disease was ravaging the north of England and the Privy Council issued an Order banning all movement of cattle throughout the district. Unfortunately for Jimmy his father had ordered a delivery of thirty-three head of Ayrshire cattle just before the disease had struck. They had been grazing for a few weeks on Flax Moor grass but this could not go on forever. Jimmy knew that by the end of the following month he would need to settle the bill for these cattle and he did not have the ready money.

The threat of bankruptcy was very real and Jimmy did not want to let the family down; if only he could move the beasts on he would hopefully have enough cash to tide the farm over until the banning order was lifted. Early on the morning of June the twenty ninth Jimmy, with the help of his brother John, set out to drive the cattle over the White Moor track to Gisburn. He had let it be known in the local farming circles that he had a stock of healthy animals to dispose of.

The brothers walked for two hours and finally arrived in the small Yorkshire village of Gisburn where they drove the cattle into a field at the back of the New Inn and waited for the other farmers to arrive. Soon there were twenty local cattle men inspecting the Ayrshires and Jimmy started the auction; the best animals brought seventeen pounds and the smallest managed eleven pounds. The whole lot had been purchased by three farmers from the surrounding district and Jimmy was well satisfied. He filled out the sales receipts and was just taking the cash when all hell broke loose.

Three policemen rushed into the field and another two blocked off the entrance. Some farmers managed to quietly slip away while others unceremoniously vaulted the thorn hedgerow. There was no such escape for Jimmy, however, and he was duly arrested and summonsed.

On the twenty seventh of July James appeared at the Bolton-by-Bowland Magistrate's Court on a charge of moving cattle contrary to a Privy Council Order and also with allowing the removal of cattle without a licence. Alongside Jimmy were the three farmers who had bought his cattle and they were charged with buying cattle without a licence.

Jimmy tried his best to get out of trouble, he hired a solicitor who stated to the court that the farmers had bought the cattle before the sale and were merely collecting them from the field. The prosecution, however, showed this to be untrue when they produced the receipts that Jimmy had made out on the day. The upshot of the case was that Jimmy was fined fifty pounds for the main offence but the magistrate, realising the difficulties that farmers were experiencing at that time, fined him one pound on only three counts of illegal removal, instead of the whole lot.

The three farmers were fined ten shillings for each head of cattle that they had bought, plus costs. Jimmy admitted that he was in the wrong and paid the farmers' costs and fines. After this setback he struggled but somehow managed to keep things going. Trade could only go one way from that point and, sure enough, cattle sales improved over the next couple of years.

In 1867, a year following James senior's death, his widow, Sophia left the farm and moved down into Barrowford where she took a house called Poplar Cottage on Ingham Street. Susannah, young Edison and his Uncle Thomas also left the farm to live with Sophia while Jimmy and John carried on scraping a living on the twenty-seven acres of Flax Moor Farm. Thomas became a commission agent in the cotton trade and as such he travelled to and from Manchester where the main cotton merchants were based. Here he met a young woman from Ramsey in the Isle of Man, and they were married in 1870. The couple continued to live at Poplar Cottage for a short while but Thomas found that the travelling was getting too much and so he took his wife to live on the outskirts of Manchester.

Thomas' brother, Richard, also moved to Manchester where he studied dentistry. He met his future wife while living in the city and they married in 1870 when they were both twenty-one. As soon as he could Richard brought his wife, son and daughter to Barrowford where he took the shop premises to the side of the White Bear Inn. Here he proudly displayed his sign:

*Mr R. Nowell, Dentist*
*The Medical Hall*
*Artificial Teeth Correctly Fitted Without Pain*
*Natural Appearance*
*Lowest Price for Good Workmanship and Materials*

In the meantime Jimmy carried on with his farming and cattle dealing operation. In 1863 he started to court a Colne butcher's daughter who loved nothing better than helping out at Flax Moor and Jimmy could see that she would make a good farmer's wife. They had a son, whom they named Oates, in 1864 and they married in the following spring. Besides being a good farm hand Jimmy's wife also brought money into the marriage, her father's extended family had been cloth manufacturers in the district earlier in the century; they were also land and property owners and so she was able to bolster the farm economy with a small dowry.

Over the coming years the family increased steadily, the youngest child being born in 1878 but, as it so happened, this year turned out to be a traumatic one for the family as, in the January, Jimmy had finally been declared bankrupt in his cattle business. Things had picked up for a while after he had taken over the farm but as the years passed small cattle dealers found it more and more difficult to earn a living.

Jimmy decided to make a fresh start and moved his family down into Higher Barrowford where he took the tenancy of Crow Trees Farm. Here, in a picturesque spot by the riverside above the Higherford Mill, he eked out a living as a small dairy farmer, assisted by his eldest son.

At Poplar Cottage, Edison was working as a weaver just across the road at Berry's Mill. His grandmother, Sophia, had been worried about her son, Jimmy, and this began to affect her health. During the winter of 1878 she caught a chill and had been unable to shake it off. As the year turned so the chill developed into pneumonia and before the new warmth of spring had arrived Sophia had died leaving just Susannah and Edison in the cottage.

During the year leading up to her mother's death Susannah had been seeing a widower, almost ten years her senior, by the name of Henry Wilkinson. Henry had been born over the Yorkshire border in the small cotton town of Barnoldswick. His father had originally been a cotton carder but by the late 1840s he had managed to buy a grocery shop in the town. Young Henry had been a handloom weaver by the age of nine and by his fifteenth birthday he was weaving on power looms. By the age of thirty he had worked his way through the mill and had become an overlooker. A lucky break came Henry's way when his sister married William Hartley of Barrowford. William was a cotton manufacturer in the Pendle Street Shed, Nelson, and Henry Wilkinson joined his brother-in-law as a junior partner in the business.

Besides his interest in the Pendle Street Mill, Henry also had the tenancy of a farm a couple of miles or so out of Blacko, off the Gisburn road. Sarah's brother, Jimmy, knew Henry and he thought that it might be good idea to introduce his spinster sister to the lonely widower. This turned out to be one of Jimmy's better ideas much to the amusement of the rest of the family as he had never been regarded as the romantic type. In fact romance had nothing to do with Jimmy's outlook on marriage as the practicalities of running the farm dictated his taste in the opposite sex.

Henry and Susannah hit it off immediately and nine months following the death of her mother Susannah married her new love. Henry had lived for a while with his sister and brother-in-law in Nelson but he realised that he would need somewhere of his own when he remarried. Just at that time his sister, who lived in the small village of Rimington, had been widowed and she found that her house was much too big for her to manage alone. She suggested that Henry, and his new family, move in with her for a while to see how things would work out. He needed little persuading as he loved the countryside around Rimington. The village lay within a vast, open plain of moor and meadow, between Gisburn and Barrowford, and there was little to trouble anyone there except the haunting cries of the kite and the curlew.

# 14

# A First Meeting

Edison Nowell had been reasonably happy at Rimington; Henry Wilkinson could not be a substitute for the father that Edison never had but nevertheless he was good to the lad. He provided a stable influence when Edison was at that awkward stage in his late teens but that is not to say that Henry found his new stepson an easy character to rub along with. The lad was uncomfortable with any show of emotion between his mother and her new husband and Henry had been aware of this from the day they had all moved to Rimington.

If they hugged or even sat too close to each other then Edison would make a dramatic and noisy exit from the room and sulk for hours afterwards. Henry tried his best to understand the young man, after all Susannah had been his only close family since he had been born and now someone else had become the focus of her attention. Edison never came to terms with this; unfortunately he did not have sufficient emotional maturity to realise that Susannah could love both the men in her life equally, but in different ways. The jealous outbursts lessened as time went along but this was only because Edison had learned to conceal his feelings.

As Edison awoke by the lakeside on that high-summer morning of 1885 he rubbed the memory of his dreams from his eyes and stretched his seized joints. Rising stiffly to his feet he shook the grass from his clothes. Packing the tartan-weave blanket that had been his bedding for the night he walked along the willow-lined banks of Old Ebby's lake and began the steep climb up the deep-sided medieval lane of Slipper Hill. As he reached the Barrowford lane Edison stopped to catch his breath. He was alone in a wide landscape and this is how he liked it to be; he was never happier than when he was walking in solitude.

Indeed, this was the reason for his night under the stars. He had set out on one of his regular visits to his Uncle Jimmy at Crowtrees Farm and, as often happened during the summer, he spent the evening daydreaming by the lakeside. He would sit for hours as the sun's reflections gradually turned to dark shadows on the still surface of the water. Finally, as the evening grew too dark for him to see the fish jumping and the swallows diving across the lake, he bedded down for the night and waited for his old familiar dream to take hold.

Having recovered his breath from the steep climb up Slipper Hill the early-morning walker turned to his left and headed along the lane towards Blacko. Within minutes he was passing below Malkin Tower Farm and as he rounded a sharp bend a loud explosion startled him. He knew exactly what the cause of this interruption to the morning peace was; looking up he saw the familiar column of smoke rising from the top of Blacko Hill, giving it the appearance of a grumbling volcano. As the smoke cleared Edison saw the tip of a tall steam crane as it swung to and fro with its heavy load of newly-blasted stone. All the farmers around here were used to the daily thump of exploding dynamite in the quarry and even the grazing animals appeared to be completely oblivious to the noise.

To the left of the lane Edison passed the rough track leading down to his Grandpa's old place of New House Farm and another five-minute walk brought the wanderer to the inn standing guard over an ancient cross-roads. Bill and Martha Holt worked the small farm here and they also ran the Cross Gates Inn attached to the farm house. Bill happened to be sweeping the steps leading up to the front door of the inn and glancing along the lane he saw the approaching figure and recognised it at once. There was no mistaking the steel-blue eyes, thinning sandy hair and pinched cheeks but the thing that instantly betrayed the figure as being Edison Nowell was his strange gait. He didn't so much walk as stumble along; his back was slightly stooped and this lessened an already diminutive five-foot five-inch frame. His arms tended to hang limply and this gave the impression that he threw them forward with each step. When he was younger his mother had constantly tried to correct this,

"Edison, stop slouching. Come on! Shoulders back, stand up lad."

Susannah's scolding proved to be to no avail; her son's odd manner of walking grew worse if anything.

"Now then young 'un," Bill Holt was almost as round as he was tall and he had a cheery word for everyone.

"How's thy mother going on. Haven't seen her since she got wed."

"Awe, not so bad, Bill. She misses her friends in Barrowford but apart from that she's alright."

Pleasantries duly exchanged, Edison set off down the hill and was soon standing at the end of the rough track leading to his birthplace of Flax Moor Farm. He looked across the twenty-seven acres of grassland and remembered the summer days of haymaking when the family would all be out together in the meadows. James senior would start to scythe the waving grass as soon as the mid-July weather looked to be settled. He always judged the coming weather by looking across to Colne; if the smoke from the mill chimneys rose straight up he knew that they would have a few fine days in which to cut and gather the hay.

Edison had happy memories of riding on top of the last load as the horses nodded in their harness, pulling the laden hay cart back towards the waiting barn. The massive red ball of the late evening sun would be rolling across the hunched back of Pendle Hill as the massive cart wheels trundled across the Far Meadow. By the time they reached the hayloft the sun had dropped behind the hill and an ochre twilight played among the sandstone buildings. The family would help to fork the twisted bundles of hay into the loft and Edison's job was to fill heavy earthenware jugs with beer from the barrels in the cellar and bring them out for the adults.

When the hay had been laid in the barn to James' satisfaction the horses were tended to before being stabled for the night and the workers retired to the farmhouse kitchen where Sophia and Susannah had prepared enough food to feed an army. Plates of pork, more gleaming white fat than meat, jostled for position on the massive pine table with sliced beef, steaming potato pie, huge loaves of warm bread and golden apple pies. Young Edison was even allowed a glass of beer - as James succinctly put it;

"If tha works like a worker tha eats like a worker!"

A cart rattled up the hill and disturbed Edison from his daydream; in the driving seat was the familiar figure of Edward Pollard. Edward, or Eddie as everyone knew him, stopped the cart and jumped down to have a word with Edison. Eddie was the son of the farmer from the Top Farm and often helped out on the Nowell farms when extra labour was required. As he approached Edison noted that Eddie's back was even more bent than it had been the last time he had seen him. Eddie had always suffered from a slight hunch and this gave him a pronounced way of walking but now, as he reached his mid-fifties, his problem was becoming more pronounced. Everyone said that his hunch had been caused by a lifetime of scything and hard labour in the fields but now that Eddie had inherited his father's farm he employed workers to carry out the hard labour.

Eddie had always made a fuss of Edison, when he was a young lad he bought him treats and showed him how to scythe a meadow and lay hedges; while Edison had liked the older man he also thought him a bit odd. As Edison grew up Eddie would often tell him that if ever he needed work there was a job for him on his farm. Eddie crossed the lane.

"Nowthen young Edison, how's it goin'? Haven't seen thee for a while."

Edison tipped the neb of his flat cap to return the greeting.

129

"Mornin' Eddie, got your grass in?"

"Aye lad, it'll just see us through this time."

Eddie was referring to the fact that the previous year's crop of hay had been poor. The weather had been unseasonably cold and a lot of farmers had to buy in fodder to feed their stocks in late winter and this year of 1885 had not shaped up to be much better. Having said that, at least the grass crop had improved enough to just about feed the cattle until they were turned out into the fields on the first day of the following May.

The two talked about farming for a while until Eddie jumped back onto the cart and, raising his old cap to reveal the reddened scalp of his bald head, he shouted across to the younger man;

"Now lad, don't forget, there's a job waiting for thee on t'farm if thy ever needs it."

With that Eddie shook the reins and resumed his climb up the hill. Edison carried on down the lane and turned along by a row of whitewashed cottages; this was the boundary between Higherford and Blacko but there were no signs to inform the traveller of this fact. Still downhill the dusty, rutted track brought the walker to Grimshaw's mansion house where the track and the turnpike road to Blacko bounded a triangle of grassland. Here stood a barn and cottage, separated from the main buildings of Lane Farm by the Marsden to Hellifield turnpike road. The locals called this fork in the road *Dicky Nook*, supposedly after Old Dick, a cobbler who had lived in the cottage there many years ago.

The large houses alongside the roadside here betrayed the wealth of their owners. Many of them had been erected by the Grimshaw family who built Higherford Mill in 1824, in fact the Grimshaws owned most of the property and land in Higherford, Jimmy's Crowtrees Farm included. Descending to the river the turnpike road passed the Bridge Inn and broached Pendle Water over the bridge that gave the inn its name.

Here, on the corner of a sharp sweep in the road stood Higherford Mill. The central portion of this three-storied sandstone building was the original spinning mill, once driven by a water wheel attached to its eastern side. Over the years the old wheelhouse had been demolished and two new buildings had been erected on either side of the original mill. The saw-tooth pattern of their roof gables gave them away as northern-light weaving sheds.

Turning along the narrow lane, squeezed between the river and the mill, Edison heard the familiar endless clatter of the Lancashire looms as they hammered, yanked, pulled and shot the cotton weft across the warp in an endless mechanical opera. Three men stood at the open mill door smoking their short clay pipes, two of them were dressed in the weaver's 'uniform' of heavy work trousers held up by braces, blue cotton smock jackets, small mufflers tied around the open neck, collarless shirts, flat caps and iron-soled clogs. They were covered from head to toe in fine down from the cotton fibres while the third man wore a navy blue bib-and-brace overall that was heavily smeared with oil and grease.

This man was the shed overlooker, or tackler, whose job it was to keep the looms running smoothly. The tacklers were often regarded as 'little tin Gods' by the other mill workers. They had worked their way up through every facet of cotton production and knew the working of the sheds inside out; they had the power to decide which weaver might have priority when breakdowns occurred. Weavers were paid by the amount of cloth they produced and if the tackler delayed the repair of a broken loom then the weaver would lose money until it was back up and running again. Furthermore, the tackler could refuse to accept a finished warp if he decided that it was not up to standard; even tiny flaws, where the weaver had not pieced broken threads properly, could be rejected and the weaver might lose a couple of day's pay.

Edison was, by this time, working in his step-father's mill and strings had been pulled to gain him the job of clothlooker; as such, he was responsible for inspecting the finished cloth before it was sent out for dying or to the customer. He knew the power that the tacklers wielded and he also knew that some of them overstepped their authority. In some mills the tacklers were downright bullies and, in particular, young women could fall foul of their ill temper. If, in the opinion of certain tacklers, a newcomer did not learn quickly enough then their lives could be made a misery. There had even been cases of young girls committing suicide over their unhappiness at work. The weaver's unions were not slow to take these cases up and often this would be the cause of a prolonged strike. The problem was that the employers usually supported their overlookers against the weavers and this could lead to a standoff between management and operatives. These cases, however, were thankfully rare as most tacklers lived amongst the weavers and everyone rubbed along reasonably well.

The men nodded at Edison as he made his way past the mill and along the riverside. Directly in front of him was the high arch of the 'Old Roman Bridge' as it was known locally. In actual fact the bridge, erected around the middle of the sixteenth century and known locally as the *Oxeystan,* was far too young to be associated with the Romans. At the far end of a line of attractive cottages stood the buildings of Crow Trees Farm and Edison opened the farmhouse garden gate. As he did so his uncle Jimmy emerged from behind the barn with the handle of a shiny tin bucket over his arm.

"Now then Edison, come to give me a couple of days have you?"

Jimmy laughed as he teased his nephew; this was the greeting that Edison always received and it never seemed to get any funnier. Jimmy, who could never truthfully be described as having a diplomatic nature, said that Edison had gone soft when he left the farm and started in the mill.

"Look at his 'ands," he would grab hold of Edison's hands and raise them for anyone within shouting distance to see.

"Like a ruddy dressmaker's 'ands they are, you need a few weeks working wi' me lad, that'll sort thee out!"

Jimmy's wife emerged from the farmhouse and chided Jimmy for his teasing the lad.

"Take no notice of 'im, Edison."

The visitor's cousin, Oates, also appeared on the scene and sided with his mother.

"I'd like to see fayther looking cloth in t'mill, he wouldn't last five minutes!"

As the little group stood by the gate they noticed two women, accompanied by three children, making their way slowly towards them.

"Good morning," Ellen nodded at the group.

Jimmy clutched the peak of his crusty old cap between forefinger and thumb.

"Mornin' Miss Ellen, grand day."

"Indeed it is. And how is your mother, Edison? We see very little of her nowadays."

Edison nodded that she was alright but his attention was taken by the young woman who accompanied Ellen. Without actually realising it he was staring at Sarah and he liked what he saw; she held herself with dignity and her broad smile lit up Edison's morning. The group passed further along the riverside and his eyes followed intently; as they climbed the stile higher up the path Edison turned to his cousin.

"Who's the lass? Never seen her around before"

Oates smiled at his cousin's sudden enthusiasm for social interaction.

"Oh, that's Sarah Davis – lives in at Atkins'. I'm surprised you 'aven't come across her, she's been here for about eighteen months now. "

The brief chance meeting played on Edison's mind for the remainder of the day and the others thought that he was behaving even more oddly than usual. That evening Edison walked the short distance to the Bridge Inn for a couple of glasses of beer. He did not drink a lot, firstly because it cost money but mainly because the one and only time he had been drunk he felt that he had not been in control of his faculties and he certainly had not liked the experience.

Bill Hall, the landlord of the Bridge Inn, was always pleased to have the opportunity to gossip. He brewed his own beer and this kept him busy during the daytime but every evening he could be found leaning on the bar, his flat cap pushed back on his head at a jaunty angle. Bill was a Nelson chap who had married the daughter of the previous landlord of the Bridge Inn.

Bill was always willing to share his problems with anyone who would listen and that evening it happened to be Edison. Bill pushed his old cap even further back up his head and took a swig of beer.

"Aye, we're having trouble wi' t'mother-in-law's will, tha knows. Th'old lass died at th'end of May this year but we can't get forrard."

Bill's story actually began back in 1876 when his father-in-law had purchased the brand new house of number eight Victoria Street, further down the village, for the sum of £155. When he died he left the property to his wife but she died not long afterwards before the will had been proved. This meant that the executors of the will had possession of the house and this incensed Bill Hall.

"I had to put up wi' th'old lass for years an' this is all't thanks tha gets!"

As Bill continued in full flow Edison noticed that the others at the bar had drifted quietly away. They had heard the story a hundred times and were only too pleased to leave Edison as the sounding post for Bill's wrath. When Edison stepped out of the Bridge, his ears ringing, the last of the evening sun was spreading a burning red glow across the sky. He cut across the road and walked over the high arch of the Roman Bridge. This brought him out at Crow Trees where he found his Uncle Jimmy puffing at his last pipe of the day.

"How were Brewer Bill? Did he mention old Nancy's house?" Jimmy guffawed so violently his stubby clay pipe shot out of his mouth and landed in a shattered clump at Edison's feet. Staring wistfully at his lost smoke Jimmy grimaced and shook his head in sorrowful resignation.

"Bugger, I'd just filled that."

Jimmy turned to walk down the path while Edison looked down at the final gasping tendrils of blue smoke rising from the charred remains of his pipe but he didn't particularly see the funny side. Loping down the path in Jimmy's wake he was indignant.

"You could have warned me about Bill, I'd have gone down to the George and Dragon if I'd known!"

# 15

# Red Skies and Lightning

The Black Country seemed a long way away as Sarah's first Christmas at Spring Hill approached. She often stood at the open kitchen door to breathe deeply of the evening air and watch the gathering dusk as it struggled against the soaring lights of a new evening. For two months now the evening skies had provided an amazing display of colour the like of which had not been seen in living memory.

On a particularly striking evening Sarah stepped into the garden from where she watched the high, distant clouds over Pendle Hill as they caught the last rays of the day and reflected them over the darkening land. The town of Colne, atop its sweeping hill, appeared to be lit as if a stage-light had been trained on it while against the golden-red hues the moon had taken on an unnatural blue tinge.

This phenomenon had first materialised within two weeks of Sarah's arrival. When she first saw it she asked if the sunsets were always as spectacular in the north and Mr Atkins had been amused by this.

"No, this is new to us. The Times has been following the story of a great explosion on the other side of the world and the meteorologists have been predicting these effects."

Sarah's employer joined her in the garden and they both stared in awe at the western sky.

"And now it would appear that they are to stay with us. But you have to say, my dear, that something so beautiful can only be the work of God."

Sarah agreed wholeheartedly, she had seen mustard skies in West Bromwich, and the fiery red night-glow of the iron foundries but the scale of these red skies was truly humbling. From that time on the local people could be seen staring heavenward every evening. They would stand at their front doors, necks craned, or even walk to the summit of Pendle Hill to behold God's new wonders.

When Sarah had been steaming her way northwards, dreaming of days gone by and days to come, an event of truly catastrophic proportions was taking place in the Far East. The warnings had been clear to see for months and had been shouted from the rooftops by certain people from the Dutch East Indies Company. Unfortunately these warnings were ignored and on the twenty sixth day of August the largest explosion ever measured rocked the whole of Indonesia.

The eruption of Krakatoa was heard in Australia and the pressure beneath this volcanic mountain exploded molten rock and ash fifty miles into the air. According to the Indonesian authorities the resultant tsunamis were responsible for around 40,000 deaths but others put the death rate at 120,000. The phenomenal amounts of ash spewed out by the volcano quickly spread around the world and this was the cause of the fantastic sunsets. There was also a severe downside to the spread of ash in that it blocked out the sun causing temperatures around the world to drop considerably.

Christmas came and went and Sarah busied herself with the daily duties around Spring Hill. She had become firm friends with all of the family but especially with Ellen and the children. Her favourite day of the week was Sunday when she would accompany her employers to the nearby Higherford Wesleyan chapel. She enjoyed helping out in the Sunday school where she met a lot of people; she was being accepted into village life and was even gaining an ear for the difficult local dialect.

Ellen showed her new friend the local area and the little group became a familiar sight as they walked the highways and bye-ways with the three children chattering and dancing at their heels. Of all the places that Ellen had shown her Sarah's favourite spot was the Water Meetings where the Blacko Water stream joined with Pendle Water higher up the valley. When Ellen first showed Sarah this walk she had been fascinated by the beautiful display of unspoilt nature.

It was the late spring of 1884 as the walkers first took the short riverside path from Lower Park Hill to the Water Meetings; they were soon passing along the lane by Crow Trees Farm where a stile in the wall marked the beginning of the footpath. The path hugged the river bank as it led the way; on the right were woods of oak, willow and birch stretching from the Blacko road down to the water's edge.

To the left, rolling meadows climbed to the high ridge farmsteads in the distance and a short way along the path a waterfall tipped the cool, peaty waters into a frothing cauldron beneath. This was the Higherford Mill weir where an iron sluice gate allowed some of the water from the river to be diverted through the meadow and into the mill lodge. From here the water would rush along to drive the mill waterwheel. This was no longer the case as the mill had been converted to run on both steam and water in 1833 but for many years now it had been powered solely by steam. However, the Lancashire boilers still required large amounts of water and so twice each day the boiler man would walk along and tend to the iron sluice-gate.

As the little group from Spring Hill walked along, the musical sound of the river formed a backing to the birdsong. Ellen had been shown the secrets of this natural world by her mother many years ago and she could name each type of bird. The vivid blue flash of a kingfisher as it darted past; the tiny, but colourful golden-crested wren and the playful dance of yellow wagtails as they hopped from stone to mossy stone in the river bed. These were a few of the birds to be seen but many others gave themselves away only by their song. Ellen knew the sounds of the linnet, the willow warbler and the meadow pipit and pointed to the trees in which they rang out their mating calls. More often than not Sarah's inexperienced eye missed these elusive creatures but their song was enough to lift her heart.

Onwards they walked until they reached Water Meetings Farm where an old, rickety wooden bridge took them across to the opposite bank of the river. The farm track rose steeply through the trees to the Blacko Road at this point but Ellen steered her friend further along the river. Soon they had arrived at the actual meeting of the rivers from where the Water Meetings took its name. From here the Blacko Hill rose swiftly to its full height and, across the narrow river valley, the steep embankment of Utherstone Wood blocked out the sun.

High in the trees the new foliage of summer had not yet hidden the huge nests of a heronry and the wheeling of their occupants fascinated Sarah. She had seen one of them lower down the river; he had been standing in the water on one leg, completely motionless, waiting for his dinner to swim by. Sarah had no idea that this was a Heron until Ellen enlightened her and, now that she had seen them flying overhead, she realised just how large a wingspan they had.

"Light as a heron." Ellen pondered a saying that her mother had been fond of.

"If something was lighter than it looked she always said that it was 'light as a heron.' I had no idea why until a couple of years ago when I found the skeleton of a dead one and when I picked it up it was no heavier than a handful of feathers. The bones were all hollow, like straw – to help them fly I suppose."

While the children took off their shoes and socks to paddle in the dark crystal pools the two women sat on a large, flat stone and took in the view. The tinkling of the water as it tumbled and spilled over countless rocks had a soporific effect and Sarah found herself beginning to nod. Ellen too was lost in deep thought but all too soon the children were complaining that their feet were cold; it was time to head back to Spring Hill. As they walked along the river Sarah thought to herself that this place would be even more beautiful in the high-summer months.

Below the farm two large, square boulders rose from the river, the larger of the two would be about ten feet square while the smaller one was around five feet square. Sarah pointed out that she thought this was an unusual formation.

"Yes, that's the 'Coach and Four,' if you think about it their shape is that of a closed coach being pulled by four horses. In 1745 Benjamin Ingham preached from that rock and, by 1749, there were enough of his followers in Pendle Forest to build an Inghamite Chapel at Wheatley Lane. It's a beautiful little chapel, Wheatley Lane.

At Easter the adventurers had climbed Pendle Hill; Ellen explained to Sarah that this was a longstanding tradition in the district. Thousands of mill workers would flow out of the towns and villages on Good Friday and head for Old Pendle's heights. The Atkins children wanted to walk to the hill, as their friends did, but Mr Atkins had previously insisted on them going in his carriage. This time, though, it had been decided that the two eldest were now big enough to cope with the six-mile round trip.

The night before Good Friday the family set about hard-boiling a dozen eggs and painting the shells with faces and patterns. The following morning they packed a picnic bag, put on their stoutest shoes, and set out for the darkest depths of Pendle Forest.

The term 'forest' as applied to the Pendle district was actually a misnomer, as Sarah soon found out. Following the Norman invasion of 1066 the word *'Forestas'* had been applied to the district around Pendle Hill by the new overlords who used the land solely as a hunting area. Although there were a great number of trees in copses and isolated woodlands there was no specific area that could in any way be termed a *'forest.'*

The happy group turned up the side of the White Bear Inn and began the long climb out of the village to the ridge top. Having passed the Temperance Hall, Green Bank Farm and the Pasture Gate Piece House they pushed on until they were half-way up the hill and level with Ellen's old home of Pasture

House. They stopped for a few moments at the end of the track leading to the house and Ellen's eyes moistened, as they always did when she thought of her short life here with her husband.

"Come on Ellen, let's not look back." Sarah took her hand and gave a playful tug. At the top of the hill the group stopped for a breather and to take in their surroundings. Sarah leaned on a heavy wooden field gate and admired the stunning scenery. From the Yorkshire hills in the far distance the green valleys and ridgeways stretched across to Pendle Hill in the west and the alpine-like view took her breath away.

"It's lovely up here! I wonder why you cunna see this view from the village?"

Looking back down the hill that they had just negotiated she immediately knew the answer. They were astride a high ridge that stretched from Utherstone Wood, through the Pendle Forest, and along to the Roman settlement of Ribchester near the town of Blackburn. Ellen explained that this ridge carried an ancient trackway that had been used as a route between the east and west coasts since time immemorial. This part of the ridge formed the height above Barrowford and effectively blocked any view to the north from the village.

"Full of surprises, Pendle Forest," Ellen knew every inch of the district, "The view changes at every turn."

Down the other side of the ridge they went, dropping into the scattered groups of farms, houses and mills that formed the village of Roughlee. Ahead of them stretched a long walk as they left Roughlee and headed towards the tiny village of Barley, nestling at the very foot of Old Pendle. The road here meandered around the hillsides as it passed above woodlands and scenic riverside mills.

Ever since they had joined the Barley road the crowds of fellow walkers had been growing steadily and now they were walking in a large, jolly group; all out to enjoy this rare day away from the clattering mills.

Ellen set out the picnic on the crowded Barley village green as the rising mass of Pendle Hill looked disapprovingly down at the annual invasion. They soon polished off their lunch,

which the two children had swilled down with a full bottle each
of *'Emmett's Barrowford Mineral Water.'*

"Steady on you two, there wunna be any privies on the hill
you know."

"Don't worry Sarah," Ellen was an old hand at this.

"They can go where everybody else goes, behind a wall at the
top."

Suitably refreshed the four set off along the well-worn
footpath as it followed the infant Pendle Water towards its
source. This was the final part of their quest and, as they grew
ever closer, Pendle seemed to Sarah to be growing in size. On
both sides the ground became increasingly rock-strewn and
the grass turned to bracken. The footpath suddenly rocketed
upwards at an alarming angle and the four climbers stopped to
gather their breath for the coming exertions. All around were
others intent on the same goal of reaching the summit; young
and old alike were smiling as they sucked in great gulps of the
crisp air.

"Right, here goes."

Ellen steeled herself for the climb she led her party up the
steep ascent and the children thought that this was a great
game, running up the path ahead of the two adults, and then
running back down to tease them.

"Alright, alright, wait until you get to my age you young
whippersnappers," Ellen shook a fist in mock anger, "see if you
can run up here then!"

Many were the times when one or other of the party lost
their footing on the loose stones but they persevered. Sarah
felt to be climbing to the heavens as her lungs burned and her
knees began to buckle - but she was not going to give up now.
They eventually spilled, puffing and panting, onto the level
plateau of Pendle's summit where the children made straight
for a mound of loose stones and started to dance around on
top of it. Ellen turned to Sarah, who was still somewhat
flushed from the physical effort.

"That's a bronze age burial mound, so they tell me."

"Is that the same?"

Sarah pointed further along the summit to another pile of stones. Ellen informed her that this was a modern cairn, created by a tradition that anyone climbing the hill placed a stone on it.

"Why haven't we brought a stone?" piped up the children.

"Well, I reckon that it's hard enough carrying yourself up here, never mind carting rocks up as well!"

They made their way to the highest point of the hill and gazed into the distance. Ellen was used to the vast panorama afforded to those who took the trouble to climb Pendle's slopes but Sarah had seen nothing like this and stared in awe at the huge landscapes unfolding before her in all directions. Ellen pointed to the distant sparkle of the waters in Liverpool Bay, beyond which were the hills of North Wales and further to the west they could make out the cliffs of the Isle of Man. Northward were the Lakeland mountains, to the east the Three Peaks of Yorkshire seemed just a stone's throw away and beyond them Ellen said that York Minster could be seen on an exceptionally clear day.

Nearer home a patchwork effect of dry-stone field walls radiated outwards in all directions, dividing the hills and valleys for as far as the eye could see. Between the walls the spreading green land was punctuated by the rising smoke of many small, scattered forest hamlets as they scrambled for shelter within Old Pendle's bosom.

Boulsworth Hill rose high above the Nelson and Colne valley and was obviously the next largest hill to Pendle in the whole area; in fact Boulsworth was considered by local people to be the male equivalent of the two. The massive bulk of each hill stood in direct opposition to the other on either side of the district and this gave a distinct sense of balance within the landscape.

All along the Pendle ridge people were peering down the face of the hill and rolling their painted eggs over the edge. Ellen, Sarah, young Ellen and Mary all rolled theirs and watched them as they bounced and crashed down the rock-strewn slopes. Most of the eggs were shattered into a hundred pieces

143

long before they even reached half-way. The object of the exercise now was to walk back down in search of an intact egg and if one had managed, against all odds, to make it to the bottom in one piece then this meant good luck and fertility for the coming year. Because each egg had an individual pattern painted on it people could recognise their own efforts among the shattered remains. However, Ellen said that she didn't know why they bothered because it was very rare for anyone ever to find an unbroken specimen.

On their way back down the precarious footpath Ellen made a detour along the hillside where they came to a pile of large stones arranged about the bubbling, crystal-clear waters of Robin Hood's Well.

"This is an ancient spring, they say that people were using this water before history began. Some people call it Fox's Well because the Quaker leader, George Fox, came here in 1652 on his northern tour. From up here he saw into the Lake District and the Yorkshire Dales and made his way there. When he arrived in Westmorland he found large numbers of Truth Seekers and gathered them together; he later said that he had a vision while standing here - the Lord was showing him where his people were gathered."

They resumed their undignified descent and Mary and young Ellen spent fifteen fruitless minutes searching the bottom of the hill for their eggs. Ellen called them over,

"Come on you two, it's getting a bit cold and we should be making our way back home."

When they reached the village of Barley, Ellen decided that the youngsters looked tired so she approached one of the hansom cabs parked up outside the Pendle Inn.

"Hello Wesley, are you free to take us home?"

"Course, Miss Ellen."

With a smile Wesley Clegg jumped down and helped each of the party to climb aboard.

"Heyup." A shake of the reins propelled the horse into life.

"We'll soon have you back in Barrowford."

Even before the carriage had rattled its way out of Barley the children had fallen asleep.

"James and Martha alright, Miss Ellen?" Wesley knew the family well. In fact he knew everybody well; his business of carting, removals, cabs, funerals and weddings brought him into contact with the lowly and the great in equal measure.

"Yes, thank you. James was only saying yesterday that if this cool weather keeps up his coal sales will hold up nicely."

The adventurers were soon passing through Roughlee and to the left stood Roughlee Old Hall, set back from the road with a large garden to the front.

"That's where Alice Nutter lived," offered Ellen.

"She was one of the famous Pendle Witches who were hanged in 1612 for bewitching people around here."

"Ooooh aye," Wesley rolled his eyes in mock terror, "You wouldn't want to be out and about around here after dark!"

"Anyway, that's another story for another time."

Ellen was tiring now, the fresh air and exercise had taken its toll on the travelling party.


On the afternoon of the fourth of July a freak thunderstorm struck Barrowford; the sky blackened alarmingly and Sarah called the children in from the meadow behind Spring Hill. They had been watching Bill Greaves, the farmer's son from next door, and the hired farm lad, Bill Illingworth, getting in the cut hay. The men had noticed that the skies over Colne had been growing angry but they thought that they would have ample time to get in another load before the bad weather reached Barrowford.

This was no ordinary storm, however, and within minutes day turned to night and the heavens opened. The two men released the farm horse from the cart shafts and began to run her back to the shelter of the farm.

Unfortunately they had gone only a few strides when the lightning struck; an ear-splitting crack rent the air and a blinding flash immediately filled Spring Hill with a surreal, blue light. The closeness of the bolt put the fear of God into everyone in the house; no one spoke and the children grabbed their mother's skirt as she gathered them to her. Then, as suddenly as it had arrived, the storm moved away and the skies cleared; Sarah and Ellen went out of the back door to see if the lightning had done any damage.

And, sure enough, it had. There in the field, about fifty yards away, lay the bodies of the two men and their horse, the poor animal lay on her back with all four legs in the air, twitching violently. Her corpse steamed in the last of the rain and from beneath the brass harness fittings rose small plumes of grey-blue smoke from her scorched hide. Ellen and Sarah stood stupefied; they could not believe that the children had been playing on that very spot just minutes before.

"Quick Sarah, go back in and, whatever you do, don't let the children see this."

Sarah did as she had been instructed but Ellen did not really know what to do at this point. Should she run down into the village to fetch the doctor? Should she climb the fence and go over to the stricken group? She quickly made up her mind to hurry around to the farm and tell the farmer, William Greaves, of his son's accident.

William was a thin, wiry man whose sunken face betrayed the fact that he had lost every tooth in his head. Nevertheless, he was of a farming stock who could trace their lineage hereabouts through many centuries past and he had inherited his ancestors' tough character. William turned ashen faced as Ellen told him the bad news, he had seen the lightning flash from the kitchen window of the farm but he had not been aware that it had grounded so close to home.

Despite his seventy-five years William ran across the field to his son's side like a whippet and Ellen followed although her shoes were hardly suitable for running across the wet grass. As she approached the group Ellen heard William shouting and a loud groaning from the two stricken men who were, by now, sitting up - they were extremely dazed and shocked but they were alive!

Both of them survived their misadventure; they could not work for a couple of weeks and they were covered in bruises from head to foot. Doctor Pim told them that he had never seen anything like it; he could only assume that the horse, being the tallest of the three in the open field, had attracted the most violent part of the lightning strike.

Friends of the stricken men lost no time in pointing out that the lightening strike had been God's retribution for their not having attended church regularly. The two Bills quickly became famous in the district as the lads from Barrowford who survived the thunderbolt that had killed a cart horse!

Bill dined out on his story for the rest of his life;

"I wouldn't have minded but th'old feller were only interested in th'orse!"

Admittedly, Bill remembered little of the immediate aftermath of the storm but this didn't stop him from embellishing the truth.

"Aye, I were layin' in t'field and he come rushin' up – 'Oh Dolly, Dolly – me lovely 'oss – Oh what am I goin' to do?' And there's me, lying there nearly dead wi' no sympathy from any bugger."

For years afterwards the mothers in the village would warn their offspring of the dangers of being out in a thunderstorm,

"If you're not careful you could end up dead as Old Greaves' horse."

The day following the accident William Greaves had the corpse of poor old Dolly to dispose of and he searched amongst the handwritten signs in the barn. He soon found the one he wanted and placed the pole in a recess in the wall separating the farm from Colne Lane. *'Nakerman plese cole,'* said the sign; William shook his head as he walked back to the farmhouse. Some of the other signs in the collection were, *'Maulman plese cole' –'Fariar plese cole'* – *'No tincars'* and *'No navays.'*

The signs had been written by young Bill and, when he had finished them he stood back to admire his handiwork.

"What the 'ell sort o' spelling do call that, lad?" William had a reasonable standard of education in as much as he could write far better than he could read. His grandfather had held classes in one of the Caul Cottages, at Lower Park Hill, in the later 1700s where he taught the 'three Rs' to local youngsters, and a few adults, for a reasonable fee. Amongst his pupils had been Ellen's father and her aunt.

William had received an education of sorts from his father who, in turn, had learned from his father. Unfortunately, William never seemed to have had the time to educate his own son.

"What good's scribin' ever done me?" William was fond of saying but when he saw the signs he wished that he had put in a bit more time with his lad. That said - he never actually took the trouble to rewrite the signs himself!

# 16

# Brollies and Clairvoyants

The year of 1885 marked a turning point for Sarah; she felt to be a part of village life and was as happy now as she had ever been since leaving The Lyndon. She still had doubts about her future, however, and could not help but wonder where her life was heading. Was she to spend the rest of her life in service – damned to an eternity of bringing up other people's children and looking after other people's houses?

Although she never spoke of Luke to the Atkins family he was never far from her thoughts. Sometimes he would visit in her dreams and the pair of them would run hand-in-hand through the Hilly Fields of Harborne or they would giggle like schoolchildren at some silly, teasing joke that Luke had made at her expense. Sarah always found the mornings difficult following one of these dreams as a deep feeling of hopeless loss invaded her sprits and often proved hard to shake off before midday.

It was not the case that Luke never wrote to Sarah. She had written to him giving her new address before she left Harborne and, about a month following her arrival at Spring Hill, a letter arrived which Ellen passed to Sarah with a wink.

"Perhaps this is from a secret beau, Sarah?"

Sarah's cheeks coloured slightly as she pushed the buff envelope into her apron pocket, she knew the handwriting as intimately as her own and intended to sit down and read it in the privacy of her room. Luke was well, and hoped that Sarah was too; he also hoped that she was getting along alright with her new family. He apologised for not having written before but things had not been going too smoothly for his family in Whitehaven. He would tell her about it some other time but suffice it to say that he loved, and missed her and would write again as soon as possible - he looked forward to her reply with all the news of her new life.

Sarah was, as usual, elated to hear from Luke but it saddened her to hear that his family were having some kind of problem; within the week she had sent a long reply. Another two months passed and Sarah received a hand-coloured postcard showing the bustling harbour at Whitehaven, again, Luke apologised for not writing as often as he would have liked.

This became the pattern of Luke's letter writing, a page or so every two to three months. Sarah became increasingly despondent at this infrequency but tried to persuade herself that he would not have much time to write, what with working and the family problems. Still . . another voice told her that if he truly loved her, as he said he did, then he would make more of an effort to correspond.

Sarah's love-life was not the only thing to be going through a difficult period; the cotton trade had been in recession for months but now the mill owners were pushing hard for a reduction in their operative's wages. On January the twenty fourth the Leeds Mercury ran the following paragraph;

*Messrs Berry Brothers of Barrowford have given notice to the weavers in their employ of their intentions to reduce wages by 5%. The firm runs about 1,000 looms and the notice will affect about 350 hands. Last week Mr Barrowclough gave notice of a similar reduction. Mr Barrowclough is the largest employer of labour in the immediate area and the combined reduction will affect over 1,000 hands. There is every reason to believe that the proposal will be accepted by the operatives.*

Barrowclough's Mill stood at the bottom of Halstead Lane on almost the very spot where Ellen's father, Richard Berry, had started his first manufacturing business.

In March, Wiseman and Smith, the owners of Higherford Mill, declared their intention to reduce wages but the workers flatly refused. They were all for a reduction in working hours, as opposed to a cut in wages, and the unions fully endorsed this. To further complicate matters a large number of small employers had broken away from their own form of 'union' known as the *Master's Association*. The smaller owners accused the large manufacturers of bargaining with their workers to keep wages artificially high in order to drive the small man out of business. And so the game of industrial cat-and-mouse continued throughout the following months.

Sarah and sister Fran managed to meet up on one afternoon every week or two when Sarah would catch the train to Burnley or Fran would come over to spend the afternoon around Sarah's home ground. The two of them would exchange their news and, depending on the time of year, they might take a walk or visit the theatre. One of Fran's favourite pastimes was to spend an afternoon at the Victoria Hall, in Nelson, where Mrs Green, a clairvoyant medium, charged tuppence for the admission to her two o'clock show. Fran would meet Sarah outside the station and the two would walk arm-in-arm to the hall in Scotland Road, catching up on the gossip of the past fortnight.

Sarah was never quite sure if her sister actually believed the things that they witnessed when Mrs Green entered into one of her trances. Some of the performances were quite convincing and Fran would leave the hall singing Mrs Green's praises while Sarah remained resolutely sceptical. On one occasion the medium had slipped into a trance and 'contacted' a chap called Ezra who was promptly claimed by a large, excited woman on the front row. Eyes closed, hands outstretched and face raised to the heavens Mrs Green began to drawl in a strange, ethereal voice;

"Have you a messaaage from the spirit wooorrrld Ezraa?"

At this precise moment a loud banging started from somewhere above the heads of the startled audience.

"Speeeak to me, Ezraa, speeeak to meee."

Bang, bang, ratt-a-tat-tat. . .

"Have you a messaaage for this siiide?"

Bang, bang, ratt-a-tat-tat.

By this time the hall had erupted into chaos. Some people were clearly moved by this obvious proof of the existence of the spirit world while others looked around, searching for the source of the noise.

Mrs Green herself was quite uncomfortable and seemed to be at a loss as to how to proceed. She was saved by the entrance into the hall of the ticket collector who, having heard the commotion went outside to find the cause. He marched the source of Ezra's message down the aisle to the front of the hall and there, shamefaced, stood two small scruffy boys with the bamboo pole that they had used to rattle the windows.

Half of Mrs Green's audience were indignant while the other half thought this was hilarious. A woman's voice rose from the back of the hall,

"Eeh, them's t' Dinsdale brothers, wait 'til I see their mother, they won't 'alf get what-for when I tell 'er what the little monkeys've been up to!"

Fran tended to agree with Sarah's doubting side after that little incident but the thing that finally convinced her was the afternoon when they arrived, clutching their entry fee, and found the hall closed. Pinned to the locked door was a small sign reading;

*Clairvoyant meeting cancelled due to unforeseen circumstances*

An annual jaunt that the girls looked forward to was the Great and Little Marsden Agricultural Society Show, better known as the Nelson Show. August the twenty second was the third anniversary of the show and it had proved to be a huge success. The mill workers were only too pleased to see how their farming cousins from the surrounding countryside lived and many thousands of people from a wide area flocked to the Seedhill Estate to see the animals and the farm produce.

Sarah loved the atmosphere of the show ground, she particularly enjoyed walking among the tents and marquees with their smell of fusty canvas mingling with the sweet scent of newly-trodden grass. Overlaying this was the not-so sweet scent of dung but this was an integral part of the atmosphere. The town dwellers could get up close to the massive bulls and the dignified bulk of the shire horses. Farmers compared their stock while youngsters dashed to the toffee-apple stalls or queued for bags of fried potato chats.

Fran's friends from Burnley were there, along with some of the people that Sarah knew from chapel, and they all grouped together in one happy gang. Not least among the entertainments to be seen that year was a hot-air balloon belonging to Mr Whealan, of Huddersfield, named '*The Duke of Edinburgh*,' and Ben Nutter's '*Freaks of Nature Show*.' Ben Nutter was a horse dealer from a well known line of Barrowford farmers and his show consisted of a small tent in which he exhibited a three-legged duck, a five-legged sheep, a six-legged heifer, a three-legged yearling filly and a Golden Water Otter.

The group of young women paid their penny entrance fee and filed through the tent to see these fantastic oddities of the natural world. Ben Nutter stood by a cage containing a shape covered by a white linen sheet. He launched enthusiastically into a spiel describing his Golden Water Otter as the rarest mammal on earth:

"In fact this, ladies and gentlemen, is one of the only two surviving specimens known to man - the Shah of Persia has the other one!"

When his audience was judged to be suitably prepared for this stunning rarity, Nutter would whip back the covering sheet to reveal a large brass kettle. This, of course, was followed by a great deal of vocal derision from the crowd but, fortunately for Nutter, they usually saw the funny side.

In the horse section Messrs Robert Hartley and Alexander Bell, the owners of Clough Springs Brewery in Barrowford, had been sweeping the board with their horse entries since the show's inception. This year they won 'Best Stallion for Road or Field' but the remainder of the rosettes went to other Barrowford exhibitors. Also with a first prize was Ellen's nephew, James Berry, for the 'Best One Year Old Mare or Gelding for Road or Field.' Sarah watched as James was presented with his small silver cup and was pleased for him as she knew that his grandson had died only a few weeks earlier at the age of eighteen.

As the afternoon wore on Sarah's group gradually drifted off and it was finally left for her to say goodbye to her sister. Fran set off up the steep hill of Carr Road to catch the train to Burnley and Sarah walked along the riverside to Newbridge from where she followed the village road to Spring Hill. It had been a nice feeling to be amongst friends, to laugh and joke and generally relax. She slept well that night.

November arrived more quickly than Sarah thought possible and with it came the blustery weather of late autumn. This year, however, the weather during every season had been unusual in one way or another. There had been the long frosts of winter, the heavy storms of summer and now exceptionally strong winds were making their presence felt.

One Thursday afternoon, in the middle of the month, Sarah had been amusing the children in the back parlour. Mr and Mrs Atkins were out visiting family and Ellen was busying herself with some job or other in the kitchen. A loud, anxious banging on the front door stirred the household and both Sarah and Ellen arrived in the hallway at the same moment. They looked quizzically at each other, it was not a usual occurrence for the door to be hammered on by visitors to Spring Hill - most civilised folk rang the bell.

Alone in the house with the three children both women felt uneasy at the prospect of opening the door to such an insistent caller.

"Who is it?" shouted Ellen from the back of the door, "Who's there?"

No reply.

"We aren't opening this door unless you state your business, we'll fetch the men of the house if you don't," Ellen was bluffing but she didn't know what else to do.

The banging started again but this time it was not as loud and, as Ellen repeated her questions from behind the door, Sarah went through to the dining room at the front of the house. As quietly as she could she pulled the heavy sash window upwards until the opening was about a foot wide. Craning her neck around the window jamb Sarah could see along the front of the house and what she saw made her run to the front door.

"Ellen, quickly, open up."

Ellen turned the iron key in the large mortise lock and apprehensively opened the door to reveal the cause of the tumult. There, on his hands and knees and covered from head to foot in blood, was a shocked and battered man. His clothes were in tatters and Ellen immediately thought that this was one of the many tramps who passed through from time to time.

They helped the almost senseless man through to the kitchen and gave him a glass of James Atkin's brandy. The man was obviously in shock and hardly able to speak but fifteen minutes or so by the fire, and a few gulps of the liquor, saw a marked improvement. Sarah went next door to bring William Greaves in the hope that he could help; perhaps he would know the unfortunate chap.

Gradually an odd story unfolded. The lane that ran past Spring Hill and onward to Colne was an ancient route that, until quite recently, had been a busy packhorse trail used by the carriers of all manner of goods. They would load up their train of Galway ponies and follow the network of trails wherever they needed to go. In fact Ellen recalled the trail being in use when the horses known as the 'Lothersdale Lime Gals' carried crushed lime into Barrowford from over the

Yorkshire border. The surviving trail from Colne now formed a parallel footpath to the side of the modern lane and was flanked on either side by mature oak and beech trees.

The unexpected visitor had left his home in Colne not an hour previously and had been walking along the old footpath. The purpose of his journey was to deliver a letter to a relative of his wife who lived in Barrowford. As he approached the canal bridge it began to rain and so he naturally put his umbrella up. This kept him reasonably dry although the wind blew the rain sideways which soaked his trousers. Mid-way between the canal bridge and Spring Hill he remembered receiving a severe blow between his shoulders and the next thing he knew he was flat on his face in the mud. He had no idea where he was, or what had happened and, seeing the glow of lights from Spring Hill in the deepening gloom, he staggered across Colne Lane for help.

Ellen brought a bowl of warm water, soap and a clean cloth and began to clean the man up; he presented an odd sight without any doubt. His overcoat had been torn down both of the side seams leaving him wearing the sleeves, collar and front which was still buttoned up. His shirt had suffered the same fate with just the sleeves, collar and front remaining. Ellen cleaned him as best she could and when the blood was removed she noticed that the whole of his back was red-raw where the skin had been removed as if he had been flayed alive.

"Oh, heavens above, what a dreadful mess! We're going to have to get you to the doctor to get this seen to."

William, Ellen and Sarah looked at each other, wondering what on earth had caused these injuries.

"You sure it wasn't lightning?"

William Greaves was understandably thinking of the events of last year when his son was almost killed in the neighbouring field but the stranger did not recall any thunder or lightning and nobody else had seen any flashes from the sky. William wondered if he had been the victim of assault.

"I'll go and get the lads and we'll have a look around."

Back in the farmhouse William picked up his gun and summoned the two Bills. They walked along the lane towards Colne and quickly found the cause of the unfortunate chap's injuries. Half-way between the canal and the house a heavy branch lay across the footpath where it had been blown from a nearby oak tree; the branch was around ten feet in length and a foot in circumference. Examining the under part of the bark William found strips of skin and blood. To the side of the path they also found a few tattered remnants of tweed and cotton.

"This is what did the damage alright."

As they walked back towards the house, Bill noticed a battered, black umbrella half embedded in the thorn hedgerow where it had been blown by the strong wind. The umbrella spike had a large splinter of wood impaled on it and the supporting metal spokes had been bent double.

"Bloody 'ell."

As the three men weighed up the situation Bill took off his crusty old cap and scratched his head.

"That gert branch must 'ave hit his brolly."

The truth of the matter dawned on them. The man had been walking along when the branch fell as he passed directly beneath the tree, the spike of the umbrella must have been directly above the man's head when the branch struck. The umbrella would have been rammed down onto his head and shoulders but this would also throw him forward thus deflecting the impact. The branch missed his head and dealt a glancing blow to his shoulders and back and, as it did so, the falling wood ripped of his clothes at the back, neatly removing his skin.

When the three farmers returned with the story Ellen and Sarah could scarcely believe them although the accident victim vaguely recalled his umbrella being torn from his grip. He also realised that if the rain had not started a few minutes earlier, or if his wife had not insisted that he take the umbrella on his errand he would almost certainly have been killed by that falling branch.

Ellen wrapped her patient in a clean sheet and William put a clean shirt and coat in a bag for him. Bill harnessed the pony and brought the trap round to take him down to Doctor Pim's house in the village.

"What is it with you people up at Park Hill?" The doctor was incredulous when he heard the story, just as he had been when he had treated Bill for the effects of the lightning strike the previous year.

Sarah received a telegram in late November and, as was the way with telegrams, it carried unwelcome news; her father, John, had passed away the previous day. Uncle Reuben had sent the telegram in the hope that it might give Sarah and Fran enough time to make it back to the Black Country for the funeral the following day. Sarah was given the afternoon off and she called on Fran to tell her the sad news. The girls were heartbroken at the loss of their dad and they sat weeping together for most of the afternoon. In the end they decided that they would have to miss the funeral as they could not get down to West Bromwich by the morning.

They went to the Telegraph Office and sent Reuben a message to the effect that they regretted that they could not attend the funeral but could he organise flowers from the sisters and let them know the cost? Sarah wrote to Reuben that night and wondered if they could contribute towards the funeral. As it turned out the Iron Worker's Friendly Society, of which John was a member, would cover the costs and there might even be a small sum left over for Sarah and Fran. Sarah took her sister's hand as she left for home.

"Just us two now, Fran."

As Christmas approached the churches of Barrowford combined in order to stage a full rendition of Handel's Messiah at Saint Thomas' church. The Wesleyan Singers joined with the Saint Thomas' choir, the Primitive Methodist Singers and musicians from various backgrounds.

Alfred Duckett brought his wife, along with Fran, over from Burnley and Sarah accompanied Mr and Mrs Atkins. The contingent from Spring Hill knew most of the singers in the chorus and all agreed that the performance had been a credit to those involved. The Duckett party went along to Spring Hill after the performance where the two men retired to discuss business over brandy while Ellen, Martha and Rachel Duckett socialised in the front parlour.

Rachel Duckett was excited by the fact that they were having a grand new house built about half a mile up the hill from their present house on Accrington Road. The new house was to be a large, detached property in a select area of town known as West End.

Fran and Sarah chatted in the kitchen and when Sarah heard the news of the Duckett's intention to move to a larger property she was concerned that Fran might have a lot more work on her hands. Fran was not overly concerned as she was sure that Mr Duckett would employ extra staff where necessary.

"Still," Sarah was looking out for her sister as she had always done.

"Just be careful Fran, we don't want you wasting away from hard labour!"

# 17

# A Fateful Meeting

Life in the village of Rimington changed little for Edison Nowell. He travelled over to Nelson every weekday with his step-father, Henry Wilkinson, and worked his hours in the clothlooking department of the mill. Every evening they would take Henry's gig back through Barrowford and homewards through Blacko. Unlike the less privileged mill workers Edison did not work Saturday mornings.

His weekends were usually spent in a round of visiting his Uncle Jimmy at Crow Trees, or taking the train the fourteen miles into Yorkshire to call on his Uncle Peter and Aunt Alice. Their son Richard, Edison's cousin, was a groom at the stables on a large estate near Skipton and Edison would sometimes spend an afternoon helping him in looking after the horses. Edison had a natural affinity with the animals that he could never have with people and loved to spend time with them, just as he had done on his grandfather's farm all those years ago.

Another of Edison's pastimes was to walk into the neighbouring village of Gisburn and call in at the railway station where the station master, Robinson Norcross, lived with his young family. Norcross knew Edison's Uncle Jimmy well through his regular dealings with rail shipments of cattle from Scotland into Gisburn. Edison would watch Norcross go about his business of signal changing and generally running his little domain.

Usually, wherever Edison went, he went alone as he had few friends outside of family members and acquaintances on whom he could call to pass the time of day. He was often to be seen loping around the highways and byways of the district, on his way here or there or nowhere in particular. He cut a lonely figure and the casual observer might be forgiven for thinking that the young man had the appearance of being lost.

On occasional Sunday afternoons Edison would walk across the White Moor from Rimington and traverse the quarry on Blacko Hill. From here it was but a short walk down the southern slopes to where the Sunday dog races took place. Edison did not like the thought of losing his money and never gambled but he did enjoy watching the whippets and greyhounds competing against each other.

These events were extremely popular and crowds would flock into Blacko from the distant towns of Blackburn and Preston thus swelling the ranks of local enthusiasts. A great deal of money changed hands on the Blacko fields and there was no shortage of subterfuge amongst the dog racing fraternity. Many were the fights between disgruntled punters, bookies and dog trainers over lost bets and Edison liked this slightly dangerous atmosphere, providing that he could stand on the periphery and stay well away from any trouble.

So popular did these race meetings become, in fact, that the Barrowford and Nelson Police Committee asked the Preston Authorities for extra manpower to police them. The Constabulary Committee submitted a report describing 'The generally rough and disorderly nature of the people of Colne, Barrowford and Nelson.'

Mr William Tunstill, of Reedyford House, represented Nelson at the Preston County Office and he objected to the wording in the report. He attempted to place much of the unruly behaviour on those people coming into the area from outside by saying that; 'The neighbourhood of Colne was no more unlawful than any other. . . people came in great numbers from the Blackburn area to race dogs on the Barrowford-Yorkshire border.'

The Chairman of the Constabulary Committee stated that regardless of where the roughs came from more Constables were required on a Sunday and the motion was carried. The subsequent increase in the police presence slowly led to the abandonment of the Blacko dog races in favour of the official Manchester dog tracks.

One of the major roads running through the Pendle Forest took the traveller from Clitheroe through to Colne; this road skirted the northern face of Pendle Hill and meandered its lonely way across the heathland between the villages of Downham and Barley. The castle at Clitheroe was the traditional home of the overlords of Pendle Forest and it was here that their armies were garrisoned and all legal records were kept. The overlords also owned a great deal of land in the Pontefract and Wakefield areas of Yorkshire and the heathland road carried their caravans to and fro between their Lancashire and Yorkshire estates. On their medieval travels the people of Clitheroe brought back to Lancashire the legend of Robin Hood and a number of sites were named after the famous outlaw.

Robin Hood's Well, on the upper slopes of Pendle Hill, overlooks the heathland road at a point where it forms a cross-roads. Here, on this desolate, windswept moor, stood the upright stone known as Annel Cross. The name of the cross suggests that this remote area, with its vast, panoramic views across the peaks of Yorkshire, was an important sacred place for the ancient local people. *'Onæl'* is the Anglo Saxon word for *'burn'* or *'consume by fire'* and the inference here is that the Annel cross-roads was once used as the site for some ancient fire ceremony or other. Until quite recently a gibbet was placed at the cross-roads where the corpses of executed criminals were publicly left to rot in the cutting moorland wind and rain.

Perhaps it is no surprise, then, that this place was still being used for public gatherings; on the first Sunday in each May the Nick O' Thungs Charity erected their 'Gypsy Tent' in a field below the cross-roads. The Nick O' Thungs was an annual meeting of many of the villages within Pendle Forest and could well have been a remnant of the ancient Saxon practice of *'moot'* gatherings. The moots were overseen by the local Saxon lord who enforced bylaws and adjudicated where disputes had arisen. In fact the name Nick O' Thungs could be seen to directly relate to this whereby *'nick'* was the old name for a road crossing a hillside and the word *'thungs'* was the local dialect for the Saxon *'thing,'* or gathering. This meant that, although they were unaware of it, the forest people could have been celebrating a tradition that had been enacted hereabouts for well over a thousand years.

The pubs and clubs of Pendleside would collect contributions of money from their regulars over the year and shopkeepers would donate foodstuffs to the Nick O' Thungs. The proceeds provided free meat and drink for the villagers and this meant that some of the poorer people of the community were able to have at least one good day out in the year.

Once the marquee had been erected huge fires were lit and the food prepared. This year the Barrowford and Colne contingents contributed some fifty pounds weight of beef, four dozen eggs and a large quantity of ham. Beside the food there were a number of barrels of beer, all set out on stillages and ready to supply the thirsty crowds.

Edison had contributed what he had considered to be an ample payment to the fund when he had been approached in the George and Dragon in the previous December. He was, therefore, not going to miss out on benefitting from his contribution by not attending the feast. At least that way he would be certain to get his money back! And so Edison walked over the moor and joined in with the Nick O' Thungs along with the lowly, the great and the good of the district.

The summer of 1885 had been another disappointing one, the aftermath of the explosive Krakatoa was still being keenly felt by farmers and growers around the world. The price of commodities, such as bread and beer, rose in relation to the poor crop yields but Edison didn't care much as he was in line for an unexpected windfall.

Loner that he may have been, when Edison turned twenty-one he had followed two of his uncles into the Barrowford branch of the King William IV Lodge of the Independent Order of Oddfellows. The purpose of the Oddfellows was to provide a mutual friendly society into which members paid subscriptions and were able to ask for monetary help if they hit upon hard times. The Barrowford branch met in a building on Sandy Lane, in Newbridge, and were closely allied with their brother societies in America.

Over the years many members of the Barrowford branch emigrated to America and so a reciprocal arrangement between the societies of the two countries was organised. This meant that if an ex-patriot Oddfellow required aid in America the Barrowford society could ask their counterparts there to provide the necessary help. The main requirements here were for arrangements to pay for funerals with the appropriate Oddfellows rites and the funeral costs would then be transferred from Barrowford to America.

Edison attended very few meetings in a year but this changed in the spring when the Barrowford Committee began to moot the idea of disbanding. The problem was that a number of other clubs and societies had sprung up in the area and the village could now boast branches of the Ancient Order of Foresters and the Horticultural Society. A number of members of the Oddfellows were also drifting away to the Conservative Club and there were plans afoot to open a new Liberal Club in Water Street.

Several meetings were held at which tempers ran high between the members who had been drifting away and the regulars who wished to see the Society carry on. On more than one occasion arguments almost ended in fisticuffs and, from a safe distance at the back of the meeting room, Edison chortled at the free entertainment. Finally, at the first June meeting it was decided that dissolution would be the best course of action. When all the property had been sold the money was distributed among the 178 members and each, including Edison Nowell, received the sum of £30.18s.0d. This pleased the young man no-end and he was cock-a-hoop for weeks, in fact he even splashed out and bought his mother a new pair of gloves.

In September Edison's step-father, along with his business partner, William Hartley, were invited to dinner at Spring Hill. James Atkins, who supplied their Pendle Street Mill with coal, wanted to discuss a matter in which he thought they could be of assistance.

When Edison heard Henry Wilkinson and his mother discussing the invitation his ears pricked up. He had been skulking, as usual, in the back room but the open door allowed him to catch the gist of any conversation. He liked it this way, he always felt that he might be the object of their conversation and listened in as often as possible to ensure that this was not the case. The mention of James Atkins made him sit up; wasn't that where the lass he had seen with Emma Sutherland lived? He took about three seconds to formulate a plan.

Hands in his pockets, Edison sidled nonchalantly into the lounge where his mother was busy sewing some item or other of ladies apparel.

"Er, did I hear you mention James Atkins?"

"Yes, son," Susannah knew very well that her son had the habit of listening in to their conversations.

"We've been invited to dinner next Saturday at Barrowford."

"Oh, er . . . can I come?"

Susannah put down her sewing and looked quizzically at the lad.

"That's not like you Edison, you don't usually want to come out with us."

Not wishing to show that he had an ulterior motive Edison played the sympathy card.

"Well. . . I was just thinking. I haven't been out much lately and it might do me good to socialise a bit."

Henry and Susannah exchanged glances. This was most peculiar, even for Edison.

"Well, James did say bring the family."

Henry was bemused but without being rude he could not refuse to take the lad and so Edison Nowell's life was about to change forever.

The following Saturday turned out to be a fine day and an evening burst of red ochre was spreading across the sky as the party from Rimington pulled into the driveway at Spring Hill. James Atkins appeared at the side door of the house to greet them.

"Good evening Henry, just thought I would save you the trouble of walking all the way around to the front. Good evening Susannah, are you well?"

Henry returned James' greeting and introduced his stepson. Edison and James had known each other by sight from around the village but had never been formally introduced.

As Martha and Ellen fussed around their guests Sarah was busy putting the children to bed and some fifteen minutes later William Hartley arrived with his wife, Nancy, both of whom Edison knew. He respected Nancy; she was still a weaver at her husband's mill but even though she could have given up working years ago she said that she loved weaving, and the camaraderie of the mill folk, and would have to be carried out of the weaving shed rather than retire.

After dinner James, William and Henry retired to the drawing room in order to discuss their business. James told the others that he was keen to expand the amount of coal gas that he supplied to the town; at present he was supplying some two hundred tons but his Reedyford site could manufacturer more than that. If the Nelson Gas Committee were to increase James' contract he might double his profits. This was where William and Henry came into his plans because they just happened to serve on the Gas Committee.

"If, gentlemen, the Committee could see the advantage of taking more local gas from me I am sure that we could take a look at the costs of the coal supply to certain mills in Nelson."

"Well James, five shillings a ton, and two shillings to bring it to the mill - your prices haven't exactly been going down lately, have they?"

Their laughter concealed a serious issue for James; if he could strike a deal tonight it could make a big difference to his business.

In the meantime the dining table had been cleared and the ladies were catching up on the gossip. Susannah, in particular, was pleased to hear the news from Barrowford and Nelson as she sometimes felt isolated over at Rimington. She knew only a handful of people there and nothing much ever seemed to happen.

Edison sat quietly in the corner of the room sipping on a sherry and grimacing; this was a drink that he loathed and he had only accepted it through not wishing to appear impolite. He was never comfortable in these situations and he fingered his stiff collar in an attempt to loosen it. When Sarah entered the room, the children having been bedded down for the night, his eyes lit up.

"Can I top anyone's glass up?" Sarah looked around the room.

"It's alright Sarah, I'll see to it." Ellen knew that Sarah was not officially working.

"Oh, I would like another glass of this delicious sherry please Miss."

Sarah looked at Edison and wondered where she had seen him before; she noted his sturdy brown brogues, brown-check tweed trousers, heavily-checked tan tweed jacket, half-turned stiff collar and woollen tie. The slight forward lean, the attempt at a walrus moustache and the thinning sandy hair – she was sure she knew this young man but could not summon up a name.

"Sorry Sarah, this is Edison Nowell, Susannah's son and Henry's step-son. You met Edison outside Crow Trees Farm last year if you recall? "

"Well, we didn't actually meet, more like passed each other."

Edison was attempting to turn on the charm. Shuffling his half empty glass to his left hand he took Sarah's hand.

"Very pleased to make your acquaintance, Sarah."

"And you likewise."

Sarah flushed slightly and was relieved when Edison offered to help her in the kitchen.

"I'll get you that glass of sherry."

Sarah felt slightly awkward as it had been some time since she had spent time alone with a man of her own age.

"Oh, it's alright, thanks. I'd rather have a cup of tea."

With that Edison thankfully poured the remains of his glass into the sink. The two of them chatted for an hour or so; Edison asked Sarah about her life in the Black Country and he seemed to be genuinely interested in her background. Although Sarah did not consider Edison to be physically attractive it was nice to have someone of the opposite sex to converse with and he seemed to be a polite young man.

All too soon it was time for the guests to leave and they assembled in the hallway.

"Thank you Martha, splendid. James, we will see what we can do about our little business matter." William and Nancy Hartley departed for the one mile journey to their home in Carr Road, Nelson.

"Are you ready for home son?"

Susannah could see that her son had enjoyed talking to Sarah as the Rimington party bade their farewells and quietly made their way homeward over the dark hill. When Edison had turned in for the night Susannah and Henry confirmed that they had both been thinking the same thing, it now became clear just why the young man had been so keen to accompany them to the Atkins household. Didn't Ellen say that Edison and Sarah had already met? He obviously had his eye on young Sarah!

Susannah was pleased that Edison had made an effort to meet a young woman. She admitted that she had been worried about him lately, what with him wandering the borough alone and sometimes staying out all night. He had never had any particular friends and if he could make a friend of the lass at Atkins' house then good for him.

That Night Sarah gave little thought to her meeting. It had been nice to pass the evening with someone who was not part of the Atkins household, someone perhaps more on her own level but that, she thought to herself, was as far as it went - little did she realise then that Edison Nowell was about to enter her life.

# 18

# A Proposal

The late winter of 1885 had been cold and dry and there was little improvement as the year turned. It is an ill wind that blows nobody good, however, and James Atkins prospered. His coal company was busier than ever and with the help of his Council friends he had won the new contract for the supply of gas to the Nelson Gas Company. Barrowford had been connected to the town gas back in 1863 and, before this, the mills had manufactured their own. Small gas plants supplied each mill with the necessary heating and lighting but now it was easier to take it from the expanding piped supply system and this was to the advantage of people such as James Atkins.

The previous year had also ended on a high note for the local textile industry. Following unrest amongst the workers earlier in the year trade had picked up and the manufacturers were able to guarantee a five per cent increase in wages. Early in this year of 1886, however, there had already been talk of a decrease in wages.

By the spring Sarah had received no communication from Luke; she had written three letters without a reply and had decided to wait for a response before she wrote again. In actual fact it had now been over three years since Sarah had seen the young man and she was finally beginning to lose faith in him. She was not getting any younger and hopes of any future relationship with him were now looking decidedly rocky.

From this point of view, then, Edison had appeared in Sarah's life at exactly the right moment. She was lonely, as he was, and she was looking on the practical side of things; Edison was here now, and Luke was not. This is why she had accepted Edison's invitation to walk out with him a couple of weeks following their meeting at Spring Hill. On Sarah's free afternoons they had walked along to the Water Meetings and Edison had taken his new friend into Crow Tress Farm to show her off to his Uncle Jimmy and family.

They walked along to where the Mile Tunnel carried the canal from the Barrowford stretch through to the Yorkshire side of the Pennines. In order to navigate the tunnel the horses pulling the barges were unhitched at the tunnel mouth and from that point onward the bargees had two options; one of these was to propel their vessel through the tunnel by means of manpower. The bargees would lay on their backs with their feet on the tunnel wall and walk, or 'leg,' the boat along the pitch-black water. The other option was to pay for the Canal Company steam tug to tow them along the length of the tunnel but most of the carriers declined this service.

Accidents were a regular feature of the tunnel and a number of people had lost their lives within its dank, dripping darkness. Less than four years ago a barge had penetrated more than half-way through when one of the bargees, John Widdup, left his colleague to 'leg' while he went to the front of the vessel to steer past the oncoming tow-tug. Having passed the tug, Widdup's mate shouted of him but received no reply. He carried on legging for the rest of the way and barely managed to make it through before collapsing. When the barge emerged into the daylight one of the workers on the Foulridge wharf saw that the two bargees were in trouble and boarded their vessel; John Widdup was found to be stone dead and his mate was barely conscious.

The coroner ruled that the cause of death had been suffocation. The steam tug that Widdup's vessel had encountered in the tunnel had been powered by burning charcoal instead of coal and this had exhausted the oxygen within the tunnel; because Widdup had been on the same side of his vessel as the passing tug he suffered the full effects. His mate, on the other hand, had been on the opposite side, away from the tug, and had been lucky enough to have a sufficient supply of oxygen to get him out of the tunnel. The operatives aboard the tug felt few effects from the lack of oxygen because they were continually pushing forward into fresh air, leaving a toxic vacuum in their wake.

Not long before the untimely death of John Widdup a young Barrowford lad named Reuben Holt had been rowing a small boat through the tunnel. The boat encountered a barge but the bargees were too busy legging to see the lad and he was crushed between the tunnel wall and the barge; unable to swim to safety young Reuben was drowned. Edison told Sarah these stories and she shuddered as she looked into the yawning, echoing blackness of the tunnel mouth.

The new-found friends climbed up to the ancient Castercliffe hillfort that dominated the town of Colne where they sat for hours looking over to the distant Yorkshire Dales. They visited the villages of Pendle Forest and sometimes they would go into Nelson or Colne to look at the shops before having a meal in one of the town centre restaurants.

By the time that Easter came around Edison and Sarah were seeing each other at least on a weekly basis and sometimes more often. On the Good Friday Edison walked with Sarah, Ellen and the two eldest Atkins children to Pendle where they rolled their eggs and generally larked around. Returning to the bottom of the hill the group sat on the village green while Edison ambled across the road to order a jug of lemonade from the Pendle Inn.

"Are you and Edison an item now Sarah?"

Sarah could not truthfully answer Ellen's question because she did not really know. They had been seeing each other for months now but there had never been any physical contact between them, they were more like friends really.

Sarah found Edison to be reasonably good company, he certainly tried his best to be so, but when she blew out the night candle she admitted to herself that he was not Luke, and never could be. She recalled the strange, light-headed feeling that she used to get between Luke's visits to Harborne and she also remembered the weakness in her knees when he kissed her. There was no getting away from the fact that Sarah did not have the same feelings for Edison but, in the cold light of day, her thoughts returned to the unarguable fact that Luke was not here. Nevertheless, she felt a strong sense of guilt, almost as if she was betraying Luke by seeing someone else.

Furthermore, she also felt that she was neglecting her sister; Fran still visited, but less frequently as much of Sarah's time had been taken up by the new man in her life. She did not know if she was doing the right thing and the doubting side would not let her forget it.

Edison was fond of calling in to see his Uncle Richard at the Barrowford Medical Hall whenever he was passing through the village. The Hall stood next to the White Bear Inn and was actually a fancy name for Richard's chemist shop behind which he carried out his dental work. Sarah also liked to visit Richard as he had a constant fund of stories relating to his work.

"Ah, young Edison and the lovely Sarah." Richard's greeting never varied.

"Go through to the back, both of you, Amelia will be pleased to see you."

Richard's wife was a plump, gregarious woman who never seemed to stop laughing. Edison had never visited here without there being large amounts of baking either in the oven, about to come out of the oven, or cooling on the kitchen top. Today was no exception and Amelia had her hands full in keeping her youngest son from eating the steaming jam tarts.

The shop bell rang as a customer left and Richard came through to the back. Sitting down heavily he puffed out his cheeks and shook his head.

"That was Ebenezer - again!"

"Oh no," Amelia was smilingly sympathetically. "What is it this time?"

"It's always the same – his bloody false teeth!"

Ebenezer King, better known locally as Clottie, was a local character who always seemed to be in the thick of it when things went wrong. Earlier in the year he had uprooted a dozen of Bill Jackson's new gooseberry bushes and replanted them in his own allotment. PC Ingleson immediately put two and two together as he knew very well that Clottie had a penchant for fruit trees, especially when they were free. Only last year he had been fined three shillings for pinching an apple tree from Water Meetings Farm.

The Constable visited Clottie's allotment and, sure enough, there were a dozen gooseberry bushes all planted in a neat little row. It took the constable another day to catch up with him and, when he did, the erstwhile gardener was aghast.

"What gooseberries Constable?"

The next day Clottie knocked on Bill Jackson's door.

"Ere, sethee Bill. What does ta think? Some bugger's planted thy gooseberries in my garden."

The upshot of the matter was that Bill had to take his handcart up to Clottie's garden, dig up his own bushes, and replant them where they had been in the first place. On top of that Clottie hinted strongly that he might be due for a reward seeing that it was him who had found the 'lost' bushes!

Clottie had come to Richard for a set of new false teeth. He lost his natural teeth years ago and had decided that his shrunken face had been preventing him from 'gettin' a woman.' This in fact had been only partly true, as Amelia put it; "Teeth or no teeth, there's few women would touch Clottie King with a barge pole!"

Richard had been reluctant to supply Clottie with false teeth because it had been so long since he had lost his natural ones. If the dentist could fit dentures quickly after taking the teeth out he stood a chance of a far better fit but, as it was, Clottie's jaw had shrunk making a decent job almost impossible.

Even worse, from Richard's point of view, was the fact that Clottie demanded that he get his money's worth. To his mind the more dazzling white ceramic that he could fit in his mouth the more attractive he would be to the opposite sex and this entailed having as large a set of teeth as possible. This was not Richard's only problem, Clottie also viewed the idea of false teeth as gaining a new set of cutting tools.

"I want 'em to be able to chomp through owt."

In the end Richard tried his best. He modelled a set of stout teeth but Clottie said they weren't big enough; he had not been satisfied until he left the Medical Hall sporting a set of dentures that would have looked too prominent on a cart horse.

"Oh, I've seen him in the village," Sarah knew that they could only be talking about the chap who was often to be seen in the Co-op stores, leering and smirking at the lady shoppers with a set of gleaming teeth that spilled out of his face like piano keys.

"He doesn't seem all there to me."

"Oh, he's all there lass, he's only daft when it suits him."

Richard had almost come to the end of his tether with Clottie. He was never out of the Medical Hall, complaining that his teeth didn't fit properly. Richard had explained that they never would because he'd left it so long to have them fitted but this went completely over Clottie's head.

Today's visit had been to tell Richard that his front teeth weren't sharp enough to cut through twine and could he put a better edge on them? Richard tucked into one of Amelia's jam tarts.

"It's bad enough him being in and out of here every week but having the daft beggar walking around with a set of teeth that make him look like a demented nag does no good for my reputation at all!"

This was not the only thing to trouble Richard at that time. Sergeant Harris, who was the steward at the Conservative Club, next door to Richard's Medical Hall, had a large mastiff dog which he kept as a guard dog. Unfortunately, during the previous week, the dog had gone mad and started to attack everyone in sight, including his owner. On the Thursday morning Harris had risen and, coming downstairs, found the dog frothing at the mouth. He could do nothing with the animal which, if it had not been secured on a stout chain, would have savaged him. Harris, being an ex-army sergeant, still had his service revolver and, trapping the dog in the half-open front door of the club, he shot it through the head.

Richard, hearing the shot, ran around to the club to see what the commotion was and there on the pavement was the dead dog with his master holding the still smoking gun. Richard took the scene in quickly, the froth around the dog's mouth, and the copious amount of sweat on his body immediately suggested one thing,

"That's rabies, you've done the best thing; at least no one was hurt. He hasn't bitten anyone has he?"

Jackson replied in the negative but the aftermath of the incident was that Richard also had to have his family pet dog destroyed as a precaution.

The summer passed, October brought the first real days of the winter to come and on the second Saturday in the month Edison proposed marriage to Sarah. His approach had been anything other than romantic; as usual he was looking at the situation from a purely practical point of view.

"It makes sense, Sarah. I'm fed up at Rimington and you could be the mistress of your own house. You could give up work, I'll bring enough money in to support us both."

Sarah was taken aback. She had not expected this and had certainly no plans to marry. She could see, however, that this would be a way of securing her future and possibly having a family of her own. And after all, Edison wasn't a bad man was he?

"Oh Edison, you've taken me by surprise. If you don't mind I'll need a bit of time to think about this."

He could see her point and left it at that. Sarah told Ellen about Edison's unexpected proposal and asked what she thought of him. Ellen tried her best to be diplomatic; along with most other folk in the village she viewed Edison as somewhat of an outsider who had never really fitted in.

"Well, he's of farming stock so he should be able to look after the money side of things. To be frank, Sarah, I always thought that young Edison was a bit of an odd sort of lad but it isn't me that he's asking to marry!"

Sarah's nights were filled by turmoil throughout the following week as she knew that were she to accept Edison's proposal then that would put a definite end to any chance that she might have with Luke. She had actually received a letter last month from Luke and, after all this time, it had been a surprise; the contents, however, were quite strange. The message was written in spidery writing and said little other than he was thinking of her.

'Yes, but not thinking enough,' she thought to herself, and so she never replied - she knew now that the time had come to make up her mind. She must choose between the chance of a life with Luke that did not look like it would materialise; or the definite security that Edison was offering in the here and now.

On the Wednesday Sarah took the late afternoon train to Burnley. The Duckett's new house was taking longer than expected to complete and so the family were carrying on as usual at twenty-eight Accrington Road. Fran was pleased to hear her sister's news but she could also see her predicament. Having talked the matter over for an hour or so Fran told Sarah that if she had been in the same position she would take the definite offer that Edison had made.

"A bird in the hand and all that . . . I hope I can be chief bridesmaid if you do get married."

Sarah gave a half-hearted laugh.

"That's a bit far down the line for me at the moment. Dunna worry though, Fran, you'll be the first to know."

When Edison came to call at Spring Hill the following Saturday he was elated when Sarah agreed to marry him.

"I can't wait to tell Mum, and Jimmy, and Richard, and Thomas and. . ."

"Whoa - slow down a bit. There's a lot to think about and we wunna go broadcasting it too soon."

# 19

# Cowboys and Canal Water

Sarah and Edison saw in the New Year of 1887 as a betrothed couple. The springtime brightened the starkness of winter but new summer growth was slow in coming; the weather remained cold and there was very little rainfall. By August the Coldwell reservoir, on the slopes of Boulsworth Hill above Nelson, had only three weeks supply of drinking water left in it and the whole district was placed on a footing of official drought. The crops were very poor and the arid soil was yet another burden for the farmers and growers to bear.

In Barrowford temporary pipes were run from the Water Meetings down into the village but this proved to be far from ideal as the standpipes were issuing unfiltered river water. Anyone who had ever walked the upper reaches of Pendle Water knew full well that the forest farmers washed their sheep in the river and, even worse, there were always a rotting sheep carcass or two to be found somewhere along the river's length.

Fortunately, Barrowford had always been blessed with a plentiful supply of fresh, clean water from the springs around the village, one of these bubbled to the surface in the field between Upper Park Hill Farm and the river. As might be expected from the name, Spring Hill had its own spring but Sarah had been surprised when Martha Atkins had told her in no uncertain terms that this water was never to be used.

The spring certainly looked clean enough but Sarah did as she was bid and now, in the drought conditions of late summer, she brought the household water from the lower spring. As it turned out Martha had been right to ban the use of the Spring Hill water. The previous owner of the house had his suspicions about the efficacy of the spring and, consequently, he sent off a sample to be tested. The results were somewhat inconclusive other than the water was not as pure as it might be. The chemist's report stated that, *'This sample equates to canal water.'*

The spring had not been used in the household since that day although not everyone shared the chemist's opinion. William Greaves, from the farm next door, said that his old dad had sworn by that spring; he had been absolutely convinced that the minerals in the Spring Hill water had stopped him from losing his hair. His dad before him had been as 'bald as a duck egg' but he himself had retained his curly locks until he died.

The truth of the matter soon became apparent. Because of the drought the whole of the Leeds and Liverpool canal system had to be closed between Wigan, in Lancashire, and Bingley, in Yorkshire. The canal company knew that, come rain or shine, they would not be able to reopen for at least a month and they took the opportunity to drain the canal to allow the clearance of accumulated sludge. Within half a day of the Barrowford canal being drained the water at Spring Hill quickly ebbed and then dried up completely. For over seventy years the local people had been using the canal water spring without apparent injury; in fact they swore by its healing properties! When William Greaves had been informed of the source of the spring he didn't bat an eyelid.

"No wonder it put 'airs on fayther's head."


Edison had been busy with the arrangements for his forthcoming marriage and it was decided that the best man would be James Bleasdale whose father ran Lower Clough Farm in Newbridge. James was a weaver at the same mill as Edison and the pair walked to and from work together almost every day. James cut a rather dandy-like figure - he was of slight build, always immaculately dressed and never without his walking cane and he quickly became the closest thing to a friend that Edison ever had. Fran, of course, would be Matron of Honour, the bridesmaids were to be Edison's cousins and so the arrangements were finalised for the wedding to take place in the following January. The couple had the choice of marrying either at the bride's parish church of Saint Thomas' or the Wheatley Lane Inghamite chapel where many non-conformist marriages took place.

Relations between the various denominations within Barrowford had traditionally been good. The Higherford Wesleyan choir sang at the inauguration of Saint Thomas' church in 1841 and both the Primitive Methodists and Congregationalists supported their Wesleyan and Anglican friends. As an example of this camaraderie, in 1876 Saint Thomas' ordered a new organ at a cost of £400 and the old one was sold at a cut-price to the Primitive Methodist chapel.

The ministers and incumbents of each church tended to stay for long periods; Reverend Smith, the first Vicar of Saint Thomas' church, served from 1842 until 1877 and lived at Grove House, on Wheatley Lane, with his two maiden sisters. These ladies objected strongly to the church school children having curls in their hair and it was woe-betide any child caught with flowers in their hats!

Reverend E Gough had been the pastor of the village Congregational church since 1862 and in 1877 the Reverend A F S Studdy took over the Saint Thomas' parish. Three years later this was to lead to the national press taking up a story under the headline, *'National Burial Scandal,'* when contrary to the goodwill existing between village denominations Reverend Studdy caused an ecclesiastical stir.

On the 3rd of November, 1881, a Barrowford weaver by the name of Edwin Wofenden died at the age of thirty-one years. Edwin had been a lifelong Wesleyan and when he died his wife, Alice, purchased a grave plot in Saint Thomas' graveyard with Reverend Studdy's consent. The plot was in a particularly good position alongside the pathway next to the church building and Alice was pleased to have obtained it. Naturally, Alice wanted the Wesleyan minister, Reverend I Fairburn, to officiate at her husband's funeral and, in accordance with the official procedure, she duly notified Reverend Studdy of her wishes in writing.

Unfortunately the good Reverend had not realised that the deceased had been a Dissenter and when he received the official Notice he was of the opinion that he had been deliberately deceived. Having taken great exception to the matter the minister notified Alice Wofenden that she could no longer have the chosen burial plot but, instead, a plot would be provided in the graveyard wherever room might be found.

According to Alice the Vicar told her that a plot might be found beneath the ash pile in a corner of the graveyard or the deceased could be found a resting place for a cost of ten shillings but this would be in with another body. Having consulted with the Wesleyan minister Alice was advised that her best course would be to keep her chosen plot and allow Reverend Studdy to officiate at her husband's funeral.

Unsurprisingly this state of affairs caused uproar within the village and the newspapers soon latched onto the story. On the tenth of November the Reverend Studdy duly carried out the burial ceremony but a protest by the other denominational clerics was staged outside of the church gates. Originally it had been planned for a large demonstration to take place at the funeral but, getting wind of this, the Church legal department reminded everyone concerned of the legal situation. Under Section 7 of the *Burial Laws Amendment Act* of September 1880 it is an offence to: *Wilfully endeavour to bring into contempt or obloquy the Christian religion, or the belief or worship of any church or denomination of Christians, or the members or any minister of any such church or denomination.*

Under these restrictions it was decided that the other denominations within the village would be represented by their officials who would accompany the hearse to the church gates but no further. In respect for the deceased they would then stand in silent congregation until the service had been completed.

Following this unsavoury state of affairs the National Wesleyan Council constructed an official complaint to the Home Secretary. Whether in consequence of this or not is unclear but the Burial Act was amended shortly afterwards to enable burials to take place within churchyards without the rites of the Church of England.

As far as Edison and Sarah's wedding was concerned Reverend Studdy had no qualms about carrying out the service and Saint Thomas' was duly booked. Edison pointed out in his own inimitable fashion that it was but a short walk from the church down to the Co-operative Society assembly rooms where the reception was to be held and this would save on carriage fees.

The month of November breezed in with the usual gusts of unsettled weather and, as it did so, Edison's Uncle Thomas offered his Barrowford relatives a day out. Salford, near Manchester, of which Thomas' home town of Barton formed a part, was to host '*Buffalo Bill's Wild West Show.*' Thomas thought that it would be nice if Jimmy, Edison, Peter and families would like to take the train to Barton from where they could all travel over to the arena where the show was to be held. In the end Edison had been the only one to take Thomas up on his offer; Susannah and Henry were busy with work, Peter wasn't really interested and Jimmy did not want to leave the farm.

Sarah did not take much persuading as she loved a good day out; she had yet to meet Thomas and this would provide an ideal opportunity to meet his family before the wedding. In truth Edison was quite excited by the prospect of seeing the Wild West spectacular as the newspapers had been covering it in great detail.

This was the year that Queen's Victoria celebrated her Golden Jubilee and the American government contributed by sponsoring Buffalo Bill's show to come to England and

182

perform for the Queen on the ninth of May. After a number of performances in London the show was to tour the provinces, the first stop being Birmingham and, in November, the show reached Salford where it was to stay for five months.

Between 1868 and 1872 William Cody had been an army scout for the Third Cavalry during the American Plains Wars. He earned his nickname by killing thousands of plains bison to feed the army and the workers who were building the Kansas Pacific Railroad. So successful had Cody and his fellow hunters been that the vast herds of bison soon dwindled to a few scattered, fugitive groups. Cody's hunting days were numbered and, in need of another outlet for his horsemanship and shooting skills, he formed his Wild West touring show.

Sarah and Edison duly travelled over to Barton-on-Irwell in the second week of November. The couple arrived at 246 Trafford Road in the early afternoon and Edison introduced his fiancé to Uncle Thomas and in turn Sara met Thomas's wife, Elizabeth, and their children Ellen, John, Constance, Percy, Susannah and Margaret. Also living with the family was Elizabeth's elder sister, Ellen.

After a pleasant afternoon getting to know each other, and catching up on the family gossip, Thomas, Elizabeth, Sarah and Edison departed for the show arena leaving the children in Ellen's capable hands. As they approached the venue the party had not been prepared for the sight that confronted them. Along the cold muddy banks of the River Irwell were hundreds of scattered tents and tepees. This was to be the home of the ninety-seven Native American 'Indians', one hundred and eighty bronco horses, eighteen buffalo and hundreds of other performers who were to take part in the show.

The indoor arena in which the show was to take place was also a sight to behold. The foursome queued for almost an hour to get into their seats and only when they were finally settled could they appreciate the vast expanse of the building.

At last it was time for the spectacular to begin and Buffalo Bill's Cowboy Band rode into the ring. This tour was the debut for the twenty-one piece band who were kitted out in wide-brimmed cowboy hats and pearl-studded gun holsters. The band struck up with Handel's *'See, the Conquering Hero Comes,'* as Buffalo Bill galloped into the arena. Slowly the arena filled with a parade of Cowboys and Indians; the Native Americans were largely of the Oglala tribe of the Sioux Nation and they rode around in their full battle dress. The Cowboys then rode into view, racing around and firing their pistols into the air to the strains of *'Buffalo Bill's Equestrian March'* and *'Tenting Tonight on the Old Campground.'*

Many breathtaking exhibitions of horsemanship and marksmanship kept the massive crowd on the edge of their seats. One of the stars of the show was Annie Oakley, the famous markswoman who was reputed to be the best female shot in the world. Annie and her husband, Frank Butler, put on an astounding display where handfuls of silver dollars were thrown into the air and every one would be hit by a bullet before reaching the ground.

The grand finale was a re-enactment of the Battle of the Big Horn. On June the twenty fifth and twenty sixth, 1876, five companies of the Seventh Cavalry had been wiped out when Chief Sitting Bull led warriors from the Lakota and Northern Cheyenne tribes against General Custer's forces. Custer had been killed and the battle became famous as Custer's Last Stand.

To finish the show Sitting Bull himself appeared and Buffalo Bill took the part of Custer. The players in Cavalry uniform formed a tight circle behind their upturned wagons and Sitting Bull's warriors attacked, guns blazing and whooping fit to burst. By this time the arena was full of smoke and the stench of cordite was overpowering but this did not affect the crowd in the slightest, in fact the smoke added to the atmosphere.

As the band played the final piece, *'Buffalo Bill's Farewell March and Two-Step,'* the ring gradually emptied leaving the solitary mounted figure of William Cody. He held his hat aloft, galloped around the ring and was gone; the crowd then erupted into a standing ovation. So fascinated had they been by this display of the Wild West that nobody wanted to leave – this had indeed been the 'Greatest Show on Earth.'

Back at Trafford Road that night Edison showed Sarah a side of his character that she had not seen before. He was like a little boy, excited and dancing around, pretending to shoot imaginary silver dollars with an imaginary Colt .45. Thomas laughed at Edison's antics, he had seen him like this before, but Sarah was slightly unsettled. The couple stayed overnight in Salford, Sarah slept in the spare bed in Ellen's room while Edison slept in a makeshift bed on the sofa.

As Sarah drifted into that state between sleep and wakefulness she mulled over Edison's odd exhibition of childishness. Triggered by the Wild West show her thoughts then turned to the conversation she had the previous week with Betty Hartley. Betty was the live-in domestic help for farmer William Greaves at Barrowford and Sarah saw quite a lot of her. The two neighbours would often be hanging out the washing at the same time, or they would meet on the way back from shopping in the village. Sarah liked Betty, she was open and straightforward and you knew where you stood with her.

When Sarah mentioned her upcoming trip to the Wild West show Betty had mentioned that relatives of hers lived out in the American West. She couldn't quite recall if the family were her cousins, or second cousins, but she had heard her mother speak of them. From what she remembered of the story Ann Ruth Hartley, of Colne, married a Burnley man by the name of Robert Parker around 1843; Parker's grandparents were from the Pendle Forest. The newly-wed couple moved over to Accrington where they attended the Mormon Church and in the following year they had their first son who they named Maximillian. Robert Parker took his family out to America in the later 1850s where they joined the thousands of other Mormon emigrants who were headed overland to Salt Lake City.

Following a harrowing journey Robert and Ann finally settled in Utah and, in 1865, Maximillian married Ann Gillies. They settled on a ranch in Circleville, Utah, over two hundred miles south of Salt Lake City and, in the spring of 1866, they were delivered of a son who they named Robert Leroy Parker.

Although Sarah and Betty had been unaware of it, on the very day of their conversation a train robbery took place near to Grand Junction in Colorado. On the third of November a certain Robert Leroy Parker, along with two accomplices, escaped with the grand sum of one hundred and fifty dollars. This was to be the beginning of a career in train and bank robbery that would see Parker, or Butch Cassidy as he was better known, go down in the annals of American history.

The wedding plans were going well, Ellen and Fran had helped Sarah with the organising of invitations and Edison's step-father had obtained the material for the bride and bridesmaid's dresses. Edison's mother had undertaken the making of the dresses along with two friends who were also dressmakers. The church had been organised, the flowers were on order and the reception was booked. As things progressed apace Sarah began to be lifted by the spirit of the occasion and found herself looking forward to setting up her own home for the first time in her life.

Having grown to be a part of the family she would be sad to leave the Atkins household and the Atkins family would also miss Sarah being around; Ellen and the children in particular would feel her absence. At least she would not be far away and would see them all at chapel every Sunday.

There had been a lot of discussion about where the newly-weds would set up home. Edison wondered about getting a house in Nelson to be near his work at the Pendle Street Mill but there was one drawback with this because Sarah definitely wanted to stay in Barrowford where she was settled and knew a lot of people.

Edison agreed to this but then he did something that Sarah thought quite odd - he insisted that they should live in a house with only a single entrance. If there was only a front door, he said, he would feel much more at ease. When Sarah told Ellen and Fran of this they could not understand the significance of

Edison's demand. When this was mentioned to Uncle Richard he just shrugged and said,

"Well, that's our Edison for you!"

Sarah did not argue with her husband-to-be and they duly put down a rental deposit on a small back-to-back cottage on Corlass Street, overlooking the river and the open fields of the Bull Holme. Sarah considered the one-up and one-down cottage to be on the small side but she consoled herself with the fact that they would not need to buy much furniture.

So, things were going along nicely, arrangements had fallen into place and there was nothing to worry about - until a Thursday afternoon, one week before Christmas.

Sarah had been busy baking in the large kitchen at Spring Hill; she was up to her elbows in dough and had placed her engagement ring in a small ceramic container on the windowsill. The door bell rang and she scurried down the passage to answer it, wiping the flour from her hands on her apron as she went. She opened the door with one hand while wiping the back of her other hand across her brow; she was feeling the heat from the kitchen range.

"Hello," the man on the doorstep had not yet quite come into focus,

"Can I help you?"

"It's me Sarah."

The voice echoed down Sarah's memory and she blinked at the visitor. She knew him and yet she could not quite place him.

"Er, hello . . ." and then the coral-green eyes jolted her mind away from the baking.

"Luke?"

Her thoughts were running wild. Surely it can't be Luke, it must be someone else. Luke can't be here - in Barrowford?

But it was Luke.

"It's good to see you Sarah."

She was flustered, dusting some of the flour from her apron she tried her best to compose herself.

"Luke, it's been five years. . . I didn't think I'd ever see you again."

"Aye Sarah, I know and I'm sorry. I've a lot of explaining to do."

Sarah was in a predicament. She could not invite a man into the house without asking Mrs Atkins but on the other hand she could hardly turn Luke away. The unexpected visitor saw her awkwardness and guessed that he had caught her at a busy time.

"I've booked in for the night down there," he nodded in the direction of the George and Dragon Inn.

"Can I call on you again when it's more convenient?"

"Er, yes, yes of course. If you call back about seven o'clock I'll have finished for the day."

Luke took his bowler hat, which he had been holding nervously in both hands, pulled it onto his head and turned to go.

"I'm sorry to spring up with no warning. See you later Sarah."

# 20

# Luke's Story

When Sarah explained her predicament to Mrs Atkins she understood and said that Luke could visit that evening, she would make sure that they had the kitchen to themselves. At seven o'clock on the dot the doorbell rang and Sarah ushered her guest down the hall. Not really knowing what to say she busied herself with making a pot of tea.

"You look well Sarah, the northern air must be doing you good."

They were both uncomfortable, just as they had been on their first meeting on the Hilly Fields.

"When did you come down?" Sarah carried on the small talk.

"This morning; down the West Coast Line and across from Preston."

Sarah served Luke with his cup of strong tea. Finally she could stand it no longer and, her eyes filling with tears, blurted out;

"Why didn't you come to see me sooner, why did you stop writing to me, you broke my heart."

Luke was shattered.

"I'm so sorry Sarah, it's been awkward for me. . . things have happened."

"You could still have written, Luke."

"I'll start at the beginning, perhaps you'll understand."

Luke told Sarah of the events in Whitehaven over the past five years. The family had moved to their new life in Cumberland and things began well for them, the company cottage in the Bransty district of Whitehaven was clean and dry and, as promised, Luke and his brother were given jobs working alongside their father in the new coal seam. For the main part of 1883 Luke's family concentrated on settling into their new surroundings and their new jobs. The time flew by but Luke found that he missed Sarah and thought about her every day. Writing letters did not come easily to him but he had tried to send one every few weeks.

All too soon the year turned and the unseasonal cold of 1884 brought with it an increased demand for the Whitehaven coal, this meant that there was overtime to be had and the Harris men took full advantage of this opportunity. In the back of Luke's mind he was hoping to be able to save enough money for the deposit on a cottage and perhaps then he could offer Sarah enough security for her to come up to Cumberland and join him.

One thing that became immediately apparent to the newly-arrived Harris men was that the Whitehaven pits were 'gassy.' The fact that the coal was of a high quality also meant that there was a high tar content and this resulted in a higher than normal incidence of pockets of inflammable gas.

The new shaft in which the three Harris men were working was providing a steady supply of coal as they pushed the seam out beneath the Irish Sea. At five-thirty one April morning Luke, his brother and their father, Ben, had assembled at the pit head, as they did every morning of every working day, to wait for the cage to lower them to the working level. When they arrived at the bottom of the shaft they joined the other members of their gang and prepared for the day's work ahead.

Ben was the Cottom Steward for the gang and, as such, was responsible for checking that the tunnels were free from pockets of gas. That morning he followed procedure and ventured along the tunnel towards the coal face alone, holding his safety lamp aloft; if the flame of the lamp were to burn with a blue tinge at the top then the presence of foul air was indicated and Ben would signal to the gang by raising his shovel. If he was out of sight then the gang were not to proceed until he returned and gave the all clear.

Occasionally impure air was encountered and this was cleared away by communicating from one ventilation shaft to another. Fresh air was admitted and discharged by two pits, one an engine pit, from which water was pumped, and the other a draught pit from which air was discharged.

On this particular occasion Luke stood at the bottom of the main shaft, along with the other colliers, and waited for Ben's return. One or two of the members of the gang were becoming restless as they considered that this part of the working day always cost them money through lost time. Most of the men, however, respected the safety rules and accepted them as a necessity. However, a couple of the lads had been drinking the night before and were in no mood to hang about. To the protests of the others they set off along the tunnel.

"Come on, we've got us lamps, let's get crackin,' coal's not goin' to dig itself."

The others grudgingly followed them but Luke stayed where he was. He called to his brother not to go as they would be in trouble with their Dad but his warning fell on deaf ears, the youngster was with the big lads now and didn't want to appear soft. As the light from their lamps faded into the dark of the tunnel Luke gave a sigh of resignation; at least he had tried to warn the lad, if he got a clout from Ben then it would serve him right.

Even though he had been a hundred yards distant the explosion almost knocked Luke off his feet. The stench of burning hair and acrid fumes filled the tunnel and Luke's lamp could hardly penetrate the smoke for more than a few inches. He stood rooted to the spot, choking in disbelief. Immediately a shout and a muffled scream echoed through the dense air and then there was an eerie silence that could almost be cut through with a knife.

Luke quickly came to his senses and pulled the emergency lever to alert the rescue team at the pit head. When he heard the cage rattling down the shaft he started out along the tunnel to find his brother and his dad. Nothing could have prepared him for what he found; as the smoke began to clear he arrived at the scene of the explosion and there, scattered across the floor, were six lifeless shapes, twisted and contorted into a grotesque parody of a dancing troupe.

Reality became suspended for Luke as he surveyed the carnage. After what seemed like a lifetime his senses were able to gather together what his eyes and nose were telling him . . . that here were the remains of the men who, not ten minutes earlier, had been laughing and joking as they were preparing for a day's work.

The faces, heads and chests of the twisted bodies were as black as the tunnel sides while the torsos had been turned a shiny, golden bronze. Luke's brain was not too shocked to realise that here, amongst that sorry tangle of charred limbs, were his brother and his dad. This was too much for him to take in and he passed out; as he did so his head glanced off the carriage rail leaving a deep gash across his temple.

Luke came round when a member of the rescue team began to slap his face and, as he attempted to stagger drunkenly to his feet, he was hit by the acrid stench of burned flesh and hair as surely as if the Devil himself had breathed on him. He fell back to his knees and vomited his breakfast over the black, dusty floor.

The rescue team quickly weighed the situation up and ordered the ventilation process to be set in place. One of the team took Luke firmly by the arm and began to lead him back towards the bottom of the shaft but he began to scream that his brother and his dad were in the tunnel and he couldn't leave them. Shrugging off the helping hand he began to run but the emergency team were too quick for him and two men grabbed hold of him by each arm.

"Come on, Lad. We'll do all there is to do here. Get yoursel' back, there might still be gas about."

On the following day an inquest was held in one of the local hotels and Luke gave a short statement. He did not remember to this day what he said; in fact he hardly remembered attending the inquest. After hearing the opinions of the rescue team, and other colliers who had been in the area, the Coroner stated that the following had been the most likely cause of the explosion:

Ben had passed through a gas pocket but no one would ever know if he had detected the foul air. He carried on towards the coal face and, in the meantime, the five members of the gang started along the tunnel. An open safety lamp was found alongside the charred body of the collier who had first suggested that they break the rules. His clay pipe was also found lying nearby and the inference was that he had taken the top off his lamp to light his pipe. The other men's lamps were found to be closed, as they should have been.

The practice of lighting pipes with the safety lamps was all too common in some pits and, even though this had been the cause of many accidents, it still went on. In this case the resulting ball of flame had killed the five men instantly but, tragically, Ben was returning along the tunnel and met up with the gang a split second after the explosion occurred. It had been Ben's scream that Luke had heard as the superheated air blasted his father's body.

The Coroner returned a verdict of 'accidental death' and referred to the opening of the safety lamp;

*"To this impudent act may be attributed the loss of life in the present case and nothing else. We trust that this sad case will act as a caution to others similarly situated."*

Luke's seventeen year old brother had been the only unmarried man amongst the victims. The colliery company issued a statement to the effect that, in future, they intended to dismiss any persons found to be in violation of the Company rules.

Relating his story was obviously taking its toll on Luke. As he sat cradling his tea cup in both hands his face was drawn, his hands were shaking and his eyes no longer had that green flash of mischief that Sarah had been so fond of.

"Oh Luke, I'm so sorry. It must have been terrible. And your poor mother, she would be devastated."

Sarah was beginning to understand why Luke had not been in touch but, in actual fact, things had been more difficult for him than she imagined. After the tragedy Luke's mother had been unable to come to terms with losing her husband and son; she lost weight, slept little and hardly ate a thing. The neighbours in Whitehaven were extremely supportive of Luke and his mother and his colleagues responded by a donation of money.

Luke struggled through the first few weeks following the accident but he was not himself. He suffered from constant visions of the charred bodies of his father and brother and the stench of charred flesh haunted his every waking hour. On top of that he had to support his mother who found herself unable to carry out even the simplest household tasks.

Eventually Luke decided that his health might improve if he were to face his demons by returning to the pit. And so, after three months of emotional turmoil, he returned to work. The manager thought it prudent to put him in another part of the pit to the one in which the accident had occurred and so he started with a new gang on another mining level.

By the early afternoon of his first day back to work Luke's new workmates noticed that he was missing. He was eventually found curled up in a recess near to the exit shaft; he was trembling from head to foot and sobbing uncontrollably. The colliery doctor ordered that he be taken to the hospital and given a few days of bed-rest after which he would check the poor lad over again. In the meantime the Miner's Friendly Society arranged for Luke's mother to be looked after by a visiting nurse.

The Company doctor had been an army medic before joining the coal industry and he had been used to attending men who had been on the receiving end of artillery fire. When he examined Luke, four days following his admittance to hospital, he saw in his patient all the signs of blast-shock. By and large the only treatment available to Luke was rest and recuperation and this could mean a long stay in hospital.

And so the time slowly passed with Luke comatose in his hospital bed and his mother, unable to function, cared for by a nurse. As the New Year of 1885 commenced Mrs Harris had given up; she had lost two men to the pit and the other to illness. By the end of January she had caught a fever and, on a Tuesday morning in the first week of February, the nurse let herself into the house and found her patient dead in her bed.

Luke had been making progress by this stage in his illness. He knew the names of his nurses, was beginning to eat again and his carers began to hope for a sustained improvement. It was difficult for them, therefore, to tell Luke of his mother's sad demise. They knew that they had little choice and when they did break the sad news they wondered if he had grasped its significance. His eyes became dull and he sank back into his pillow without a word. Two days later they dressed Luke and two nurses accompanied him to his mother's burial where he stood impassively at the graveside. He shed no tears; in fact his face betrayed no emotion whatsoever and the doctor's initial diagnosis of 'blast-shock' seemed to be an all too accurate description of his condition.

Now, at last, Sarah was seeing the full extent of Luke's problems and the reason why his letters had been so inconsistent.

"Lord above, you poor thing. So . . . when the letters stopped . . . that's when you were in hospital?"

"Aye, I honestly didn't know what day it was. If I'd been capable the first thing I'd have done is write to you."

Things grew worse for Luke after the death of his mother, he began to slide into a state of complete withdrawal where darkness had been his only companion. He was aware of his surroundings and he knew that he was not well but he was unable to respond to anything or anyone. The decision was made by the hospital doctors to transfer him to the local asylum where the specialised care would be better able to cope with his condition.

For the next eighteen months Luke's life passed in dreary inactivity interspersed with meals and short walks along the corridors and around the gardens. There was little stimulation on the asylum ward other than the occasional outburst of the more vociferous inmates but gradually an improvement was recognised in Luke's condition. It had been almost imperceptive for the first year but the following six months began to show a positive change.

By the Christmas of 1886 he had been recuperating in the asylum for almost two years and he appeared to be on the road to recovery. He teased the nurses and conversed with the doctors and was helping out in the gardens. He received visits from a couple of the friends he had made before the accident and the outside world no longer seemed like such a dangerous, alien place. Gradually he was allowed outside of the asylum grounds; he walked into the town, under supervision, and was soon able to walk around the harbour on his own. He would sit for hours in the watery winter sunshine watching the colliery boats come and go and he now realised that life was carrying on around him – he slowly realised that he deperately wanted to be a part of it once again. He was eventually discharged and returned to the empty family home that the Company had retained for him.

"During all the time that I was really unwell I never stopped thinking of you, Sarah. I'm sorry but it had been so long that I didn't know what to say to you. I wasn't well enough to put it all into writing. In fact this is the first time that I've actually spoken about it properly to anyone accept the doctor."

Sarah could well believe it, she could see that the poor lad was struggling; his voice was becoming husky and his face was pale.

"I'm glad that I've been able to tell you, it's a weight off my mind."

Luke had made good progress during the past six months. He had integrated back into society and could look after himself, providing that he knew there was back-up from the colliery company if he needed it. He knew, however, that he

196

was a long way from being his old self, in fact he accepted that he would never be the man he was before he lost his family.

Sarah was at a loss for words. With mixed emotions she sat quietly at the kitchen table and listened to Luke pouring out his tragic story. She now understood why he had stopped writing but, on the other hand, she had come to terms with the fact that she had lost him; she had moved on - or so she thought.

"Luke I can see that you're tired. Why don't you turn in for the night and call again in the morning?"

This would give Sarah a chance to come to terms with the day's turn of events and to clear her head. If Luke were to call back in the morning Sarah could tell him that she was very sorry that things had worked out this way but she was about to be married and that was that.

Luke turned at the end of the hallway and took Sarah's hand.

"I'm so sorry Sarah, I know I've let you down," and with that he closed the door behind him.

The doubting side had a glorious time that night. Sarah hardly slept with the prospect of telling Luke that it had been nice to see him but she would have to say goodbye forever. Why couldn't he have asked someone else to write a letter on his behalf? Why, oh why was his timing so rotten as to turn up a month before her wedding day? On the other hand the poor lad had lost his family and none of this was his fault - after all, he hadn't wanted to move to Cumbria in the first place.

Ellen told Sarah to take an hour or two off the next morning so that she could straighten things out with Luke. When he appeared at the front door she put on her tweed overcoat and Luke immediately noticed that she still wore the jet-black rose. He recalled the happy day that he bought the brooch for Sarah but that day now seemed to have belonged to another lifetime.

Sarah did not want to be seen walking with a young man in the village in case Edison heard about it. She would find it difficult to explain her relationship with Luke to her fiancé, especially as he was not very mature when it came to these matters. With this in mind the two of them left the house and turned left towards the canal. They strolled slowly along Colne Lane and they were both reminded of the many Sundays when they had strolled hand-in-hand around the Hilly Fields.

Sarah steered her visitor along the narrow canal path towards the lock house where they sat together on a long wooden bench. After a moment of silence they both spoke at once. Slightly embarrassed Luke invited Sarah to speak first.

"Well, it's very nice to see you Luke but I cunna help wondering what you expect from me after all this time?"

"Oh, I can understand that. I had to come if only to tell you why I let you down. Now that I see how hurt you've been I know I'm lucky that you didn't turn me away."

It was time for Luke to put his heart on the line.

"You see, Sarah, I've never stopped thinking of you. You've been on my mind every single day since I left you in Harborne. The doctor says that my way to full recovery is to face things and to get them out in the open. I told him about you and he said that I should speak to you and see where we stood one way or another."

Sarah had been expecting something along these lines as Ellen had put it to her that perhaps Luke needed to know if she still had feelings for him.

"I came down here not knowing if you'd be at the same place, or if you'd hate me and slam the door in my face. The doctor had warned me that anything might happen and that I had to be prepared. He also pointed out to me that you might be married by now, perhaps with children running around."

Sarah was just about to reply when she stopped. Perhaps it was better to let him finish before she spoke.

"It's been a long time, Sarah and I know that you might not want me back in your life. I've been hoping against hope that you might still have feelings for me and that we might slowly pick things up again. I've my cottage in Whitehaven and the company have found me a new job on the pit surface – I go back in the New Year, all being well. If we could pick up again then perhaps you could come up to Whitehaven? You'd love it there; there's the harbour and the mountains and there's plenty of work."

Luke could see that Sarah was uncomfortable.

"There, I've not said it very well but that's why I came. I had to know."

With tears streaming down her cheeks Sarah told Luke of the loneliness she had felt when he first left and the hurt that she felt when he stopped writing. Finally, she held out her left hand and for the first time he saw the glitter of Sarah's engagement ring. It took a moment or two before the penny dropped and then Luke knew that it was too late.

"I'm engaged to be married, Luke. The wedding's in January."

Although he had half expected that Sarah might have found another man the blow was nevertheless just as deeply felt. He saw how difficult this was for Sarah and, not wishing to prolong her discomfort, Luke rose wearily to his feet.

The pair of them presented a sad sight as they walked slowly back along the grassy towpath and over the little hump-back canal bridge. Sarah felt desperately sorry for Luke and she longed for the clock to be turned back. Moving to link her arm through his she felt a strange unease and stopped - perhaps this is not how things were meant to be? Perhaps she should be marrying Luke and not Edison? These questions were to haunt Sarah for the rest of her days.

# 21

# Marriage

On Saturday, the seventh day of January 1888, the bells of Saint Thomas' pierced the sharp afternoon as they told the village of Barrowford that Edison Nowell was about to marry Sarah Ann Davis.

Edison's family turned out in force and his mother was as 'proud as a peacock.' The polished pitch-pine seats were full from the back to the front of the church with Wesleyans and Anglicans alike, all united in wishing the happy couple well.

The night before the wedding had been a sleepless one for Sarah. Her doubting side had been in full control and she agonised over whether she was making the right decision. She slept in fits and starts and each time she had managed to drop off to sleep the same recurring dream startled her awake again. In the dream she stood with Edison at the altar of a huge cathedral but there was no vicar to officiate. Instead a grim judge stood behind the altar in his full legal regalia of gowns and a powdered wig. As Edison took Sarah's hand the judge pronounced in a deliberate and chilling voice;

"And so I sentence you, Sarah Ann Davis, to serve in marriage to Edison Nowell."

Needless to say the bride was somewhat nervous on her wedding morning but thankfully Fran had stayed overnight at Spring Hill and she was a great comfort to her sister. Fran looked stunning in her bridesmaid's dress; her red hair shone like the embers of an elm-wood fire and she turned a few heads that day.

The Reverend A F S Studdy closed the door of his grand new vicarage on the hill and walked the few yards to church where he changed into his flowing robes. The organ-blower's face turned crimson with the effort of thrutching manically at his bellows while the organist made the rafters shake until the dust flew. James Atkins walked Sarah proudly down the aisle as her husband-to-be and his best man waited nervously at the altar. Edison looked every inch the country squire in his tweed suit and heavy brogues and his best man, Jim Bleasdale, was particularly dandified with not a hair out of place. Everyone commented on how radiant Sarah looked.

All too soon the deed was done and the new Mr and Mrs Nowell, along with their witnesses, disappeared into the vestry where they signed the register. When the Registrar handed the couple their crisp new wedding certificate Sarah saw that in the box headed *'Father's name, Surname and Occupation'* Edison had written 'James Nowell deceased, Cattle Dealer.'

The newly-weds led their wedding party down the hill to the reception at the Co-operative rooms and in the midst of the celebrations Edison's mother sat down next to Sarah and had a quiet word in her ear.

"Now, you will look after my son, won't you lass?"

"Of course, Susannah. Don't worry."

As the afternoon wore on Sarah thought about this conversation and it dawned on her how strange Susannah's earnest request appeared to be. Surely her new husband would be expected to look after her – not the opposite way around?

In the late evening the happy couple left the celebrations for their new home in Corlass Street in the company of a group of the younger guests. The youngsters formed a mock procession and, banging on pots and pans, they danced around the bride and groom. Bystanders along the short route through the village clapped and laughed at the spectacle. Unusually for Edison he had taken a few brandies in celebration and he laughed at the antics of the unlikely escort; he even threw a few handfuls of coins to the youngsters as they went along. Sarah felt a little self-conscious at being the centre of attention but soon enough they reached the welcome quietness of their new home.

The cottage was sparsely furnished but the pieces that they did have were simple but sturdy. Everyone had rallied round and contributed; Uncle Jimmy had obtained a bed and a massive dark-oak sideboard from an auctioneer friend at Trough Laithe Farm. Richard had picked up a table, chairs and a tallboy from a customer whose widowed mother had just died. Unfortunately, from Sarah's point of view, none of the furniture was made from her favourite mahogany but, nevertheless, there was still plenty of polishing to be done.

On the wedding night Sarah retired to bed a little apprehensively; up to now Edison had never shown any physical affection toward her but she had taken it that this had been out of respect for her. Now they were married things would surely change. She had been advised by Ellen not to expect too much too soon in the bedroom department as they were only young and had a long way to go before they would grow together as a couple. As it turned out, Sarah's expectations of at least some degree of romance from her new husband were to be unfounded. He came into the bedroom twenty minutes after she had retired, blew out the candle, stripped down to his long-johns and slumped into bed. And that was that.

Sarah didn't know what to make of this. Her lack of experience with the opposite sex meant that she was not well placed to judge whether Edison's behaviour was normal or otherwise. This state of affairs carried on for weeks and the couple settled into a routine of Edison working his five days and Sarah running the house.

At first the new bride felt a strong sense of pride in running the household as best she could. She cooked and cleaned with a new-found vigour and the cottage soon shone like a new pin. The main part of the weekly wash was carried out on Mondays when many of the women from the neighbourhood came down to the river in front of Sarah's cottage. Here they rubbed the clothes and bedding with carbolic soap and beat the cloth against large stones set in the riverbank. The steady flow of water rinsed the washing thoroughly and the clothes were folded into piles before being pegged out to dry on the spider's web of clothes lines that criss-crossed every back street. Their work done the women would sit for an hour gossiping and sipping the tea provided by the Corlass Street residents.

Fran was a frequent visitor to Sarah's proud new home and in the spring Sarah told her that Edison had still not attempted any physical show of affection,

"I'm still *'virgo-intacto'* Fran. Do you think that he loves me?"

Fran did not really know what to say to her sister. She had never heard that odd phrase before and assumed that Sarah had picked it up from one of her neighbours. However, she could see that she was upset and confused by Edison's apparent lack of interest in his matrimonial duties.

"I wunna bother too much Sarah. From what I hear from the Burnley girls men are a strange lot. Some just want what they can get before they move on and some are happy with a bit less. From some of the stories I've heard down the Mechanics you might think yourself lucky!"

Fran did not consider herself to be an expert on matrimonial matters and she knew that she was floundering.

After a couple of months at their new home Sarah noticed that Edison was beginning to behave quite strangely. He could not relax when he came home in the evenings; he was constantly either walking around the house or walking around the village. Sarah wondered if he was worrying about work as things were going their usual unpredictable way in the local mills. A strike had just been called at Higherford Mill because the owner, Robert H Wiseman, had attempted to reduce the weaver's wages by five per cent. Wiseman had quoted 'local difficulties' as the reason for the wage reduction and in some ways he had a point.

Because the mills in Barrowford were over a mile from the Nelson and Colne railway stations, and not much nearer to James Atkins' Reedyford coal wharf, the cost of transporting raw materials was relatively high. Henry Wilkinson was paying two shillings per ton for coal delivery to his Nelson mill but Wiseman found himself having to pay almost twice that amount. Over the ridgeway, in Roughlee, the delivery of coal rose to five shillings per ton and this was as much as the cost of the coal itself. The cost of transporting raw cotton was also higher in the outlying villages and Wiseman therefore argued that he could not compete with town mills on a level playing field.

This did not impress the weavers as they had heard this old argument many times over the years so they held a meeting at Higherford at which they set fire to an effigy of their employer. Also, because Wiseman bred English Bulldogs, an effigy of his prize animal was constructed; an old shirt was stuffed with cotton-waste and an unfortunate image of the dog's face was painted on a marrow to form the head. The crowd took great delight in drop-kicking their effort up and down the road before it was unceremoniously booted into the river to the accompaniment of loud boos and jeers.

Edison explained to Sarah why some of the village weavers were striking; the textile trade in Nelson was brisk, so much so that two new mills were being built to accommodate three thousand more looms. In fact there had been such an expansion in production capacity that there was now a shortage of weavers to run the looms.

Having said that, on March the seventh a large meeting was held in Nelson's Victoria Hall because the Master's Association had refused to provide a coloured goods list in Colne. The Northern Counties Association of Weavers voted to compel them to do so by bringing the weavers out on strike and a resolution was carried to support the striking weavers at Wiseman's Barrowford mill.

For the time being at least Edison remained unaffected by the ups and downs in his trade and it was apparent that this was not the reason for his strange behaviour. However, another odd trait soon began to emerge where he would question Sarah closely on what she had been doing during the day. Who had she seen and where had she been? At first Sarah accepted this as simply the concern of a husband for his new wife; after a while, though, the questioning became rather too insistent.

As it so happened, the Nowell's next door neighbour was a quack doctor by the name of James Brown. James earned his living by charging the villagers a few coppers to supply them with tinctures, potions, salves and balms for their many ailments. He knew the local flora like the back of his hand and had earned quite a reputation as a good practitioner. This was much to the chagrin of Doctor Pim who, as the qualified village doctor and surgeon, had little time for James Brown or his quack methods.

Sarah mentioned to James that Edison had not been at ease for the past few weeks,

". . . don't tell him I've mentioned it to you. Perhaps if you call round one evening and bring it up in conversation?"

Sarah did not think that Edison would approve of her telling the neighbours that he appeared to be having problems.

And so James Brown popped into the Nowell household a few evenings later on the pretext of a neighbourly visit. He sat with a cup of tea for half an hour or so and observed Edison's jittery manner. Finally he broached the subject.

"Edison, you look a bit edgy, are you alright?"

"Well . . . I'm on edge all the time these days, don't know why though."

# 22

# Potions

Although James Brown did not say as much he had seen this situation before, settling into a new way of life could be difficult for newly-wed couples, especially where one of them had been particularly close to a parent. James' neighbour, Edison Nowell, appeared to be having more difficulty than usual and James suggested that he might have the answer.

"Tell you what, Edison. I'll make up an infusion and see if it helps, how'll that be?"

Edison agreed and the next day James brought round a large jar of reddish-brown liquid.

"Here you are Sarah. When he gets home tell him to take two big spoons three times every day. If it works I'll make him some more."

Two evening later James called on his neighbours to find Edison much more relaxed.

"How's it going?"

"Oh, it's good stuff Jim. Stinks to high heaven but it's doing the trick. I've been sleeping like a log. What's in it?"

"It's just boiled Valerian leaves and a bit of comfrey - never fails."

Sarah made their visitor a cup of tea and she asked how he had acquired his skills. James related that he had been born at Black Moss Farm, on the outskirts of Barley village at the foot of Pendle Hill; his father was from a large family who had farmed in the district for generations. James's mother was a skilled herbalist as her mother had been before her and as such she was familiar with every inch of the fields, woods and hedgerows around the forest; if a flower or herb grew locally she would know where it could be found.

"Course, what I do now, and what my mother did all her life, could have seen us accused of witchcraft not all that long ago."

Edison nodded in agreement.

"Aye, you'd have been off to Lancaster with Old Demdike's lot!"

Sarah had heard this name before, she had heard mothers scolding their children and threatening them with a visit from Old Demdike.

"What did she do then, this Demdike?"

"Well," James smiled, "If you ask ten folk round here you'll get ten different stories. But I reckon us foresters know as much as anybody about what happened."

Sarah lit the gas mantles and put a couple of lumps of coal on the fire while James began to recount the travesty of justice that had occurred in the forest only a few generations ago.

From the earliest times women have learned the skills of healing and midwifery from their forebears and, as these practises were honed, the more effective they became. The forest poor could not afford doctors but even if they could have found the money the medical profession was little more advanced than the local healers. Each district within the forest had its own favoured healer, they were usually women but men occasionally practised and they all guarded their territory jealously.

They were asked to help in cases of disease or injury and often provided potions and spells for such things as increased fertility and crops. Farmers were not slow to call on the local wise person to treat his animals when necessary. Payment was usually made in farm produce; a steady supply of thin blue milk and the odd capon would bolster the few coppers earned elsewhere.

This, then, was the way things were within Pendle Forest in the latter part of the 1500s. Within this culture two widows gained a strong reputation as healers and practitioners of the natural arts. Elizabeth Southern had earned the nickname of

Old Demdike through being a formidable character. The sobriquet of Demdike was commonly used in those days to describe a strong, older female and had the meaning of 'Demon Woman.' Demdike's arch rival was Ann Whittle, also known as Old Chattox and between the two of them these women exercised a monopoly on the practice of healing within the forest bounds. Some people favoured the one and some the other but, eventually, their rivalry was to prove their nemesis.

"The old ways didn't die out at that time, though." James went on.

"There are still people on the forest farms who cast spells for good weather for their crops. You can still buy love potions and spells if you know who to ask."

Sarah could well believe this; she had been to the forest villages and knew how isolated the district was around Pendle Hill. The people who farmed the hills and secret valleys there were the offspring of people who had farmed the same land for many hundreds of years. The old country ways were passed down as a natural matter of course and were not considered to be anything other than a way of harnessing the natural bounty of the land.

"It's only a generation ago that old Mrs Greaves was thrown out of the Wesleyan chapel at Higherford, you know."

James had been told the story by his father.

"Old William up at Park Hill, it was his mother. The chapel Leaders found out that she'd been 'consorting with conjurors and witches' and they asked her to leave the fold. Old Will's lot farmed over at Barley about seventy years ago and this particular year, around 1824 or thereabouts, was a bad drought year and the sheep on Pendle were suffering. All the farmers from around Barley used to share one shepherd who tended their stock right over the top of the hill."

"This year things were bad, all the springs and wells on the hill had dried up and the shepherd could only watch as his flock worsened. Old Will's mother knew a woman from over the hill that had a reputation for being a 'watter-finder' and she asked her for help. This woman went up on to the hill and walked about with her hazel wand and she eventually told the farmers to dig a hole in a hollow. They dug the hole and water gushed out; they called it Deep Clough Spring and it's been flowing ever since. Anyway, as far as the chapel Leaders were concerned old Mrs Greaves had consulted with conjurors and they threw her out."

A thought suddenly struck James and he rose from his chair.

"Hang on a minute, I'll show you something."

He went round to his house and within minutes reappeared clutching a battered and yellowing old piece of parchment.

"Here, have a look at this. It's a spell that my dad was given a long time ago to protect the farm house and the family from witches."

He laid the small square of parchment on the table for his hosts to peruse. Sarah and Edison squinted at the faded writing and could just make out the words;

*Omnes spiritu laudet domnum mason hebent*
*dusot propheates exurgrat disipentur inimicus*

"My dad kept it in a space behind a loose stone over the front door. He had another spell for protecting the cattle in the field. He used to put it in a gap in the field wall and if any of the cattle fell sick he would put it over the shippon door."

"What happened to the witches then?" Sarah wondered.

"Well," James put his hand around his throat and made a gurgling sound.

"Nineteen people were taken to Lancaster Castle on charges of witchcraft in 1612. In the end Demdike died in prison before the trial and Chattox was hanged along with her daughter. Demdike's daughter and two grandchildren were also hanged - altogether nine folk from Pendle Forest were executed that day for doing little more than I do now."

# 23

# Fran

Village life went on much the same throughout Sarah's wedding year of 1888. The mills worked in fits and starts, people stood on almost every street corner in gossiping groups and, as was their way, the farmers moaned about anything and everything. The weather had not been as unseasonably cold during this summer and as winter drew on everyone noticed that the brilliant reds and pinks of the evening skies were fading.

James Brown's valerian potion kept Edison on a relatively even keel but it did not stop him from questioning Sarah's every movement. If the truth were to be known Sarah actually missed her work at Spring Hill, she longed for the camaraderie of a bustling household and the constant demands of the children. But most of all she wanted to be out of her home on Corlass Street as the confines of the tiny cottage were beginning to feel like a prison to her now.

She knew that she had not been replaced in the Atkins household and had broached the idea of going back to work at Spring Hill but her husband was not pleased.

"I'm having no wife of mine going out to work. People will think that I can't keep you."

And that was that; Sarah did not mention the idea again. The housework demanded little of Sarah's time and she found herself leaving the house on the flimsiest of pretexts. Instead of collecting all her daily shopping in one trip she would walk to the butchers and take the meat home, then she would walk up to the greengrocery, take the vegetables home and then return to the Co-operative store and so on. She was always pleased to stop and talk about the weather, the goings-on at chapel, the village gossip, in fact anything that would pass a few minutes of her empty day.

The two things that now filled Sarah's life were the chapel and her sister's visits. Fran had seen a change in Sarah over the year and was concerned.

"Things still the same with you and Edison then Sarah?" She had hoped that marriage would lift the new bride out of her doubting moods but, if anything, things appeared to be going in the opposite direction.

"No change really, Fran. He dunna seem to want to touch me. There are times when it would be nice to have a hug but he won't even do that. He just gets flustered and shuffles off."

It was becoming quite obvious to the younger of the two sisters that this was not to be a marriage made in heaven.

Sarah's thoughts turned to a Sunday afternoon when she had called for Fran and the two of them walked down into Burnley.

"Do you remember when we went to that songbird contest a couple of years ago?"

A sign outside a church hall told them that there was a songbird contest there that afternoon and, intrigued, they went in. The hall was lined with trestle tables upon which were hundreds of small wooden boxes. These held all manner of local songbirds from linnets and thrushes to willow warblers. It soon became apparent to the sisters that by far the most popular bird was the skylark whose collective melody filled the musty hall. The sisters walked around the tables peering into the boxes and were amazed that a beautiful, melodic sound could be produced by such small, drab, sad-looking birds.

Fran soon found herself in conversation with one of the bird keepers and she asked him where they got the birds from. He told her that he specialised in 'showing' the lark and that most of the birds in the contest were taken from nests as fledglings. Each species of songbird had a different song and, within each species, the individual had a specific song. The young birds learned their song from the older birds around them and these were used to protect their territory and to attract a mate. It was especially in the male songbird's interest to sing well because a female would generally be most interested in the male with the best song.

In the case of the skylark the keepers would allow the domesticated birds to learn their songs by taking them out onto the hills and moors. Here, the young lark would sit entrapped in the small box and listen to the singing of his wild cousins. As the free birds soared their hearts poured out a melody that descended to the ground where the caged bird heard and imitated it. This plucked a chord in Sarah's heart. The practice of exposing the caged birds to a natural world in which they should be enjoying their God-given freedom seemed barbaric. She listened to the creatures in their boxes, echoing and mimicking the songs that belonged to the wild and a tear welled in her eye.

"I feel like those caged skylarks must feel, Fran." Sarah's hand swept around the room.

"This is my cage. . . I'm living my life through other people. I even stop folk in the street to talk about nothing so as to pass a bit of time."

At nights Sarah's dark companion had now assumed a very real shape and her heart sank; she was married but at the same time she had never been more alone. Above her, just out of reach, a huge pair of black wings would slowly envelope her until a troubled sleep took over.

As Christmas approached Edison let it be known that he could not spend another year in the tiny cottage; he felt claustrophobic within the confines of the four walls just as Sarah did. He now had to admit that taking a house with only a single entrance had been a mistake on his part so he took Sarah to look around some of the new houses in Newbridge and she agreed that if they could move into one of them then they would have much more room. These were terraced houses with a back door leading into a private yard, they had two bedrooms and, luxury beyond luxury, each house had its own toilet. Sarah had become accustomed to the private upstairs bathroom and the downstairs toilet at Spring Hill and she hated the outside 'long-drop' privies shared by every block of eight houses on Corlass Street. Edison told her that this was far better than some of the properties in the Old Row where twenty houses might share a single privy.

The couple settled on number five Joseph Street and in the January of 1889 Wesley Clegg moved their scant belongings down the road to their new home. Sarah busied herself with getting the house as she wanted it while Edison kept out of the way as much as he possibly could.

Joseph Street was one of a large number of new terraces that were springing up all around Barrowford. They were good quality, stone-built properties with high ceilings, large window openings fitted with quality sash fittings, coal fires in all the rooms, running water and provision for gas cookers.

The Nowell's new neighbours were almost exclusively mill workers, the exception being Henry Goodier next door at number three. Henry, nicknamed 'Harry Soot' because he always seemed to be covered in coal dust, had migrated over from Preston a couple of years ago to work as a filler at James Atkins' coal yard.

Taking pride of place in the front room of the new house, or parlour as Sarah liked to call it, was a massive sideboard of the finest West Indian mahogany. Sarah and Fran happened upon this behemoth in a Nelson auction room and Sarah fell instantly in love with it. The price of the sideboard took all of the few pounds that Sarah had been left by her father but she considered it to be money well spent. It took three men and a hand-truck to manoeuvre the sideboard into the house and its new mistress took great delight in polishing every inch of the glowing surface for the rest of the afternoon. When Edison arrived home that evening his jealousy demanded to know if she had spoken to the delivery men.

"'Course I spoke to the men, I cunna just ignore them could I?"

There was one slight problem with the move to Joseph Street and that was that Edison no longer had James Brown's valerian potion to keep him on an even keel. He noticed that he had become increasingly jittery over the first couple of weeks following the move and Sarah suggested that it was because he was no longer taking the potion. She offered to ask James if he would make a regular batch and she would collect it once or twice per week. Edison, however, thought otherwise. He became angry at the suggestion that he had become reliant on a few boiled leaves to keep him calm. If this was indeed the case then he had lost a certain amount of control over his own body and he was not having it; that was the end of the matter as far as he was concerned.

The Ducketts were now settled into the new home on Padiham Road, in Burnley, which they had named Fern Royd. Fran was in good company here as there were people from her native Midlands living on both sides. At Daisy Bank the head of the household was a tailor who had originally moved north from Staffordshire; living with him were his wife and eleven children who ranged in age from twenty-three to four years. On the other side, at West End Villas, lived a retired cotton manufacturer and his domestic servant came from Shropshire.

Fran loved the new house, on sunny days she would take her breaks in the front garden and take in the fresh air. Fern Royd had been built on the western edge of Burnley, away from the factory chimneys, and was situated on the edge of the ancient rural district known as Ightenhill Park. From her bedroom window beneath the eaves of the front gable she had a superb view of the Hameldon Hills and beyond to the high moors.

Sarah was most impressed on her first visit to the new house. She took the train as usual but stayed on to the next stop from the Barracks Station where she used to leave the train when visiting Accrington Road. Leaving Rose Grove Station she climbed the hill to Gannow Junction and walked along past the Tim Bobbin public house. Within minutes she had reached 363 Padiham Road and there, chiselled into the gateposts, one on the left-hand and the other on the right, were the words Fern and Royd.

If the weather happened to be fine during Sarah's visits the sisters would board a tram down into town or walk around the leafy lanes of Ightenhill. Sometimes they walked towards the small town of Padiham and wandered the paths around the stately Gawthorpe Hall or, if the day was really nice they would simply sit out in the garden and put the world to rights.

On the first Sunday in August Sarah called at Fern Royd, as she had arranged with Fran the previous week, and had been surprised when Rachel Duckett answered the door.

"Oh, hello Sarah. Fran is not feeling very well today. A stomach upset I think. She has not been out of her bed. Come, I'll show you up."

Sarah found her sister in bed with the heavy eiderdown pulled up to her chin and her cheeks a fiery red.

"Now sister, what on earth have you been doing with yourself?" Sarah thought a light hearted tone might cheer the invalid.

"You must be roasting under all that bedding, I'll open the window."

"No, no . . . I'm cold. I haven't been able to get warm since I came to bed last night. Mrs Duckett brought me the winter quilt but I'm still frozen."

"Well, you look as if you could toast muffins on your forehead. I wonder what you've picked up? Have the children been poorly? I was always catching colds and tummy upsets from the children at Spring Hill."

"I've no idea. Might be something I've eaten. I've been on the privy half the night and I feel rotten."

Sarah stayed with Fran for a couple of hours, fussing with her bedding and plumping her pillows. Finally it was time to catch her train.

"Now, is there anything I can get you Fran?"

"No thanks. I've plenty of water here. I feel so daft with Mrs Duckett having to look after me."

215

"Never mind. You'll be better in a couple of days and I'm sure Mrs Duckett won't mind. You're part of the family now."

On the way out Sarah spoke to Fran's employer.

"She's not very well is she? I hope she picks up soon but she's worrying that she is being a nuisance to you."

"Oh, that's nonsense. I've told her not to worry. The important thing is for her to be back to her old self."

Sarah said that she would call again later in the week and took her leave. When she told Edison of her sister's illness his first thought had been the same as hers,

"She'll have picked it up from the youngsters, or it'll be something she's eaten."

Sarah had intended to call at Fern Royd on the following Thursday but the sight of her sister in her sickbed had unnerved her. Fran was never ill, it was true that she caught the odd cold but she certainly never took to her bed. Unable to settle, Sarah caught the mid-morning train to Rose Grove on the following day.

As she approached the house she noticed a pony and gig at the kerbside and thought that the master of the house must be at home. She had almost reached the front door when it opened and Rachel Duckett appeared, along with a distinguished looking man of about thirty-five.

"Ah, Sarah. This is Doctor Mackenzie, he has been examining Fran. Doctor, this is Miss Davis's sister, Sarah."

Doctor Mackenzie raised his bowler hat and addressed Sarah in a soft Scottish brogue.

"Good morning my dear. Mrs Duckett has summoned me to your sister, she is worried that she is making little progress. I am afraid that the news is not good."

Sarah's gaze moved from Rachel's worried face to the concerned expression of the doctor. Something was obviously amiss.

"What is it? What's wrong with Fran? Is she alright?"

"Well, there is no need to panic at this stage my dear but I am afraid that your sister has contracted typhoid fever. We will do all we can for her."

216

Typhoid! Sarah's mind raced . . . what did she know about the illness - was it fatal, was it crippling? She knew that the disease had been widespread before she had been born but it was much rarer now.

"Oh no. Typhoid. People die from that don't they?"

"Now, now. It is early days yet. Your sister is young and I am sure that she is well fed living with Mr and Mrs Duckett. Many people fight off the disease given adequate care and there is no reason to suppose that your sister cannot make a full recovery."

"Can I see Fran?"

"I will tell you what I have told Mrs Duckett. You must not touch your sister, nor must you handle anything that she has touched. The disease spreads from person to person and through contact with contaminated food. The patient's clothing and bedding must only be handled with great care and it is to be boiled for at least ten minutes. I cannot overstress the importance of hygiene in cases such as this."

He turned to address Rachel.

"I will call again in the morning Mrs Duckett and I will bid you ladies good day."

The doctor pulled on his gloves and walked down the path to his waiting gig. Rachel saw that Sarah was struggling to come to terms with the unwelcome news.

"Doctor Mackenzie recommended that Fran should be in isolation but I said that we could take care of her here. She has to be quarantined as far as possible and he is to organize a private nurse. Visits will have to be strictly controlled and the children must be kept away from Fran's room."

Sarah could hardly credit that her Fran was so poorly that she should be put into quarantine; nevertheless she was grateful to Rachel.

"I can't thank you enough Mrs Duckett. It's very good of you and I know that Fran will appreciate your kindness."

Rachel showed Sarah up to Fran's room at the very top of the house and they quietly opened the door. To Sarah the patient appeared to be very much the same as she had been a couple of days ago.

"Hello Fran. You're in the wars this time. What'll we do with you?" Sarah sat in an armchair that the doctor had strategically placed under the window and away from the bed.

Fran attempted a half-hearted smile for her visitor but she was too ill to manage it. Her temperature had been soaring for almost three days now and she was suffering with constant diarrhoea which left her absolutely exhausted. Her head throbbed as if it would burst and her bowels felt to be on fire.

"The doctor says it's typhoid, Sarah. What's gunna happen to me?"

"Don't worry Fran. Mrs Duckett says she'll get a private nurse in to look after you. What with that and the doctor coming every day, you'll be right as rain in no time."

When it was time for Sarah to leave she told her sister that she would be back in the morning and, wagging her index finger in mock admonishment, she wanted to see an improvement in her condition. As she reached the bottom of the stairs she saw that Alfred Duckett had returned home. He had been summoned from his office at the Pipe Works by his wife and they were deep in conversation.

"Sarah, Mrs Duckett has just been telling me of the situation. A poor show, a poor show indeed. Poor Fran. Rest assured that we will do all that we can for her."

"Thank you Mr Duckett, we really appreciate your kindness. I've had an idea . . . Fran wunna be able to do her work for a while and I wondered if you'd like me to do it 'till she's well again?"

Fran's employers exchanged glances; Alfred rubbed his chin and nodded.

"What do you think Rachel?"

"Well, it sounds like a good idea. Fran will have her sister nearby when she most needs her and I will certainly need help of some kind around the house."

And so it was agreed that Sarah would move into Fern Royd and take over Fran's duties until she recovered. Edison was not best pleased with the idea and demanded to know who would be in the house - who would Sarah have contact with at Fern Royd?

"If that's all you can bloody-well think about then it's too bad. I'm going to Fern Royd in the morning and that's that!"

Edison was taken aback by this show of defiance. For the first time since he had known her Sarah was making it plain that she was in no mood for her husband's stupid games. Realising that he had spoken out of turn, and not for the first time, he attempted to pour oil on the troubled waters.

"Why don't we go up and ask Uncle Richard what he thinks?"

Sarah thought that this was not actually a bad idea; as a chemist Richard would have come across cases of typhoid before and might be able to offer some useful advice.

"Oh dear, I'm very sorry to hear that Sarah. When was the poor lass diagnosed?"

"Today really but she started to feel ill last Sunday."

"Ah well, you can expect her to have a raging temperature for the first week or so after which it should abate. The following weeks will show how badly she's going to react to the disease. Let's hope she can throw it off, at least she has youth on her side."

Richard was trying his best to look on the bright side for Sarah's sake. He knew that there was a fair chance that Fran would recover within about six to eight weeks but he also knew that there was a chance that serious complications could set in. Fran might even end up as a carrier of the disease and spend the rest of her life in quarantine.

"What can I do to help her? Is there any medicine she can take?"

"I'm sorry Sarah, there's actually not much that modern medicine can do in the case of typhoid other than care for the patient. Your sister should be kept as dry as possible, cold compresses will ease the effects of the fever but it is really down to the individual's response as to what the outcome might be."

Richard went on to tell Sarah of an outbreak of typhoid that had occurred twelve years earlier in Barrowford.

"It started on a farm in Blacko where the family had typhoid but they carried on milking their cows and delivering the milk around the village. People in the village were going down like flies and nobody could understand why. In the end the Medical Officer traced the source and stopped the farmer from selling his milk but by that time there were around fifty cases of the disease in the village. Out of the fifty who contracted the disease only eight died and they were mainly older people."

The point that Richard was trying to make was that the majority of people who caught typhoid stood around a seventy per cent chance of recovery. Edison knew the farmer who had inadvertently started the 1877 outbreak.

"I felt sorry for the family really, they had no idea that they shouldn't have been selling the milk. The old lad was never the same afterwards."

At 10.45 the following morning Sarah arrived at Fern Royd clutching the same small travel bag that had carried her possessions from Harborne to Barrowford six long years ago. Having looked in on Fran, who was sleeping fitfully, she unpacked her two sets of working clothes and a Sunday dress before going down to the kitchen. Rachel was pouring a pot of tea for them and informed Sarah that there had been no change in Fran's condition overnight, she was still running a very high temperature.

"Doctor Mackenzie should be here any time now Sarah. Let us hope that he can give us some encouragement."

"He seems to be a nice man, does he live locally."

Alfred and Rachel Duckett had known James Mackenzie ever since he came to Burnley ten years ago. He had been born on his father's farm in Scone, Scotland in 1853. He then worked as an assistant chemist in Glasgow for a year before deciding that he wanted to study medicine. He took private tuition in Latin, passed the university entrance examination and entered medical school at Edinburgh University.

The newly qualified James Mackenzie M.B & C.M then worked as a locum in a colliery practice in Durham until, in the November of 1878, a residency post came up at Edinburgh Royal Infirmary. He completed his residency in the following year of 1879 and moved south to Burnley where he joined the partnership of Doctors Briggs and Brown.

Here in Burnley he found himself in the midst of an industrial town crying out for medical help. Disease was rife and in his first year there were fifty-six deaths from scarlet fever alone while the infant mortality rate was running at almost twenty-five per cent. The newcomer saw between sixty and seventy patients every day and would attend at least three birth deliveries per week.

The dour Scot remained undaunted by his heavy workload and found time, in 1882, to complete an MD thesis on the subject of Hemi-paraplegia Spinalis. On top of this his spare time was occupied by a study of German and Greek, he also played golf and began to write a novel on the social depravation that he saw all around him. He married in 1887 and went on to publish a large number of papers on the study of the heart in which field he was making quite a name for himself.

"So you see, Sarah, your sister is in very good hands. Ah, speak of the Devil!"

At that moment Doctor Mackenzie let himself in through the front door and stood in the hallway. Sarah took his hat and gloves.

"Good morning ladies. How is my patient, any change?"

"Not really doctor," Rachel lowered her voice in case she could be heard upstairs,

"She still seems to be running a high fever and she has hardly eaten a thing."

"Early days yet, early days."

The following Monday saw Fran's illness entering its second week and Doctor Mackenzie was of the opinion that her temperature was abating. Sarah took this as a positive sign that her sister was getting better although she had to admit that, if anything, she looked worse. Whatever morsel the patient managed to eat made its way through her body with frightening speed; she was also suffering with severe abdominal cramps and this made her reluctant to eat anything at all.

This carried on for the following two weeks and Fran grew weaker, the private nurse saw to her every need while Sarah helped with the domestic duties. If the circumstances had been different Sarah thought that she would enjoy working in the Duckett household as the children were well behaved and the family were undemanding. When Rachel broached the subject of wages with Sarah she refused payment saying that she was only too happy to help out. They eventually decided between them that the temporary domestic help would work for her keep and Fran would be paid seventy-five per cent of her wages during her confinement.

Sarah returned home to her husband every Saturday and would be back at Fern Royd by noon the following day. She admitted to herself that she would rather stay at Fran's side than return to Joseph Street but she also felt that she had a duty to her husband to at least make sure that he was looking after himself. She needn't have worried because, although he did not tell his wife, he spent most of his time either with Jim Bleasdale or over at Rimington where his mother cooked for him.

This state of affairs continued but, at the end of Fran's sixth week of illness, the doctor was becoming less optimistic.

"I have to say, Mrs Nowell, that I would have hoped for more improvement in your sister's condition by now. However, she is well cared for and these things must run their course."

Poor Fran looked dreadful and it broke Sarah's heart to watch her suffer. Her fine features were hardly recognisable now, her face was swollen and her once-sparkling eyes were sunken and dark. There was no spark left in Fran as Sarah sat by the window hour after hour watching her sister deteriorate.

The strain was beginning to tell on all involved at Fern Royd; Sarah became increasingly tired, the children could not understand why they had to be quiet around the house at all times and Rachel was becoming emotionally drained with the constant stress. However, they all thought the world of Fran and the important thing was that they did all that they could to get her well again.

It was now the end of the third week in October and Fran was not recovering. She had been suffering for ten full weeks and this did not bode well. Doctor Mackenzie knew now that his patient stood only a small chance of a full recovery but he tried not to let his fears show. Each day he expected to see the signs of secondary complications and on the morning of the twenty second of October Fran took a turn for the worse.

She had been coughing for most of the night and Sarah had kept a vigil in the chair by the window. When the doctor arrived he listened to Fran's chest with his stethoscope and frowned. He asked the nurse to sit the patient up and he tapped her back with the tips of his fingers.

"Oh dear. I am not happy with that. I'll call back this evening, nurse. In the meantime you would perhaps keep turning the patient."

Fran's coughing fits had increased and she was finding it difficult to breath by the time the doctor returned that evening. He listened, tapped and looked at the nurse - now he was sure that it was double pneumonia. He paused on his way out of the front door to speak to Sarah and Rachel and they knew from his demeanour that the news was not good.

"I'm very sorry ladies but there is little that I can do now. Miss Davis' fate lies in God's hands."

Sarah and Rachel sat down at the kitchen table. Sarah had not fully taken in the doctor's words, her whole being was numb.

"God Sarah, I am so sorry."

"But . . . she'll be alright won't she? She'll get better when her cough clears up?"

Rachel could see that Sarah was in shock and placed a comforting arm around her shoulder.

"Sarah, Fran is very ill. We are told that where there is life there is hope and we must pray that it will be so."

Rachel tried her best to think of something more reassuring to say but in the end she just held Sarah's hand. Over the following four days Sarah hardly left her sister's side. She slept in the window chair and saw to Fran's every need until the nurse returned in the morning. Fran was suffering now and her sister knew it.

As Sarah sat and watched over the patient she saw the brick-red hair contrasting sharply with the clean white pillow and for a moment she caught a glimpse of Fran the lovely young woman, not Fran the patient. She saw the beautiful translucence of her face crease and her eyes flash as she tilted her head back in laughter.

Fran's breath rattled deep within her heaving chest and the harsh sound brought Sarah back to earth with a sickening jolt. After a few minutes, exhaustion took over once more and Luke entered her thoughts; a feeling that she had not had for a number of years overwhelmed her. Once again she was lost. She was not simply looking for a place that she could not find; she was keenly aware that she would never find anything other than that dark void into which the pain and hopelessness of life constantly poured.

How different life would have been had Luke never left the Black Country or if Fran had never moved to the north. And her husband, the one person who should share her inner fears, was the last person she could tell. In the blink of an eye Sarah saw with the clarity that only desperation can provide that she had traded her life as a paid domestic help for that of an unpaid servant. The recurring dream of her wedding eve floated into her mind;

"I sentence you, Sarah Ann Davis, to marriage with Edison Nowell."

These words had turned out to be only too prophetic and she regretted marrying Edison Nowell with all of her heart.

A new day dawned but the normal bustle of the house seemed dulled by that heavy atmosphere created by the heavy, stalking footsteps of severe illness. Fran lay still, she did not recognise Sarah any longer. The doctor paid his morning visit and, shaking his head, replaced the sheet over his patient and sadly uttered a single word;

"Pleurisy."

As he left the house he told Rachel that he did not think that Fran would last out the day. And so it proved; Sarah held her sister's hand as her lungs rattled and the corners of her mouth dribbled blood. The nurse sat by Fran's bedside and constantly mopped away the blood and the sweat from Fran's face and here the deathbed scene was set for the demise of Miss Fanny Davis at 2.30pm on the twenty sixth of October. She was aged just twenty-four years.

Alfred Duckett did not skimp on Fran's funeral. He purchased a grave plot for her and provided a magnificent horse-drawn hearse to carry her on the final journey. In a quiet corner of Burnley cemetery Fran was laid to rest with all the love and dignity that Sarah knew she deserved.

# 24

# Football and Fire Engines

Edison had been on his best behaviour for the few months following Fran's death. He realised that Sarah was fragile and he tried his best not to bother her. In actual fact this was through no altruistic motive, he kept out of her way in case she snapped at him again. He had not liked his wife standing up to him.

A couple of times each month he would go along with a group of people from work to watch Burnley play at the Turf Moor Football Club. Edison and Jim Bleasdale would stand together and bellow at the referee which always made Edison feel better. On a crisp, sunny Saturday afternoon at the end of February, 1890, the group went along to Turf Moor to watch a derby match between the Football League teams of Burnley and Blackburn Rovers.

These derby matches were always keenly contested and this match in particular turned out to be no exception. This was a cup match and feelings were running particularly high as, just before the kick-off, it became known within the ground that the referee was to be a chap named Robert Horne. The problem here for the Burnley fans was that John Horne had joined Blackburn Rovers at the beginning of that season as their goalkeeper and it just so happened that he was the referee's brother.

There was much muttering and grumbling in the stands as the match kicked off and before long there was an incident where a Burnley player was fouled. The referee ignored this but soon afterwards gave a foul against Burnley which the home fans strongly disagreed with. The Burnley players were so incensed that they walked off the field in protest. The fans were now howling for the referee's blood and were sure that the match was fixed in view of the fact that his brother was playing for the opposition.

Finally the Burnley players returned to the field and the match ended in a 2-1 victory for Blackburn Rovers. The supporters in the Burnley stands erupted and stormed the pitch and, seeing them swarming across the grass towards him, the referee dived for cover under the grandstand. The club Committee had to form a protective circle around the hapless match official while the police tried in vain to clear the pitch. Reinforcements were called in and, in the meantime, the referee was escorted into the shelter of a neighbouring house.

Eventually it was decided to bustle the referee into a cab which hurried away just as the howling, stone-throwing mob appeared on the scene. The cab was pursued half-way across town and it was generally agreed afterwards that the life of Robert Horne had been in very real danger.

Edison and the rest of his group managed not to get caught up in the crowd as it flowed out of the ground in search of Horne. They made their way along the cinder track past the cricket field and onwards to the Central Station.

At the end of the month Blackburn Rovers won the League cup but this did not impress the people of the Burnley district. Later in the year Blackburn were in the news again when their players took umbrage at a refereeing decision and walked off the pitch; the match was subsequently abandoned.

As for John Horne, the goalkeeping brother of the fugitive referee, he joined Nelson Football Club in the following season. Many Nelson supporters also followed neighbouring Burnley and Horne received a decidedly mixed reception at his new club.

By the end of March the East Lancashire district was feeling the effects of a prolonged coal strike. James Atkins had almost exhausted all of his coal stocks and other yards were in the same position. In Colne most of the mills, and other factories, had to be stopped through a shortage of fuel and, in Barrowford, Berry's Mill stopped their 1,515 looms thus laying off 600 workers for a week. The mill started up again but was restricted to a four-day week of seven hours only.

The coal stocks at Nelson railway station were down to a few tons and the shortage started to affect the public; where the price of one hundredweight had been nine pence before the strike the cost had now doubled. Luckily many people had enough reserves of coal in their outhouses to see them through the worst of the shortage.

On the twenty third of February Barrowford was buzzing with the news that Ellis Fell had been found dead. Ellis' father was also named Ellis and, as a former landlord of the Fleece Inn he had been a well known character around the village. Ellis junior was a weaver at Berry's Mill and his brother, John, was a small cotton manufacturer. On the morning of the twenty third Ellis junior had set out with his dog and gun for a day's shooting in Pendle Forest. Around six o'clock in the evening a farmer by the name of Hartley was seeing to his stock at the very foot of Pendle Hill when the pitiful howling of a dog pierced the sharp evening air.

He set off across the fields in the direction of the sound, lighting his way with a storm lantern and a few hundred yards away Hartley saw the dog sitting by a wall. He hesitantly approached and as he came up to the animal the reason for its behaviour became all too apparent. Laid on the wet grass at the base of the wall was the body of a man; as Hartley attempted to get closer the dog snarled at him and he withdrew a couple of yards.

Not knowing if the person beneath the wall was dead or alive Hartley called on the help of his farm hand and between them they managed to get a rope around the distressed animal. Hartley examined the man with the light from his lantern and could see no sign of life. He pulled him by the shoulder, in order to get him onto his back, and immediately regretted doing so. The whole of the left side of the poor man's head had been reduced to a bloody pulp. In a state of shock Hartley and the farm hand stumbled back to the farm with the dog in tow. The police were summoned and by midnight the case had been solved to their satisfaction.

The body was identified as being that of Ellis Fell and it appeared that he had died sometime in the late afternoon of the twenty third. Lying beside his body was his double-barrelled shotgun, both barrels were still loaded. No foul play was suspected as it was apparent that the deceased had slipped against the wall in an attempt to jump over it. When he stumbled he had dislodged a large stone from the top of the wall which landed on his head and crushed his skull.

Ellis, aged fifty, left a wife, three sons and a daughter. He was interred in Saint Thomas' graveyard, to the south of the church, where he joined the illustrious company of deceased members of the manufacturing families of Berry, Grimshaw and Barrowclough.

The summer passed quietly enough with everyone looking forward to the celebrations arranged for the thirtieth of August. The town of Nelson had been lobbying for the grant of charter status for around three years and finally, in this year of 1890, they were successful. Queen Victoria granted the town its charter as a Municipal Borough and the Charter Day celebrations were all set to go ahead.

This was to be a massive celebration; the streets around the town centre were transformed into medieval thoroughfares by fronting the buildings with wooden castellations and huge crimson flags. Over 80,000 people flocked into the town and a procession some two miles in length snaked proudly through the crowds. All the trappings of civic pride were on show; the Fire Brigade, the East Lancashire Volunteer Battalion and its band, the Police, trades people, chapels, churches and Sunday schools - all walked rank upon rank in their thousands. In the evening a spectacular firework display lit the sky and the 'electrical illuminations' were a popular feature in the town centre.

Sarah and Edison walked the mile up into Nelson to watch the celebrations. They were a little too late to see the procession along Market Street, in the very centre of town, and so they made their way down Leeds Road where the Fire Brigade were to mount a demonstration of their new steam water-pumping engine.

Nelson Fire Brigade had been formed in 1873 when eight firemen were appointed. Now the Brigade, consisting of a Superintendent and twenty men, was the proud owner of a gleaming new steam pump grandly named the *Lord Nelson*. The engine had been built by Messrs Shand, Mason and Company and had three steam cylinders capable of pumping 600 gallons of water per minute. The engine had four wheels with wide rubber tyres and was designed to carry an engineer, stoker, seven men and the necessary coal to fuel it.

The horses used to draw the steam pump were also used by the town's Cleansing Department but this was not an ideal situation. When the fire bells rang at the town hall the horses had to be unyoked from the 'muck' carts, wherever in the town they might be, and rushed around to the fire station on Booth Street. This meant that there were often long delays where the pump stood idle until the horses arrived accompanied by a sweating, grumbling cleansing operative who might have had to dash the length of the town. Occasionally the carters would not hear the fire bell, sometimes by accident and at other times by design, and this rendered the engine useless.

The scene was set for a grand show of the powerful steam apparatus. The Superintendent kept his men busy polishing the brass-work for days before the exhibition and the engine shone like burnished gold. The *Lord Nelson* was positioned in Leeds Road, to the front of Bridge Mills, and a large expectant crowd gathered around. The Superintendent gathered his men and with their helmets and axes shining in the late summer sun they made an impressive spectacle. The engine was checked to ensure that the boiler held enough water and the inlet end of the hose was thrown into the nearby Walverden Stream.

A number of lengths of heavy canvas hose had been joined together in order to raise the water to a height that would amaze the spectators. The Superintendent was proud of his position, he was proud of his men and he was proud of his gleaming fire engine. He wanted to show the public that their rates were being well spent and what better way of doing this was there than to give them a demonstration of the Brigade's new and powerful technology?

Their first mistake was to use pine-wood sticks to stoke the engine's firebox. In his enthusiasm to please the Superintendent the stoker began frantically heaving armfuls of pine onto the fire in order to get a quick head of steam going. However, when the engine was set in motion this resulted in a huge plume of burning, sparking embers being launched skyward. Accompanied by 'ooohs' and 'aaahs' from the crowd the fireballs drifted high on the wind only to fall still glowing on the heads of the spectators. The crowd began dancing around like demented Dervishes in an attempt to beat out the hot embers as they burned through their caps and bonnets.

Eventually the onlookers managed to push back against the weight of the crowd to a safe distance leaving the fire-spitting machine to stand in disgraced isolation. The Superintendent berated the stoker who, muttering into his thick grey beard, raked out most of the wood kindling and replaced it with best coal. In no time at all the boiler had raised 100lbs of pressure and before long a plume of black smoke replaced the belching embers as the engine began to give off a satisfying hiss. The Chief gave the signal and his 'bugle boy' sounded 'all hands to the pump.' The crowd grew in confidence and approached the engine once more.

The Superintendent was determined that his new machine would earn its keep that day and his objective was to raise a column of water to the height of the towering Bridge Mills chimney. The water jet spouted from the hose and six men were required to hold it steady. Higher and higher reached the white column of water as the steam engine joined in with the excited atmosphere of the day.

Soon the hose was propelling a powerful water jet to the top of the 190 foot mill chimney and the crowd were highly impressed. Clapping and cheering they threw their caps into the air, this was truly something to behold!

For a full half-minute the water reached even higher than the chimney - until the canvas ripped. A huge rent appeared in a length of hose lying along the road in front of the crowd. Within seconds the whole of the front ten rows of the crowd were soaked through to the skin and, as they turned to escape the violent shower, the crowd pushed back *en masse*. In the ensuing melee a number of people were trampled and crushed and in the end very few escaped without suffering either minor injuries or a thorough drenching.

Fortunately Sarah and Edison were on the edge of the crowd and were able to escape the deluge with little more than a light shower. They enjoyed their day at the charter celebrations and as they walked home Edison became unusually talkative. He brought up the subject of his mother and mentioned to Sarah that he was worried about her health; his step-father was also worried about Susannah and had taken Edison to one side in the mill.

"Have you noticed a change in your mother lately?"

"Well, when I called last weekend she still had that cough. It seems to be weeks now since she started and she can't get shut of it."

"I know, I know. I've had the doctor to her four times now and he says it's probably a cold that's turned to bronchitis. He says she's to keep warm and have plenty of rest."

Edison rarely spoke of his family and the fact that he was now doing so showed Sarah that her husband was concerned.

In what to Sarah seemed like the twinkling of an eye the first anniversary of Fran's death appeared on the horizon. On the morning of the twenty sixth of October she slipped out of the house and took the train to Burnley. Having bought a bunch of autumn flowers on her way from the station Sarah walked the short distance up the slight hill to the cemetery. She said a prayer in the small chapel inside the gates and then set out on the half-mile walk to where the Dissenters' plots were situated. The path sloped steadily downhill as it passed row upon row of sandstone, polished granite and marble memorials until finally Sarah stood by the small stone that indicated the final resting place of Fanny Davis.

As Sarah gently laid the flowers against the stone a deep sense of melancholy overtook her. She stood, hands clasped and head bowed, as the damp air swirled the young grass on Fran's grave. Overhead a rookery stirred and the cawing breath of a hundred wheeling birds steamed in the grey-damp morning. Fallen leaves rotted on the footpaths and combined with the clammy earth to create a thick atmosphere of decay that penetrated Sarah's very bones.

Head bowed and unmoving she stood in the heavy autumn air as her mind raced with thoughts of Fran running along The Lyndon in her new, pink Whitsun dress. Of her dad picking his youngest daughter up and rubbing his stubbly chin across her face until she squealed with laughter. Of that upright, proud figure with the flowing, deep amber-red hair that framed such a beautiful face.

After what could have been a few minutes or an hour Sarah noticed a middle-aged woman tending a neighbouring grave. The mound of soil at the foot of the gravestone had hardly grassed over and Sarah knew that this woman had suffered a recent bereavement. Looking up the woman saw Sarah's tear-stained cheeks and, pulling her grey woollen shawl tight to her body, slowly shook her head. This woman's grief was written deep in her face and Sarah guessed that the grave over which she stood did not hold the only loss in her life.

"Life can be a bugger, lass."

Sarah nodded and the two strangers shared a moment of mutual grief that spoke louder than any church scripture or sermon could ever have done. Here were two people who found themselves pitted against a world of which they had little understanding.

233

As Sarah made her way slowly through the cemetery gates she felt fragile and alone. In fact, in the physical sense of the word, she was now truly alone in this world; as the woman's words echoed in her ears she thought that she could not sum up her sense of loss in any better way.

"Yes," she said to herself, "It's a bugger alright."

# 25

# Amalgamation

Uncle Thomas sent for Edison's mother, Susannah, when he heard that she was not improving. He knew of a convalescent home near the Lancashire coast at Ormskirk and he had offered to pay for her to take a break there for a month or two until she recovered. Susannah's cough seemed to improve at first and everyone held high hopes that she would soon be back home; but it was not to be. In the November, Thomas sent a telegram to his Barrowford family with the sad news that Susannah had passed away at the age of fifty.

Edison was inconsolable. He was unable to cope with the situation and began to lash out at his step-father saying that he had not looked after his mother properly. This deeply hurt Henry who was confident that he had done all he could for his dear wife. Sarah also bore much of the brunt of Edison's immaturity, his aggressive behaviour grew worse and she became increasingly unhappy.

As the year of 1890 progressed Edison found that he was been becoming unpopular with certain people in the village, and it was through no fault of his own.

Nelson had been granted Municipal status and the town was now far bigger than its village neighbour of Barrowford. Now that the charter celebrations were out of the way the Nelson Councillors decided that the year of 1891 was to see the start of civic expansion on a grand scale. The first thing that they were determined to do was to annex Barrowford by providing it with two wards within the Nelson Borough.

The Barrowford people were having none of this and the case for amalgamation was taken before a Parliamentary Committee. Over the four-day hearing in London the Nelson representatives employed bullying tactics against their smaller neighbour but, by and large, their case was nothing less than shambolic. The Committee refused Nelson's request to absorb Barrowford and the Nelson contingent set off for home with their tails between their legs.

This was not the case with the victorious Barrowford representatives who were met by a cheering group of village people at Nelson railway station with a wagonette to draw them like conquering heroes through the streets. They were elated with their victory and processed their heroes past the town hall with much jeering and rude gesturing in the direction of the Council chambers.

When the party arrived back in Barrowford a large gathering greeted them at the White Bear Inn and the speeches went on long into the evening. Conspicuous by his absence, however, was Edison Nowell. Both Henry Wilkinson, and his partner William Hartley, had been part of the Nelson deputation to London and because of his relationship with Henry the unfortunate Edison had been on the wrong end of many unfortunate comments.

"'Ere he comes, the little squire,"

"Which way you voting then Nowell?"

"Why don't you move to Nelson with yer fancy family?"

These were some of the less ribald remarks he had to endure. This had been the last straw between Edison and his step-father and he gave in his resignation notice at the Pendle Street Shed.

Fortunately there was work much nearer to home now; just around the corner from Joseph Street the large new cotton factory of Lower Clough Mill had recently opened. The mill was operated as a 'room and power' company whereby the owners installed the latest steam technology and leased space within the mill to manufacturers. The first tenants in the newly opened mill were Christopher Atkinson and Company and they were looking for skilled workers; Edison was duly taken on in the clothlooking department.

No sooner had Edison started his new job than more bad news hit the family; brother Thomas' wife, Elizabeth, had died following a short illness at the age of forty-four. This tragic loss left Thomas with a young family to bring up. This was yet another blow to Edison and his temper became no sweeter. Sarah was sad to hear of Elizabeth's demise as she had liked her right from their very first meeting. She also liked the children and asked Edison if he thought she should go over to Salford to help Thomas out with the youngsters for a while but he was adamant that this would not be a good idea. Coping on his own had been hard enough in the ten weeks that his wife had spent away from home when Fran was ill but this time he wouldn't have his mother to run to.

The couple at number five Joseph Street were not happy and that was obvious to everyone who knew them. The loss of family members had changed the attitudes of both Sarah and Edison. She had become hardened to the hectoring and endless jealous questioning of her husband while he seemed to be ever more resentful of his wife. If she let him have all his own way he resented her weakness and if she stood up to him he became furious.

The first time that Edison hit Sarah she stood frozen to the spot in a state of shock. They had been arguing about a trivial matter, as usual, and Sarah had tried to bring the shouting to an end by calling Edison a 'little tyrant.' It had not been a full-on blow, rather a slap to the side of her head but, nevertheless, it hurt and she knew that this was a turning point in her husband's strange behaviour. It had been bad enough when she was taking his constant verbal abuse but physical violence was something that she had never experienced before in her life.

The following week saw Sarah calling at Spring Hill; she had thought long and hard about Edison's outburst and had

237

decided to talk with Ellen as she looked upon her older friend as a mother figure and always valued her advice. Sarah told Ellen the story of Edison's behaviour, about his jealousy and the fact that he had worshipped his mother to the point of obsession.

Ellen was not in the least surprised. She was sorry that Sarah was unhappy in her marriage but she never had liked young Edison Nowell. There was something about his shuffling gait and slightly devious manner that had always repulsed Ellen.

"From what you have said, Sarah, things have deteriorated since the death of his poor mother. I would not be surprised if he were punishing you for still being alive while she is dead."

Sarah took a minute or so to let this sink in. She came from a straightforward, loving family who would not under any circumstances have hurt each other. The fact that Edison appeared to have mental problems was way beyond her experience and she did not know how to deal with the situation.

"In the end, Sarah . . . and I hate to say this . . . you could always leave him. I honestly do not think that he will improve as he gets older. Perhaps you should consider getting out now?"

In actual fact Sarah had thought about leaving her husband many times. But this train of thought inevitably returned to a single fact – she had nowhere to go.

"But I've no family now, Ellen, and I wunna know what to do."

She consoled herself with the thought that at least Edison worked and provided for her, he kept a roof over her head and food on the table, surely that must count for something? Her thoughts turned to Poor Rosy Malone and how easily a woman without money could end up in the depths of depravity.

"No, I'll see it out. I married him for better or for worse, you never know, he might mature as he gets older."

Ellen doubted this very much but seeing that her young friend was upset she did not press the point.

"Well, I'm sorry I can't offer you more advice, Sarah, other than keep out of his way when he starts his antics."

There was no more violence in the few remaining months of 1891 although Edison's jealousy did not lessen; in fact he suspected Sarah of having liaisons with almost every man in the village. No matter how vehemently she denied it he would not be placated and this is how the unfortunate marriage progressed into the following year.

# 26

# Fire and Fraud

Edison settled into his job at Lower Clough Mill. The new factory could boast all the latest technology and the clothlooking department was airy and warm. There was also the great advantage of living within a few hundred yards of his work, especially now that the winter snows had arrived.

The new mill was attracting many people from outside of Barrowford and new houses were springing up at a great pace. The mill also brought a lot of trade to the Co-operative stores directly across the street and the many corner shops in Newbridge thrived. On the hill above Lower Clough Mill a new street had recently been erected and named after a local manufacturing worthy; the terraced rows of Dixon Street reached high into the open fields where there were no other houses to overlook them. This reminded Sarah of her childhood home on The Lyndon and she told Edison that she wouldn't mind living in one of the new houses.

At a quarter-past six on the evening of the sixth of January, 1892, the engine at Lower Clough Mill broke down. The horizontal cross-compound engine had been built and installed by William Roberts' Phoenix Foundry in Nelson and was around one year old. During the day the engine tenter had noticed that one of the bearings was running hot and he decided to stop the engine in order to let the mechanic have a look at it. This meant that there was to be no work in the evening and most of the workers left for home. This was fortunate because within two hours fire had broken out in the cotton twisting room. The twisting room occupied one end of the mill building and it was here that the warps were set up for the weaving process by threading the warp threads through the eyelets of a metal strip known as a heald. Along with the heald a comb-like reed controlled the separation of the warp threads.

On the evening of the engine breakdown two men remained in the twisting room with the wall-mounted gas mantles lighting the room. In one corner of the room, unnoticed by the workers, a heald was hanging too close to one of the gas lights and two minutes later the inflammable material covering the heald burst into flames. By the time the fire had been noticed it was too late to contain it and the twisting room had become an inferno.

The Nelson Fire Brigade were called out but the poor state of the road at Newbridge held them up and twenty minutes passed before they reached the blazing mill. The *Lord Nelson* engine was set up at the rear of the mill where the building backed on to the river. This meant that there was an ample supply of water to fight the flames but the fire was too far advanced. The main building was three floors in height with twenty-two windows along its length and as the flames reached the upper levels a strong wind began to fan them alarmingly. The Fire Brigade realised that they could not save the main part of the mill and so they concentrated their efforts on trying to save the engine house and lower weaving shed.

By this time an excited crowd of almost 2,000 people had gathered to watch the spectacle and the police struggled to keep them away from the burning building. Sarah and Edison watched the fire from the safety of the riverbank and Sarah was worried that her husband would now be out of work.

By midnight the Fire Brigade were satisfied that they had saved the lower part of the building and it was now a case of damping down the smouldering ruins throughout the night. In all there had been 1,250 looms at Lower Clough and many of these were in the shed which the Fire Brigade had managed to save. Over £9,000 worth of stock was lost in the gutted warehouse and the damage to the building was estimated at not less than £6,000. Some 300 employees were thrown out of work as a consequence of the fire.

Fortunately for the mill owners and tenants the buildings and contents were insured and work quickly began on rebuilding the factory. A single-storey weaving shed was to replace the lost three-storied building and this meant that the mill could be up and running again within a few months. Many of the employees, including Edison, found temporary work at other mills in Nelson and Colne and before the end of the year they were back in their old jobs at Lower Clough.

At this time Sarah had been thinking of approaching someone for advice on her marital problems. She thought that her husband might listen to an outsider but she had no idea who to approach about the matter. As coincidence would have it an advertisement appeared in the local newspaper where a Barrowford man, by the name of Albert Veevers, was advertising his professional services.

Sarah had heard of Albert and knew that he was one of the local characters; he often had letters and poetry published in the church newsletters and the local newspapers. Albert had been born in Church Street, Barrowford, the son of a shoemaker and a baker. He became a joiner by trade but in 1878 he fell from scaffolding and landed on his head, this left him stone deaf and not a little odd but he was well liked around the village. Following the accident Albert never worked again but fortunately his family were not without money; they had acquired a number of properties over the years and the rental income from these eked out his writing.

An example of Albert's humour was published in the local paper when a man named Robert Moore died in February at the grand old age of 101. Robert lived for a number of years at Brownley Park Farm, in Blacko, with his son Thomas and his family. Never one to miss an opportunity Albert penned the following ditty;

*Old Moor no more walks o'er the moor,*
*For he is now no more,*

*Five score and one old Moor did score,*
*Sure few score more than Moor.*

Albert turned his hand to many things to make a living and his latest wheeze was to advertise himself as a marriage guidance expert. The first advertisement that Sarah noticed was spread across two columns of the classified pages;

*Marriage in Trouble?*
*Albert Veevers – Park Hill*
*Phrenologist and Physiognomist*
*The Greater the Fee the Greater the Stimulus*

Sarah noted the advertisement but, not knowing what it was actually referring to, she did nothing about it. The following Friday another two-column piece advertised Albert's newfound skills;

*Albert Veevers – Professional Peace Maker*
*9 Church Street, Barrowford*
*(Note the address - - Ancestral Residence)*
*A New Departure*

*Whatever Brawls Disturb the Street*
*There should be peace at Home*
*When Wife and Husband are Unsweet*
*To Sweeten them I'll Come*

Tentatively Sarah mentioned Albert's services to Edison and asked him what he thought. She was left in no doubt;

"You're pulling my leg; I'm not having you tell anybody about our private life!"

And so Sarah's only ever attempt to rescue her failing marriage ended before it had even begun.

There was certainly no shortage of scandal to occupy the village gossips in the year of 1892. In March the news broke that James Aston, treasurer of the Barrowford and Bootle Co-operative Society, had embezzled Society funds. Aston, aged

243

thirty-eight, lived in Higherford with his wife and three young children and, unfortunately for all concerned, he had been listening to one of the local sages in the George and Dragon propounding the ease with which money could be made in stocks and shares. Like many of the village weavers Aston was finding life difficult and he thought that the idea of investing on the Stock Exchange would be the answer to all his problems. Of course, it never crossed his mind that the pub sage didn't appear to have two pennies to rub together!

All that was needed was an initial sum with which to buy the first shares and after that it was foolproof. The stocks would go up, they would be sold at a profit and this would be reinvested in yet more stock until the speculator became rich beyond all imagination.

When he completed the Co-operative returns for the period to the beginning of February Aston saw that he had in front of him the sum of £865 in cash. This proved too much for him and the vision of vast profits swam before his eyes. He consequently bought an amount of Company stock through a Burnley broker and waited for the money to roll in. Except the money did not roll in - rather it rolled out and it stayed out. Aston had planned to replace the February funds in the Co-operative books from his profits and nobody would have been any the wiser. Now, however, he could not replace the money and his supervisor reported the loss to his superiors.

Aston appeared before the Lord Chief Justice at Preston Crown Court in April and he was not a happy judge. He said that societies of working men had to depend on someone to keep their accounts and he could not look upon this betrayal of trust as a light issue. He took into account the fact that the prisoner had been a collector for the Society for around eleven years and had previously been of good character. Nevertheless, in light of the seriousness in which the Court viewed this offence Aston was sentenced to penal servitude for a period of five years.

Edison and his money had a narrow escape in the embezzlement scandal. He had inherited a sum of money from his mother and most of it was invested with the Co-operative but fortunately he had withdrawn the whole lot at the end of January in order to purchase two more houses. Across from his home on Joseph Street stood a terraced row called Duckworth Street and two of these properties had come up for sale. The words of his Grandfather, James, rang in his ears when he saw the properties;

"Narthen lad, never let thy brass fester."

In other words James had been offering the advice favoured by most farmers - do not trust banks - put your money into land and property. When the neighbours found out that Edison had bought another two houses the appellation of 'Little Squire' began to be aimed in his direction on an increasingly frequent basis.

Everett Stansfield was a well-known figure in the village and a friend of Edison's Uncle Jimmy. Everett was quick witted and ready to have a laugh with anybody he happened to meet, be it the vicar or the night-soil man. He invariably wore large, iron-soled clogs with his baggy trousers tied half-way up his calves with twine. Everett also liked a drink and his favourite pastime at weekends was to rise early and walk a few miles to pubs in other areas of the district. By late afternoon he would have had enough beer to float a battleship and anyone who met him on his unsteady walk home would be treated to a full-blown song and dance routine, whether they had requested it or not!

He rose as usual on Sunday the first of May and decided to stroll over to the Hare and Hounds Inn in the village of Foulridge. Everett arrived at the inn at eleven-thirty and, because it was a Sunday, he sat down to wait for the landlord to open up at 12 o'clock. Sure enough, as the grandfather clock in the tap room struck twelve the large red face of James Carr, the landlord, appeared at the door.

"Narthen Everett. Been out all night 'ave you?"

"Ne're mind that Jim, pour me a pint afore I die o' thirst."

By ten past twelve Everett was settled contentedly at one of the ricketty wooden benches looking out at the rising, bracken-strewed view of Weets Hill. At that moment the village policeman walked in and looked imperiously around the almost empty pub; spotting Everett his eyes lit up.

"Ahh, Everett Stansfield from Barrowford I believe?"

"Guilty."

The constable turned to the landlord who had an idea of what was coming next.

"Right Mr Carr. You realise that it is an offence to serve alcohol to persons from within a three mile limit of the premises at this time on a Sunday?"

"Oh come on Constable, we've 'ad all this before. Barrowford's outside the three mile limit; always has been an' always will be."

The three mile limit was a law passed to ensure that people from the local area did not flock to the local pubs on a Sunday when they should have been attending church. It was recognised that travellers would have need of the services of inns when they were away from home and so the notion of a distance limit was introduced.

The problem for James Carr was that the police were tightening up on the drinking laws and they had re-measured the distances between each village and town boundary. The previous Constable had accepted that the nearest boundary between Barrowford and Foulridge was three miles and forty-four yards by public roads. Now, however, the new police measurement had been taken to include the canal towpath. This was said to have been a private road but used by the public under sufferance and therefore, when it was used as an official route, the boundary distance from Barrowford to Foulridge was less than three miles.

Everett Stansfield was duly summoned for being on licensed premises within the limit at twelve noon on a Sunday. James Carr was also summoned for opening his house on the same charge and they appeared at the Colne Police Court on Wednesday the eleventh of May. The police gave evidence that

Everett's house was two and three-quarter miles from the Hare and Hounds.

In his defence Everett originally intended to use his own measurement of the distance and so, to this end, on the Saturday following his alleged offence he set off from home with a borrowed hundred-foot tape measure of the type used by surveyors. His intention had been to drag the extended tape behind him and count how many one hundred feet lengths there were between his house and the Hare and Hounds. However, after dragging the tape for twenty minutes he was getting tired of people stopping him with witty remarks such as;

"Hey up, Everett, thy dog's escaped!"

A small crowd of children followed him out of Higherford shouting;

"Where's thy dog mister?" and this had proved too much for the amateur surveyor to take.

He stopped off at the Cross Gates Inn with the intention of having one jug of ale but he didn't stagger out until the late afternoon. By that time he had completely lost interest in his project but from then onwards he liked to impress people by telling them that the distance from his house to the Cross Gates was exactly 2,036 feet.

The upshot of the court case was that the prosecution won the day. James Carr was fined twenty-four shillings plus costs and Everett Stansfield was fined ten shillings plus costs. Everett thanked the judge and wished him a very happy Easter but it was just a pity that his Sunday pint of ale had been the most expensive one of his life!

# 27

# Death in the Mill

By this year of 1892 Edison's Uncle Jimmy had moved from Crow Trees Farm to take the tenancy of a farm on the ancient slopes of Castercliffe. James was cattle dealing once again and employed the services of various cattle drovers to move his stock around the district. In the Nelson area he employed a chap by the name of John Easton who, on the twenty seventh of July, did a rather naughty thing.

John Kenyon owned the Barrowford Clough Springs Brewery and the Rossendale Brewery near Blackburn and like many of his fellow brewers Kenyon had the tenancy of a number of pubs throughout the district. Elichia Dickinson was employed as a commercial traveller for the Barrowford business and in this capacity was driving his pony and gig from Nelson to Colne when John Easton flagged him down.

"Hey up Ely, where you off to?"

"Now then Jack. Bit of business in Colne to attend to."

"Can I have a lift?"

"Well, you can tend the horse while I talk to the landlords if you want."

And so the pair set off on the mile or so journey; Dickinson noticed that his passenger smelt strongly of drink but this was nothing new and he wasn't so drunk that he could not hold the horse. Arriving at Colne Dickinson made several calls at the public houses where he might sell his employer's products while Easton remained outside and looked after the horse, making sure that the local lads didn't play on the gig.

At the Cross Keys Inn the traveller was invited to stay for a meal and so he paid Easton one shilling to take the horse and gig back to his stable in Nelson. Later that evening Dickinson was offered a lift back and when he arrived to check that the horse had been attended to it wasn't there, neither was the gig.

It later transpired that Easton, spotting an opportunity to make a few easy pounds, had driven the gig from Colne straight over to Cliviger on the other side of Burnley. There he approached the landlady of the Ram Inn and offered to sell her the horse and gig. The landlady was suspicious of the offer as people did not just turn up out of the blue offering to sell such things and she sent him away with a flea in his ear.

Undaunted Easton drove for another two hours and ended up at the Windmill Inn on the outskirts of Rochdale, Manchester. Here the same thing happened and Easton was again sent packing so, at this point, he gave up his attempts to sell the outfit and had a few pints of ale instead. The following morning he woke in the gig and as his frozen senses slowly returned he decided that there was nothing for it but to return to face the music. He begged a bag of horse feed from the landlord of the Windmill and set off on the long drive home.

Needless to say John Kenyon prosecuted Easton and he was remanded on a charge of stealing the horse and gig, a set of harness, two cushions, one rug and one whip altogether valued at £59: 10s: 0d. Easton pleaded guilty and expressed his remorse, blaming drink for his actions. He was committed to stand trial at the following Preston Quarter sessions and, needless to say, James Nowell had to find himself a new cattle drover for the next few years.

While the Lower Clough Mill was being rebuilt other mills in Barrowford were struggling to cope with another downturn in trade. Albert Mills stood on the hillside on Pasture Lane where the massive southern facade of its spinning department towered uncompromisingly over the White Bear Inn. The first part of the mill had been built by John Barrowclough back in 1852 and his grandson, also John Barrowclough, took over the running of the mill upon the death of his father in 1886. John junior had no real love for the cotton industry and in consequence the mill had not been doing well.

In 1892 Albert Mills ceased trading and on Tuesday night, the thirteenth of September, a meeting of the principal inhabitants of Barrowford was held to consider the steps to be taken to alleviate the great distress in the village caused by the stoppage. It was reported that a great many people had, through the stoppage, an average weekly income of less than one shilling each. It was resolved to make collections at places of worship and workshops in the township and to invite private subscriptions to a relief fund.

On the twenty sixth of October the Liverpool Mercury ran the following paragraph;

*At Barrowford, chiefly owing to the long-continued stoppage of the Albert Mills (which have changed hands), the distress is on the increase. Enforced idleness of a large number of the inhabitants has led to the distress which a local relief committee has done, and is doing, its best to meet.*

The Mercury mentioned the fact that Albert Mills had now changed hands and this was indeed the case. John Barrowclough junior had finally sold the mill and the purchaser was Sarah's former employer. James Atkins had long harboured a wish to get into cotton manufacturing and, along with two new partners, he saw an opportunity to purchase Albert Mills at a knock-down price. When trade picked up again, as it always did, he would be in a good position to take advantage of the upturn.

Atkins and partners registered the new firm of West Hill Manufacturing Company Limited with £6,000 raised in £20 shares. The initial partnership contract stated that the firm was to carry on business as; *'Spinners and weavers of cotton, woollen, silk or other fibrous substances and the winding, warping, beaming and sizing of yarn and the dying, bleaching, colouring and printing of any of the aforesaid substances.'*

Things did not improve in the local industry and November saw over 5,000 looms running on short time in Nelson and Barrowford with a further 3,000 looms about to close down operations. James Atkins' Albert Mills was weathering the storm to a certain extent but an event was about to unfurl that would have a great impact on his life.

James Howarth, the engine tenter at Albert Mills, had been in to see to his boilers on Boxing Day in order to get them settled after the Christmas break. Early on the day after Boxing Day he rose early from his bed, gulped down some of yesterday's thin porridge, put on his overalls, clogs and jacket and set off for work. The morning was black as pitch as he closed the door of his cottage to the front of the Old Row. He walked along the main road, the clattering of his clogs echoing from the walls of the buildings, and turned up the hill by the White Bear Inn.

The engine house was a two-storied building attached to the Middle Mill and, to James Howarth, this was the hub of the whole factory; if the engines did not turn then the mill did not run. By the time that James' young stoker arrived the engines had been checked and oiled and the boilers were ready to be nurtured into life.

Manfred Halstead was eighteen years of age and had worked under James Haworth long enough to know his job. He was certainly no expert, he had a long way to go before he could claim to be an engine man, but he was, nevertheless, a competent stoker. Manfred lived a few hundred yards from the mill, on Queen Street, with his parents and two younger sisters.

By six o'clock the milltown symphony of a thousand clog-irons told the men in the engine house that the looms would soon be demanding power and Manfred set about stoking the boilers. There were two steam engines of 450hp under James's control and these ran the looms in the two weaving sheds. By half-past six the boilers were up to pressure and James threw the lever that started the overhead shafting in the sheds rumbling.

Things went smoothly for a couple of hours and on the upper floor of the engine house James filled his tin mug with strong tea before putting his feet up for ten minutes. No sooner had he done so than young Manfred bounded up the wooden stairs.

"Boiler pressure's droppin' James. Come and 'ave a look will you?"

"Nay, bloody 'ell lad. They can't 'ave lost much pressure, it in't five minutes since I last looked."

With a sigh of resignation James told his stoker to sit down and not to touch anything as the engines were ticking over nicely. His heavy clogs shook the dust from beneath the stair treads as he noisily descended to the boiler house to check the pressure gauges. A few minutes later he had satisfied himself that all was well and climbed back up to give the lad a ticking off for wasting his time.

But the lad was not there; James called out but there was no reply. Knowing that Manfred would need to come down the stairs to pass through the boiler house, and this had not been the case, James assumed that the lad was still somewhere within the engine house. He walked around the other side of the engines but he still saw no sign of his stoker until he happened to glance down into the engine crank pit - and what he saw would make his blood run cold until the day he died.

The long crank rod from the engine reciprocated within a long trench, or pit, set into the engine house floor. As the massive crank slid backwards and forwards on its never-ending mission small jets of steam escaped from the cylinders and mixed with grease and oil to form that distinctive smell of the steam engine. However, James noticed that there was something else mixing with the steam and oil – the bones, blood and brains of young Manfred Halstead.

As soon as he realised that the lad had fallen into the pit James stopped the engine, this caused the overhead line-shafting connecting the engine with the mill machinery to groan with the momentum of a thousand looms. Slowly all of the shafts piercing the building of the West Shed stopped, leaving the weavers looking at each other with raised eyebrows.

James summoned help from the manager and the shed overlookers, one of whom, seeing the tragic scene, ran from the mill and was not seen for two days. There was very little left intact of the poor lad; every bone in his body had been smashed and the limbs were separated from the torso, in fact the body had almost been reduced to a bloody pulp. An overlooker and the mechanic went down into the pit and shovelled the sorry remains of young Manfred into a sack. They were then placed in a weft-box, the most suitable container that could be found, and taken to his parent's home.

Nobody ever knew exactly how Manfred had fallen into the crank pit that morning. The Coroner was satisfied that all appropriate hand-rails were in place around the engine and the crank pit had been particularly well protected by rails. Needless to say, the Halstead family were devastated by the loss of a son and brother at such a young age.

James Atkins also took Manfred's death to heart as, to a certain extent, he felt that as part-owner of the mill he had to take some responsibility for the accident. This did not auger well for James and the coming years would see his health deteriorate alarmingly.

# 28

# Ice and Slander

The tragedy of Manfred Halstead's death saddened the whole village and neighbours rallied around his family to offer as much support as they could. Within a few days the village almost had another tragedy to endure when a group of lads decided that it would be a good idea to go ice skating on the canal.

The winter of late 1892 had been quite severe, but only for short periods; over the New Year there had been a reasonably thick layer of ice on the canal and this attracted people from miles around. One of the most popular skating venues was the canal reservoir at Foulridge where it was not unusual to see hundreds of people on the ice. During protracted periods of cold weather traders would set up their catering stalls along the banks of the reservoir, and on the ice, and the flames from a hundred torches would add to the surreal atmosphere on the frosty, night-time lake.

Official 'ice testers' would inspect the quality of the ice each day and when they were given the all clear men, women and children would glide around to their heart's content. Some had shop-bought skates but the majority had cobbled-up contraptions made by the local blacksmiths. These strap-on efforts worked, but only just, and many were the times when a skater would be unceremoniously dumped on their well-padded backsides when a slip-on skate slipped off.

Because of its length the canal was far more difficult to control than the reservoir and there was little checking of the ice for quality and thickness. This meant that some stretches of ice were highly dangerous. And so it proved on the second of January 1893 when a group of Barrowford lads set out from William Green's home in David Street for an afternoon's entertainment on the frozen canal at Hodge House.

Here a wide stretch of the Leeds Liverpool canal ran alongside James Atkins' coal wharf; here the water formed an expansive 'pool' that ice attracted skaters in their droves. On this particular Monday, however, the lads were the only ones on the ice as the workers were back at their looms. All was well for ten minutes or so, Ambrose Clough moaned a bit when the ice started to 'thunder' but, there again, Ambrose was always moaning. He complained again when a huge crack appeared beneath his feet and this time he made his way back hurriedly to the safety of the bank. When the others had finished jeering at their soft pal they resumed their skating only to see William Green disappear from view.

Ambrose Clough had been right to worry about the crack in the ice because it had now opened up exactly beneath young William's feet. The rest of the gang panicked and made for the bank as fast as their skates would carry them. As they assembled on the towpath there was no sign of William whatsoever - he was beneath the ice.

The lads knew they could not go back onto the ice as they were likely to suffer the same fate as their unfortunate friend and so they decided to go up onto the road bridge passing over the canal at this point in the hope that they could summon help. Looking down from the bridge they could see that William had surfaced in the hole in the ice.

They began to shout and scream for help but there was nobody to hear them on the road. Luckily for young William at that moment a young man emerged from beneath the bridge on the towpath below. Hearing the lads clamouring for help he quickly summed up the situation and, taking off his jacket, slid down the banking onto what appeared to be the thickest part of the ice. He slid along on his stomach so as to distribute his weight; inch by inch he crawled ever closer until he finally reached the frightened lad. The rescuer edged his way to within inches of the jagged sides of the hole and managed to get hold of William's collar.

By this time, at the nearby Atkins' wharf, Sarah and Edison's neighbour, Henry Goodier, had heard the commotion and dashed along the opposite bank with a rope. He threw one end of the rope to the rescuer who tied it around William's chest and it was then simply a matter of dragging the sorry bedraggled boy across the ice to safety. The rope was thrown again and the procedure repeated to bring the hero across the ice.

The coal workers took young William into their shed to warm him up and dry him out. Fortunately he was little the worse for wear following his near-tragic accident; in fact the clout he received from his dad proved to be the most physically painful part of the whole affair.

As for the young passer-by; nobody ever found out who the shy hero was - when he saw that William was in safe hands he walked quietly away.

Things at number five Joseph Street had progressed from bad to worse since Sarah had approached Edison about seeking marriage guidance. He had now developed an obsession with all things to do with the New World, especially Australia. In the autumn of 1892 new neighbours had moved into the Clock Cottages across the street from Edison and Sarah. They had recently returned from America where the man had been to seek his fortune. He never did discover monetary riches but he did return with an American wife.

Edison listened in awe to his neighbour's stories of the open country and massive cities that he had seen on his travels and from that moment he was hooked; he bought every magazine and travel brochure that he could lay his hands on. He commandeered one of Sarah's laundry drawers for his ever-growing collection and would devour them every night. He was particularly taken by the advantages of Australia; from what he read it was simply a case of booking a passage out there and riches would then beat their way to your door.

In the early summer the matter came to a head when Edison rushed into the kitchen manically waving his arms around. After finishing work on Friday evening he had called in at the reading rooms above the Co-operative stores to skim through the Nelson and Colne Express and the Times, this saved him the expense of having to buy a copy. That day the Times ran a story that immediately took Edison's eye;

*'Finds Lead to New Australian Gold Rush.'*

"What did I tell you?"

Sarah was startled by her husband bursting into her kitchen. This usually meant he was winding up for yet another assault on her.

"They've found a massive gold-field in Australia and they say that you've only got to turn up and start digging. There's gold everywhere, you can just pick it up off the ground."

The newspaper had been referring to an incident in June when three Irish prospectors had been travelling through the Kalgoorlie district of the Australian outback. One of their horses cast a shoe and, as the others were waiting for the horse to be re-shod, they found traces of gold in the dirt and gravel. They immediately decided to set up camp in order to search the surrounding area and on the seventeenth of June an official reward claim was filed. The news spread like wildfire and the Kalgoorlie gold-field became world famous almost overnight.

Sarah tried in vain to reason with her starry-eyed husband. She was rooted firmly in reality and knew very well that riches were the reward of hard work and good fortune wherever you happened to live. But he would have none of it, he refused to listen to common sense and finally declared that they were going to emigrate.

"Not likely. If you're going you go on your own."

Sarah could think of nothing worse than being reliant upon Edison in a foreign country, he was difficult enough to live with here!

Edison flew into a rage and sent his wife flying across the room with a blow from his fist. She picked herself slowly up from the kitchen floor and brushed down her dress with the palms of her hands; at least she was no longer shocked when he hit her. He was always careful never to hit her in the face where bruising would show and give the game away to outsiders. He wanted to keep his little outbursts a secret between them.

Sarah composed herself and with undisguised venom she spat out;

"I wish you would go - as far away as possible. You might even find yourself a one-door house and another woman to thump!"

Edison slammed the door behind him and disappeared onto the village streets. And so things scraped along; Sarah was trapped in the monotony of a loveless, violent marriage and Edison felt equally trapped within a marriage that prevented him from pursuing his dream. He became ever more peevish towards his wife and finally the reason for this became clear when he let something slip during one of his violent rages.

"You should think yourself bloody lucky that you're here. My mother's not here and she should be – not you!"

This jogged Sarah's memory; she recalled Ellen's advice when she had suggested that Edison had been looking for a mother substitute and that he resented his wife for being alive when his mother was dead. At the time Sarah had difficulty in coming to terms with this concept but she understood all too well now.

On Monday the fifteenth of May Sarah travelled to Colne in order to support a friend of hers at the County Court. Helen Walker had followed much the same path as Sarah had done whereby they had both entered service at a young age and had subsequently found it necessary to move far away from home. Helen Walker had been born in the city of Liverpool in 1867 and at the age of thirteen had found herself working as a domestic servant for a Barrowford family.

Her employer was an accountant at John Kenyon's brewery and lived in a large house on the main road with his wife and six children. As the 1880s progressed, and the children grew up, Helen used her spare time to learn the craft of dressmaking; she learned well and slowly built a good reputation for her skills. When she was no longer required as a domestic help she rented a cottage where she set herself up as a dressmaker and there was soon enough money to open a small drapery shop in the village. Sarah used Helen's services from time to time and the two became friends. Sarah would often stop by to see Helen when the shop was not too busy and they would swap stories of their earlier lives in service.

Next door to the drapery shop was a grocery run by Bulcock Dillworth and his wife Jean. Dillworth had been a joiner and cabinet maker in the village for a number of years but he had put his money into buying the grocer's shop so that he and his wife could work together. Unfortunately Jean Dillworth, who was Barrowford born and bred, had taken against Helen Walker. Jean considered her own family to be of a somewhat higher social standing than most and to her Helen was a jumped-up newcomer who did not deserve her place amongst the tradespeople of the village. Jean was also keenly aware that the twenty-six year old spinster attracted the attention of local men and if the truth be known she was jealous.

One morning, just after Easter, a friend of Helen's had been shopping in Dillworth's grocery and had overheard a conversation between them and another customer. She quickly realised that the gossip revolved around Helen.

"Aye, she's no better than she should be, that one." Mrs Dillworth was warming to her subject.

"She reckons to be all prim and proper when you go in her shop but we know where she goes at night. Isn't that right Bulcock?"

"Oh aye. We know for a fact that she keeps company with eight or nine married men and walks the lowest streets of Burnley at midnight in their company. Aye, what do you think o' that?"

There were many 'oohs' and 'aahs' from the customer who was impatient to finish her shopping and spread the news around the village streets. The eavesdropper reported the conversation to Helen who promptly went round to the Dillworth's shop and caused a scene.

She gave the grocer and his wife a thorough earful and threatened to sue them for slander if she heard of them pedalling their lies again. The grocers were defensive; they were certainly not going to take on Helen face-to-face, her city childhood had taught her how to take care of herself and the Dillworths knew it.

However, a few days later Helen learned that her neighbours had been spreading their lies once again and this time she went straight to a solicitor. The Dillworth's were summoned to appear at the Colne Court where Helen was to claim fifty pounds in damages for slander.

The defendants hired a high-flying solicitor from Manchester and he argued that the words in the plaintiff's claim 'Did not impute unchastity or adultery and were not therefore actionable under the Act of Parliament.' Helen's solicitor said that 'The whole act of incontinency was imputed by the words used.' In the end Judge Gates agreed with the Dillworth's solicitor and dismissed the action.

Helen was heartbroken. She had been hurt when she heard the malicious rumours circulating around the village and she just wished to put a stop to them. She had a number of supporters in the court and they were aghast at the Judge's finding. The fact of the matter was that the Dillworths had accused Helen of having loose morals but this was implied rather than specific.

"That my dear," one of Helen's more elderly supporters took her arm on the way out of court, "Is what happens when men judge the female of our species."

Not long afterwards Helen married a farmer from Blacko who let it be known in no uncertain terms that anyone caught spreading rumours about his new wife would be on the receiving end of his double-barrelled shotgun. The gossip stopped very quickly.

As the days lengthened Sarah's thoughts once again turned to her predicament and she felt even more undervalued in the marital home than at any time since her fateful marriage. Her frustration boiled over and she approached Edison with the fact that she wanted to learn to weave but she did not ask him this time as she knew what his answer would be. Taking the bull firmly by the horns she announced that she had been across to Atkinson's Mill where she spoke to Bob Hargreaves, the shed manager. He had told her that he would find somebody who would be willing to take her on as a 'helper weaver' and she could go on from there.

"Oh, right. And you know all about the mill don't you? You won't last two minutes in the shed."

To a certain extent Edison was right as most of the weavers he had ever known were born to the trade. Not long ago they started at the tender age of nine and were weaving by eleven or twelve, the shed was in their blood and they had never known anything else. Sarah, on the other hand, had known nothing other than domestic life; she had never worked in a factory and she certainly knew nothing about operating machinery.

Undaunted Sarah started as a helper at Lower Clough Mill and on her first day wondered what on earth she had let herself in for. She knew that the weaving sheds were noisy as she had been in Atkinson's on many occasions when she needed shopping money from Edison. However, it soon became apparent that she had not been prepared for the reality of a weaver's life.

The new recruit had been taken on by a middle-aged woman who ran twelve looms but when Sarah stood at the end of the aisle and looked across the clattering, banging sea of twisting, jerking iron and cloth she was speechless. To the uninitiated this was a hell-hole with no apparent method or structure; people rushed along the narrow space between the raging looms, pulling a bit of cloth off here, putting a bit more on there; stopping the strange beasts and starting them again while dodging the deadly flying belts connecting the looms to the groaning overhead drive shafts.

This madness was repeated incessantly across the hundreds of looms that crammed the shed building. There were no windows in the walls, all the necessary light streamed through the glass saw-tooth panels of the north-light roof. Some of the glass panels had been removed in a vain attempt to moderate the stifling dusty air but the heat from a thousand tons of rattling machinery was not to be got rid of easily.

The unbearably hot air was saturated with floating fibres from the juddering, loom-bound cotton threads and it settled everywhere. It clogged the nostrils and throat and worked its way into the scalp where it caused many allergenic skin problems. Almost all of the older weavers had been deafened by a lifetime in the sheds and they communicated by hand-signs and lip-reading and this left Sarah feeling even more isolated.

Sarah's mentor had shown her the wicker skips in the warehouse from which she was to collect the required weft, put it in weft boxes and carry it to her looms as and when her weaver needed them. They were then threaded through the shuttle by means of a tiny hole through which the weaver sucked the end of the thread. This was the practice of 'kissing the shuttle' that left many weavers with diseased lips and mouth. The reloaded shuttle was placed back on the loom ready once more to be fired back and forth across the warp threads.

Occasionally a shuttle would fly off the loom and it was sheer luck as to whether or not it hit anybody. Most weavers carried the scars of the flying shuttle, some had lost an eye or suffered some other facial disfigurement. Yet other unfortunate operatives became entangled within the moving machinery. The turning gear-wheels and the twisting, writhing drive belts were always on the lookout for a nice, soft piece of human flesh to devour.

Sarah knew that she had made a mistake; this was not her world and she would never get used to it as long as she lived. On the afternoon of her second day at the shed she was busy contemplating how she should tell Bob Hargreaves that she was not cut out for this work when something happened to save her the trouble.

The summer was waning and the last time that Edison had seen his Uncle Thomas had been a few months ago. Thomas had been to Berry's Mill on business and, as he often did when he found himself in the locality, he called on one or other of the family. On this particular occasion it had been the turn of Joseph Street to receive a visit. Sarah thought that Thomas looked very tired and drawn but this was understandable given the loss of his wife. He had taken on a live-in domestic to help with managing the household but, nevertheless, he did not find life easy. His work had become ever-more demanding, with the fluctuations in the textile trade and this was another unwelcome source of stress. Sarah and Edison waved goodbye to Thomas on that wet, early spring day.

"Take care Tom, don't forget we're here if you need anything."

And that proved to be the last that they were to see of him. As the wasps droned ever more drowsily about their business, and the trees bled a myriad of russet hues across a browning landscape, Thomas fell ill. He had been suffering from aches and pains in his arms for months but now he felt really poorly. The family were now living in the fashionable Manchester suburb of Chorlton-on-Medlock where the doctor visited Thomas and promptly ordered bed-rest. Within an hour of the doctor leaving Thomas collapsed and died in his eldest daughter's arms; he was forty-two years of age.

The insistent knock on the door told Edison that something was wrong and, sure enough, a distressed Richard stood on the doorstep. Both Sarah and Edison were stunned when they heard his unwelcome news. They liked Thomas, his unassuming manner and gentle humour had won him many friends and he would be sorely missed by his family. It was decided that Richard and Edison would travel to Manchester to see what could be done as Thomas's children were orphans now with no relatives living within many miles of the city.

Richard arranged the funeral and visited his deceased brother's solicitor to set the legalities in motion. Sarah, Edison, Richard and Jimmy attended Thomas's funeral and afterwards the family gathered in the drawing room to discuss the future. There was no problem for the eldest of the family; John was twenty now and working in a Manchester bookshop while Percy had made up sixteen and was a Post Office Boy. The problem was that young Margaret at eleven, and Susannah aged thirteen, were minors and would require the supervision of an adult. The eldest daughter, Constance, was a capable young woman of eighteen but she was too young to run the household.

In a flash Sarah saw the answer to the problem. Either one of the adults in the family would have to move in with the youngsters or they would have to come over to stay with the adults.

"It's simple." Sarah addressed the room.

"The girls can live with me and Edison and we can get the boys somewhere nearby."

Eventually all were agreed that this would be the best solution although it would be wrench for the youngsters as they would be leaving their jobs and their home. They could see, however, that there was nothing else for it and so the arrangements were made.

When the first opportunity arose for Edison to speak with his wife alone he voiced his doubts about the arrangement. For one thing their house wasn't big enough but Sarah had seen her opportunity. She hoped that with his three cousins living with them Edison would stop his violence and, furthermore, she would once again have a family of sorts to look after.

"It's easy," she was in no mood to lose this chance.

"We'll move house."

And move house they did. Sarah had harboured a wish to move to Dixon Street since the properties were erected and, as luck would have it, John Aldersley and his family were moving out of the house next door to Bob Hargreaves, the manager at Atkinson's Mill. Edison took the tenancy of the house; he was already buying two houses and he knew that the rental income for these would more than cover the rent for the new home.

In due course Sarah's massive sideboard was trundled up the steep hill of Dixon Street where it was destined to take pride of place in the parlour of what she hoped would be a happier home.

# 29

# Trouble at the Mill

Christmas passed without incident and the house welcomed its new occupants into the new year of 1894. To the rear a yard held the coal shed and privy and a gravel lane ran along the back of the two rows of Dixon Street. The back lane separated the houses from allotments behind which stood the flag-roofed building of Lower Laithe Farm.

Although the Nowells had barely moved eight hundred yards from Joseph Street their new home on the hillside proved to be much quieter than the bustle of Newbridge. It was fair to say that the rumbling of the mill sheds could clearly be heard when the heavy sash windows of the house were open but the only real disturbance was created by the heavy tread of the weaver's clogs. Every morning, except Sunday, at half-past six the mill workers made their way down the steep street and their iron soles struck an unmistakeable chord within local hearts. When the clip-clop of iron on the sandstone flags mingled with the early song of the blackbird all was well – the mills were operating and that meant there was work.

Sarah and Edison shared the front bedroom overlooking the street and as the spring advanced the sun rose ever-earlier above the ancient mounds of Castercliffe. Almost every morning the bright billowing rays of a new day penetrated between the bedroom wall and the closed curtains where it burned its presence into the room. The morning air split with a fiery glow just as the weavers and the birds broke the peace of the dew-laden air and this left a lasting impression on Sarah.

266

The three girls quickly grew to trust Sarah and they settled well in their new home. Constance, or Connie as she preferred to be known, grew particularly close to Sarah and the two of them would set off arm-in-arm on various outings. This brought memories flooding back as Sarah thought of the happy days spent with Ann Johnson at the Royal Oak. The feeling of someone's arm linked closely with her own also brought the heady fragrance of Fran's favourite lavender drifting through Sarah's senses.

Sarah was conscious that the two younger girls were presenting a brave face to the world but she knew that their hearts were breaking from the sudden loss of their parents. She was careful to support young Margaret with her schooling while not pushing her too hard. The middle sister, Susannah, was anxious to start work on the part-time system but Sarah was less enthusiastic. Not wanting her to make the same mistake that she had so recently done she took the youngster down to the weaving shed to allow her a glimpse of the real factory world. There were other trades that a young woman could enter; perhaps shop work or dressmaking would be more suitable?

Susannah was having none of it. She had accompanied her father on a number of his travels around the mills of Manchester and had been fascinated by the noisy, living entities that were the weaving and spinning sheds. She did not see the same dangerous, alien world that had presented itself to Sarah; instead she saw the textile trade as a way of life and she wanted to be a part of it. And so she started as a cotton winder for Christopher Atkinson and Company where her neighbour, Bob Hargreaves, kept a watchful eye on her.

At that time Atkinson and Company was suffering from the same trading pressures as were all the other textile mills. Many of them were now operating 'dobbie' looms where punched-card attachments to the machinery allowed for the weaving of patterns and designs into the finished cloth. In April the Nelson Manufacturer's Association refused to pay the same wages to their dobbie weavers that their counterparts in

Chorley were earning and consequently 1,600 weavers walked out of thirteen mills leaving over 6,000 looms idle.

In the meantime a problem in Barrowford had been simmering for months; the 150 workers at Smith and Wiseman's Higherford Mill made it clear that they were to resign *en masse* because they were not being paid the same rates as their counterparts in the other village mills.

Relationships between the employers and their operatives did not improve but a decline in trade was the reason for a prolonged stoppage of the mills in August. On the ninth of the month 15,000 looms ceased weaving in Nelson and Barrowford, a prolonged closure of mills on this scale had been unparalleled for many years. In September the Higherford Mill operatives were again at loggerheads with their employers and once again came out on strike – and this time they were serious.

The whole district was a hotbed of claim and counter-claim whereby the manufacturers were printing propaganda against the unions and the workers circulated rumours about the owners. A weaver claimed to have overheard two manufacturers in conversation on the platform of Nelson Station where one of the well-heeled men was reported to have said to the other;

"Aye, we've now got the buggers down to one bowl of porridge a day."

Letters flew back and forth in the Nelson and Colne Express, one manufacturer offering a reward to anyone who could prove that this conversation actually took place. The reward was never claimed but this was an illustration of the extent of the industrial unrest.

James Atkins' mill weathered the worst of the downturn but he was not immune from the general industrial strife as closed mills did not use coal and his sales suffered. He still supplied gas to the town but the lion's share of the gas supply had been granted to a Burnley firm and James could see that he was never going to improve his position. The death of Manfred Halstead had affected him and business worries played on his mind; he and Martha now had six children at Spring Hill and he began to lose sleep. Preaching began to take a more prominent role in his life and he no longer described himself as a coal merchant and farmer; his main occupation now was that of a Wesleyan Minister.

Edison saw that Sarah and the girls were getting along well and he realised that they would gang together against him in any dispute. This meant that he had been reasonably subdued over the first half of the year. This was not to last, however, and by the onset of winter he was up to his old tricks; coming in from work one day in November he had been determined to pick a fight with his wife. He was in a foul temper and finding Sarah alone in the kitchen began to throw the usual accusations of infidelity at her. He had it in his mind that she had been a little too over attentive to the Co-op butcher at the bottom of the hill.

It was true that Sarah liked the strapping young butcher; he had a ready smile for her and was always attentive when she went into the shop. But that was as far as it went and Sarah was at a loss to know where her husband had got his silly notion from. Her denial did nothing other than provoke Edison and he knocked her to the ground and, placing his knee on her chest, pinned her down and pummelled her around the head.

Little did Edison know that Connie had been upstairs throughout his outburst and came running when she heard Sarah's shouts. Connie was aghast when she came upon the violent scene; she had enjoyed a sheltered upbringing and had never dreamed that a man would be capable of hitting a woman, let alone his own wife.

"Edison, what are you doing? Leave Sarah alone."

Surprised to have been caught red-handed Edison released Sarah and slouched out of the house leaving his wife to explain the situation.

"You might as well know the truth, Connie. He's been thumping me for years. If he's in a mood, or I say something

269

he thinks I shouldn't have, he flies into a temper and takes it out on me. I can't even so much as look at another man before he's accusing me of wanting to run off with him."

Connie had realised that things were not good between her cousin and Sarah. As a married couple they certainly did not behave towards each other in the same way that her parents had done. Having seen Edison's outburst she now realised how bad things had become between them.

"You shouldn't have to put up with that, Sarah. Have you told anybody about it?"

"What can anyone do Connie? I've been advised to leave him more than once but I've no money and I wunna know where to go. Besides, he's not all bad really. Mostly he works and brings money in and we just get on with things."

The Christmas of 1894 had been a relatively good one for Sarah as for the first time since her marriage she had someone to share it with properly. Edison never liked the Christmas season as it reminded him of his family and he became maudlin and awkward. Sarah, however, looked on the season as a religious festival and enjoyed the atmosphere at the chapel. Everyone in the Higherford Wesleyan congregation was involved in organising the village festivities and Sarah helped out wherever she could. Her new house guests approached the festivities with a mixture of sadness and hope and they proved to be good company for Sarah.

As the year of 1895 took hold the weather grew decidedly cold. In Scotland the temperature was measured at minus twenty-seven degrees Fahrenheit and this was the coldest measurement since records began; fortunately there was no shortage of coal and the fires at Dixon Street blazed day and night.

Although Edison had been ashamed when Connie had caught him assaulting Sarah it did not prevent him from doing it again. The only real change had been that he began to bring Sarah flowers after his violent outbursts. He would appear with a small bunch of seasonal blooms bought from the old lady who travelled around the mills selling cut flowers. There was never any meaningful apology to accompany his pathetic attempts at a peace offering, he would simply hand them over, grunt and sit down for his tea.

"It's alright you bringing me these Edison," Sarah said whenever a bunch of flowers appeared, "but it'd be far better if you kept your temper. That would mean a lot more to me."

Sarah hadn't the heart to throw the offerings away even though she would really like to have done. Every time the girls came home to find a vase of blooms on Sarah's mahogany sideboard they looked at each other knowingly – their cousin had been lashing out again.

On the sixteenth of March the strike at Higherford Mill finally ended; the stoppage had lasted thirty-six weeks in all and had not been without incident. The owners had decided to close the mill and advertised the contents for sale but when the workers saw the advertisement they were incensed. On the day of the sale a number of the men armed themselves with heavy wooden sticks and physically prevented the auction from going ahead saying that the firm owed them money and payment of this should be a priority.

In the end the owners capitulated and work resumed but not before the Weavers Association had distributed over £3,000 to the operatives in strike pay. The total losses sustained by the workers over the thirty-six week strike amounted to £7,000 thus bringing the overall costs to £10,000. That is not to mention the losses of the mill owners.

The workers at Atkinson and Company had no such problems and life went along much the same for their employees on Dixon Street. One Sunday morning in September the Nowell household was preparing for the morning chapel service; Sarah and Connie were finishing the breakfast things when Margaret came into the kitchen. She looked over her shoulder and whispered to Sarah;

"What's wrong with Edison this morning?"

Sarah had not seen her husband since coming downstairs as he had been lighting the parlour fire and reading his newspaper.

"Why, what's he doing?"

"Just come and have a look. I think he's having some kind of funny turn."

The three of them moved quietly down the passage and looked tentatively into the parlour. Sarah saw immediately what Margaret meant; her husband was staggering about from one item of furniture to another in a most alarming manner. He gripped the back of the sofa and then lurched over to the sideboard and held on to it for all he was worth. He then lurched over to one of the wooden high chairs and slumped heavily onto the seat. He teetered back to his feet in another attempt to walk unaided across the room and his audience could see that he was bent over almost double.

Edison had always had a tendency to lean forward when walking as if he were impersonating a chimpanzee but now he was leaning so far forwards that he could hardly keep his feet for more than three paces without a real danger of falling flat on his face. When he caught sight of the three observers he hurriedly sat down in the armchair and picked up his paper as if nothing had happened. They left him to it and returned to the kitchen.

"Well," said Sarah, shrugging her shoulders, "I'm not going to ask!"

When the girls returned from chapel Edison had returned to his normal self and nothing was said about his strange antics that morning. On the following day Connie and Margaret came home for their dinner and told Sarah that someone from the clothlooking department had mentioned that Edison was lolloping around the place like a monkey. They wondered if he was taking pills or something.

"It's the badness coming out I expect."

Sarah did not really care what her husband was suffering from as long as it wasn't contagious. The situation of Edison's silly walk continued until the Thursday when, after tea, Sarah found a half-burnt piece of cork in the fire ashes. Enquiring as to what it might be Edison owned up that it was something that he had been experimenting with. He had been reading a magazine called *Sketchy Bits* in the Co-op reading rooms when he noticed the following advertisement;

*Are you little?*
*If so, you are recommended to wear the*
*A. D. Invisible Elevators, Registered.*
*Increase your height up to four inches.*
*Detection is impossible.*
*Inexpensive.*
*Send stamp for particulars to;*
*The Oriental Toilet Company,*
*F Department, 87 Strand, London.*

Keen to improve his height Edison sent off three shillings and nine pence as payment for the 'best' shoe elevators and duly received them. The elevators turned out to be wedge-shaped layers of cork and the idea was that they were placed inside the shoe with the thicker end beneath the heel. The cheapest elevators were a single piece of cork, said to raise the height by one inch, while Edison's 'best' elevators were four of these glued together. They were, therefore, supposed to increase his height by a full four inches but when he tried them he found that he was exactly one-eighth of an inch taller because they threw him forward in a most alarming manner. When wearing them he very much resembled a circus clown whose shoes had been nailed to the floor enabling his body to lean forward almost parallel with the ground without falling over.

"I haven't used the bloody things for two days but they hurt my feet so much I still can't walk properly."

"And so you chucked them on the fire?" Sarah held the charred bit of cork between her thumb and forefinger.

"Aye, too bloody right I did. I've been swindled and no mistake."

273

When Sarah told the girls the reason for Edison's peculiar behaviour they thought that it was hilarious.

"It'd have been less obvious if he'd used a pair of stilts," Connie rather cruelly observed.

Edison forgot all about his unfortunate experience with the shoe elevators until he received a rather official looking letter in mid-November. The letter was from the Common Sergeant of the London Law Courts asking Mr E Nowell if he had been satisfied with his purchase of a pair of shoe elevators from one Arthur Lewis Pointing, trading as *The Oriental Toilet Company*. If he were indeed to have been dissatisfied would he be willing to attend a hearing at the Old Bailey in a few weeks time?

Naturally Edison was not going to trail all the way down to the capital in pursuit of compensation amounting to three shillings and nine pence. He did, however, write a letter stating his experience with the goods and saying that he considered the whole thing to be based upon sham practice. He received a letter in return thanking him and enclosing the statements of others who had bought the elevators. These were to be offered as evidence before the court.

Mr Frederick Dry, of Old Trafford, Manchester, had bought the two inch elevators because he was an amateur actor and wanted to increase his height on stage:

> *The elevators made no difference to my success on the stage—the heels are an inch thick, but do not make you an inch taller, because they threw me forward. In fact someone was required to hold me up throughout my whole performance—I did not care for more practice—I put them in my boots occasionally, but never went on the stage again with them'—I said at the Police-court they affected my spine, because they gave me a pain in my back—the pain lasted about half an hour.*

Sarah Trunkard, of Cambridge, complained that she had applied for a single elevator because a girl in her care wore a surgical boot. Because she had one leg shorter than the other she quite reasonably expected the elevator to raise the short leg to the length of the other:

> *I got these two pieces of cork—I put them into the girl's boot—we had to hold her up or she walked continuously around in a circle—they were no use—I wrote in about December to say I required my money back, as they were not suitable for the purpose I required of them.*

James Graham of Walworth had an equally unpleasant experience:

> *When I got them I put them in my boots—they threw me over on my knees—my idea was my personal appearance—they hurt me by throwing my toes forward in the boot, and making them very uncomfortable—I wore them a few minutes, and sent them back the next day, and asked for a return of my money—I got no money back.*

Stephen Gent, a plumber of Hattersley Street, Burnley stated that:

> *I received a pair of elevators one inch thick—I tried them twice in my shoes, and found them very uncomfortable—they caused me pain in the back and across the feet—I wore them in the street but they forced me to run everywhere, leaning forward— I complained to the company, and received the offer of other goods, but not the toilet list—seeing it was a toilet company, I asked them to send me a hand mirror for one of my daughters—I got a box of pills.*

Herbert Chapman, of Walworth was also dissatisfied with his purchase:

> *A detective came and asked me to give evidence, and I went to Bow Street—I am a butcher, and serve in the*

*shop—I did not get a better price for my meat—I wore them on Saturday, and served in the shop till eleven p.m. but had to be assisted home—I did not tell anybody I had got them on, and never had them on again—I did feel about an inch taller when I was wearing them.*

When the court hearing concluded the defence lawyer submitted that there was no case to go before a jury as there was a genuine business being carried on and, although half-a-dozen people considered the elevators uncomfortable, that was not enough. It was stated that they were capable of raising the wearer four inches, which it was clear that they were, and contended that all that had taken place was exaggeration. The Common Sergeant agreed and directed a verdict of *not guilty.*
Edison thought that this verdict was typical of the justice system whereby business people could get away with continuously swindling the workers. In fact he was quite indignant about the matter,

"That's the last thing I ever buy from out of a magazine. You can't trust anybody nowadays."

Before they knew it another Christmas had appeared upon the horizon. Connie, Susannah and Margaret, were determined to enjoy themselves; they were all now working at Atkinson's Mill and had money to spend. New dresses and bonnets appeared at Dixon Street and Sarah was the recipient of more presents than she had seen in her life.

# 30

# Mischief and Murder

The winter of early 1896 could not live up to the extreme cold of its predecessor but nobody complained. The months rolled away and soon the daffodils brightened the village gardens, early Mayflowers filled the meadows and swallows began to return to East Lancashire. In stark contrast to the burgeoning beauty of another spring a dark episode in the history of Nelson was about to be played out.

Jackson Healey was a weaver at the same mill as Edison and they knew each other as work colleagues. Healey was one of eleven children born to a Trawden farmer, a village on the Yorkshire side of Colne, but he had worked in Nelson for a number of years. He was a handsome individual with jet-black hair, a rakish pencil moustache and an eye for the ladies.

In 1892 Healey married Elizabeth, the daughter of a local jeweller, and the newly-weds set up home in Pendle Street on the edge of the Nelson town centre. In 1895 they had a child but all was not well within the household. Healey was well known for his fiery temper and his wife did not have an easy life; she complained that he constantly kept her at the household chores even when she was exhausted from her work at the mill.

There were many parallels between the Healey family of North Street and the Nowells of Dixon Street. The husband was insanely jealous of his wife and continually questioned and harangued her about her every movement. In the third week of April, in this year of 1896, Elizabeth had been out choosing new wallpaper for the house and she was excited to

277

see how it looked. A decorator had been hired and he was busy with stripping the old paper and hanging the modern floral patterns that Elizabeth had chosen.

However, Healey's jealous nature could not cope with the fact that there was another man around the house and he convinced himself that Elizabeth was having an affair with the decorator. Finally, on Thursday the twenty third of April, his patience snapped. He called into Walton's Cycle and Hardware Shop and, telling the assistant that he needed to kill a dog, asked what might be the most effective way of doing it. He was shown a centre-fire, six-chambered revolver that would do the job nicely and so he paid the ten shillings and six pence cost of the gun and returned to work.

At ten-fifteen that evening Elizabeth went up to bed with the child leaving her husband sitting quietly by the fireside. She bedded the child down in the small bedroom and had just dropped off to sleep in her own bed when she was woken by her husband ordering her to get out of bed and shouting that;

"I'm going to put an end to you."

He knocked her to the ground, pinned her down with his left hand and proceeded to shoot her four times with the revolver. So close was the gun to Elizabeth that the flames from the barrel set fire to her night clothes.

Healey ran downstairs just as a concerned neighbour knocked on the front door, he made his escape out of the back door and along the darkened alleyways. Elizabeth, still sensible despite her wounds, was paralysed on the right side of her face but she still managed to remove her burning clothes and put a petticoat on. At this stage she had no idea where her husband was and, fearing that he would come back and finish her off, she slid open the sash window and sat outside on the windowsill. If Healey were to return to the bedroom she was ready to jump to the street below.

Elizabeth, shocked and bleeding profusely, began to shout for help and within minutes a small crowd gathered. At that moment two Barrowford men were driving past the end of the street and stopped at the house when they heard the commotion. Ben Nutter, the horse dealer whose animal freak show Sarah had seen at the village agricultural show, and a companion, broke the downstairs window and were attempting to get in when the police arrived.

Constables Featherstone and Bell had been patrolling nearby and were able to reach the scene quickly. PC Featherstone made his way to the bedroom and saw Elizabeth outside the window with the crowd shouting for her to jump. He told her to stay where she was and opening the sash dragged her back into the bedroom. He then heard the child crying in the other bedroom and handed it over to the safekeeping of a neighbour. Doctor Little was called and he put Elizabeth back to bed and dressed her wounds as best he could.

The family rallied round and it was decided that Elizabeth, being too ill to move to hospital, would be nursed at home. The first problem for the doctor was the fact that the bullets in Elizabeth's body could not be located although the wounds were more than evident. The doctor noted that the victim's tongue had turned black as a result of a wide bullet wound close to the back molar and the tonsil on the right side of the throat. The mouth, nostrils and right ear all bled profusely.

Another wound showed the entry of a bullet into the left jaw, half-way between the ear and the chin, and another in the middle of the neck with an entry hole of one-eighth of an inch. All the wounds were surrounded by black scorch marks due to the close proximity of the gun when fired and a large area of Elizabeth's shoulder had been badly burned when her clothing caught fire.

Doctor Little was aware of the reputation that the newly invented x-ray photographs were gaining in cases such as this and he asked for the help of the eminent Professor Arthur Schuster, a leading radiological scientist at Owen's College, Manchester.

Professor Schuster was ill at this time but he immediately despatched his two assistants from Manchester to Nelson; this was no easy undertaking as the x-ray equipment was bulky and fragile. They carried with them three Crooke's tubes, one being a spare, and a number of plates. They could not hope to carry the batteries for the operation and Nelson Corporation stepped in by sending two around to the house.

This was the first time that an attempt had ever been made to take x-ray photographs of a patient outside of a hospital. In fact it had only been four months since Willhelm Conrad Roentgen had published his scientific paper on his discovery of x-rays and the discipline was still in a decidedly embryonic state.

Having set up their equipment the two scientists proceeded to take the x-rays of Elizabeth's body; the first one took an hour to complete while the second one took almost seventy minutes. Elizabeth's suffering was evident for all to see and because they were not medical practitioners this had a profound effect on the scientists. So novel were the proceedings that the Mayor of Nelson and the Town Clerk were in attendance to watch history being made.

The exposed photographic plates were taken back to Manchester and on Thursday the thirtieth of April Doctor Little received a telegram from professor Schuster stating that the experiment had excited great interest in medical circles. Three bullets had been located by the photographs but the fourth remained elusive.

On Saturday the second of May Professor Schuster himself made the journey to Nelson, along with all of the necessary equipment, in order to attempt to locate the missing bullet. With great difficulty the plate was placed behind Elizabeth's skull and exposed. This time the plate was sent around the corner for a local photographer to develop and the results showed the missing bullet clearly lodged in the back of Elizabeth's skull. Unfortunately the experiments proved to be in vain; Elizabeth's injuries were inoperable and she passed away on the following Saturday, May the ninth.

As for Jackson Healey; when he left the house on that fateful night he went without a coat or shoes. He walked along Clayton Street to the Pendle Street bridge from where he threw himself into the canal. At first light on the following morning PC John Featherstone dredged Healey's lifeless body to the surface and the corpse was taken to the house of Elizabeth's parents. This was not a pleasant experience for them because they had never liked their son-in-law, they had been of the opinion that he was a strange man and that Elizabeth had married beneath herself. To rub salt into the wounds Healey had now shot their daughter and they were responsible for keeping his body until after the inquest.

The Coroner heard that Healey had left a very strangely worded letter in which he named the decorator and blamed his wife for having an affair with him. Elizabeth's father was represented by Samuel Davies, a local solicitor, who insisted that the name of the decorator should not be made public as he was an innocent man. Healey's sister also gave evidence and stated that her brother was well known for 'not being right in the head.' The jury passed a unanimous verdict that Healey had drowned himself while being of unsound mind.

The news of the North Street tragedy spread through the district like wildfire. Many people knew Jackson and Elizabeth Healey and were shocked to learn that he had committed suicide and his wife was not expected to survive. When Edison heard of the shooting he became quiet and thoughtful, in actual fact something about the episode had touched a nerve deep within him and he became obsessed.

On the Saturday morning following the shooting Edison joined the small crowd outside number twenty North Street where they waited for any snippets of news that might be forthcoming. He then walked around to the back of the house, from where the murderer had made his escape, and followed the footsteps that he would have taken to the spot where he had drowned himself. He stood on the edge of the water trying to imagine what must have been in the killer's mind that night. What had driven him to shoot his wife and what were his final thoughts as he stood on this very spot, enveloped in the dank midnight and ready to throw himself into the dark void of cold, muddy water?

The more that Edison thought about Jackson Healey's actions the more he realised that there was, after all, a way out of his life of entrapment. True, the shooting of his wife had been extreme but Healey's actions had opened Edison's eyes to the fact that there were options open to him.

Following the untimely death of Elizabeth Healey, Edison became ever more withdrawn while his jealousy toward Sarah increased. With this the periods of calm between his violent attacks grew shorter and the girls at Dixon Street became increasingly stoical in their support for Sarah.

At the end of October each year the young men of Barrowford practised the ancient custom of Mischief Night. This was the one night of the year in which they had licence to wander the neighbourhood and commit minor acts of vandalism. Gangs of lads would congregate on the far borders of the district, usually at the Moorcock Inn on the moor between Yorkshire and Lancashire and they would then walk the two miles to Newbridge carrying out as many acts of minor vandalism as possible.

Handcarts were a favourite source of amusement; they would be loaded up at Blacko with all manner of items from people's gardens and sheds and then allowed to run down the hill into the river far below. Gates would be taken from their hinges and carried a long distance before being abandoned. Windows were smeared with treacle and flour and door knobs were tied together with strong twine along a whole row of houses so that the occupants could not open them in the morning. Eventually the lads would return to their homes leaving the village strewn with the evidence of their night's efforts. The villagers would quietly set about clearing up in the morning and cartloads of gates, flower pots and even dismantled garden sheds were returned to their owners in the outlying areas.

This year, however, the Mischief Night celebrations were to be marred by sadness, and not, as might be expected, because some daft lad had injured himself while engaged in some prank.

On the run-up to Mischief Night it had been the practice of local confectioners to make special toffee and sweets for sale to the village youngsters. There were three confectioners in Barrowford and all of them made good quality produce. This year, however, many of the corner shops had taken stocks of a sweet called 'Hanky Panky' from a supplier from outside of the district. These sweets were bright-green in colour and an added chemical caused them to fizz violently on the tongue. Word spread amongst the village youngsters and quarter-pound bags of Hanky Panky flew from the sweet shop shelves.

Henry Tatham was a bright young lad of eight with a shock of blonde hair and a cheeky grin that won the hearts of everyone he came across. On Saturday morning, the eighteenth of October, Henry and his pals dashed down to the sweet shop in the Nutter Buildings and immediately decided what they were going to exchange their halfpenny spending money for. The new, bright-green Hanky Panky was irresistible at the front of the sweet display and the lads were soon back out on the street with a bag each.

They passed under the archway next to Daniel Nutter's butchers shop and, emerging onto the village bowling green, they made themselves comfortable on the river wall. They goaded each other waiting to see who was going to be the first to try the green stuff and decided to try it together. As soon as they tasted a small quantity their mouths exploded with the strange frothing sensation and their lips were bubbling with green saliva. This was great fun but they had better save some for tomorrow as there would be no more spending brass this week.

The first indication that something was wrong came on the Monday night. Young Henry began to feel ill, complaining of a bad stomach ache and his mother put him to bed suspecting the usual tummy upset. But the lad deteriorated rapidly - in the middle of the night he vomited a green substance about the size of a hen's egg and then fell into a coma. By morning young Henry was dead.

His distraught parents had called Doctor Pim to their son in the early morning but he could do nothing to save him. This was not to be the only case as both Doctor Pim and Doctor Hungerford would see a number of similar poisoning cases around the Nelson and Barrowford district. Fortunately the other cases were less severe than that of Henry Tatham.

November brought with it a particularly clammy dampness, no breeze penetrated the valley and the mill chimneys vied with thousands of domestic chimneys in an unsavoury competition to pump out the largest amount of choking, sulphurous smoke to blott out the horizon. Colds and influenza were sweeping the district and the clinging smoke that swirled around every street corner filled the lungs of all those who lived below the eight hundred feet level; this happened to be all the people in the village except those living on outlying farms.

Eighteen people aged between twenty-two and eighty-eight years died from the effects of the 'flu. On top of this there was a protracted outbreak of scarlet fever and measles and, consequently, many children fell ill. The village schools and Sunday schools were closed in an attempt to contain the epidemic. Fortunately most recovered but a few unfortunate ones would suffer from the side-effects of these commonplace diseases for the rest of their lives.

Edison, however, had far too much to occupy his mind than to worry about the fog. He was feeling increasingly isolated in his own home as Sarah grew ever closer to the girls. Sarah and Connie were fond of their shopping trips into town and would be off on the flimsiest of pretexts. Edison, of course, saw this as a threat and he convinced himself that as Connie was young and fancy-free she would be mixing in the company of young men - and that meant that Sarah would be too.

Considering himself to be far too clever to be outwitted by his scheming wife Edison formulated a plan to follow her on her supposed shopping expeditions. The first part of the plan was to shave off his moustache. This was to allow his wife to become accustomed to his clean-shaven appearance before he put the second part of his plan into operation.

"Why has Edison shaved off his tash? He looks plain daft if you ask me" Susannah asked Sarah.

"Aw, don't ask Sue, I've given up trying to make head nor tail of him."

The Nelson Theatrical Supplies shop in Market Street sold all manner of strange things to the local thespian community. Since the opening of the Grand Theatre in 1888 demand had been increasing for their wares and they now carried an impressive stock. Here you could buy or rent any manner of wigs, costumes, powdered carbide for the footlights, makeup, stage explosives, false noses etc.

Edison shuffled around the wonderland of props and suits of armour like an excited child. His reason for being here was that stage two of his plan involved disguising himself to the extent that even his own wife would not recognise him. To this end he tried on a huge, warty false nose and asked the assistant what he thought.

"Well Sir, why don't you try on one of our false noses? Nobody would recognise you then."

The assistant's little joke went completely over Edison's head and he dropped the prosthetic hooter back into the box with all the others. Little did Edison know but the assistant happened to be Ebenezer Edmondson, better known as *'The Incredible Shrinking Comedian.'* Edmondson's act was stand-up comedy coupled with contortionism and was popular on the local theatrical circuit. This did not pay very well, however, and he eked out his income by assisting in the shop.

Edmondson often worked with a Barrowford stage act known as; *'Captain Fox, The Ten Figure Ventriloquist and Farm Yard Specialist.'*

Alex Fox performed with his partner, Eugenie Chesswell, who advertised herself as a; *Mezzo-soprano vocalist (just concluded a third season with Rossini's Opera Company). At liberty for piers, halls, dioramas and pantomime. Address: The Post Office, Barrowford.*

Edison found himself the object of Edmondson's wit once again when he asked to try on a hat. He wanted something out of the ordinary to aid his disguise and he was thinking along the lines of a fedora. Edison had always had trouble in buying caps and hats because of the large proportions of his upper head; his face was not proportionate to his cranium and he eventually had to place a special order for outsize headwear with his outfitter. He was hoping that the theatrical suppliers would stock outsize hats because, after all, the theatre types were odd people anyway, weren't they?

Edmondson opened a number of hat boxes, each of them holding an increasingly large fedora until he finally came to the largest hat in the shop. With a sigh of resignation he handed the hat to Edison.

"Well, if this one doesn't fit I'm afraid that Sir will have to wear the box!"

Again, Edmondson was playing to a hostile audience and Edison wandered off in search of another type of headwear. Eventually, with the encouragement of the assistant, he settled on a French beret. No matter that it made him look like the least disguised person in the whole of Nelson; in fact Edmondson knew that his customer would stand out like a sore thumb with that thing on his head. However, a sale was a sale and the customer seemed pleased with his purchase.

Edison's final requirement was to be a set of false whiskers and he was on much firmer ground here. The shop stocked every style, size and colour imaginable and a fine set of huge red sideburns was soon decided upon. A bristly walrus moustache of roughly the same colour was purchased and, as Edison was about to take his leave, Edmondson could contain himself no longer.

"May I make so bold as to ask Sir to what end he might be putting the apparel?"

Edison had been expecting this question.

"It's a surprise for the wife," he answered in all honesty. When he had gone Edmondson turned to the shop manager and rolled his eyes.

"I knew I shouldn't have asked - it doesn't bear thinking about!"

# 31

# A Cunning Disguise

Before Edison had a chance to use his cunning disguise Sarah came to the end of her tether and threw him out of the house. It was the same week in which he had been to the theatrical shop and his behaviour had been particularly violent. The problem did not concern Sarah alone now; there were young girls in the house and they should not be subjected to this sour atmosphere.

The support of the girls gave Sarah a determination that she did not previously have and when Edison hit her once again things came to a head. With the three girls backing her up Sarah confronted her husband and he was taken aback.

"I want you to go, you're a brute and I've had enough. This is no way for these girls to live, they shouldn't have to see a man hitting his wife. If you don't leave then I'm going to the police."

True to form Edison stormed out of the house and did not reappear for hours. Eventually he could see that there was no arguing with Sarah and he agreed to move out. After all, he told himself, it would only be for a short while as she would soon miss him. He rented a small cottage overlooking the Reedyford Bridge and moved in on the eighth of November.

The thought crossed Edison's mind that in actual fact he was now free to do whatever he liked with his life. He could follow his dream and emigrate to the New World, leaving his old life well and truly behind. There was, however, a problem with this; he would be leaving his properties on which Sarah might have a claim if he were still married to her. But this was not the only drawback; if he left for good Sarah might very well meet another man and, as far as Edison was concerned, if he couldn't have her then nobody else was going to have her. No; having given the matter a good deal of serious thought he decided that there were more ways than one of skinning a cat.

There was no problem covering the rent at Dixon Street without Edison's income. All three of the girls were working and, on top of that, they had now received their inheritance from their father's estate. In September Sarah had accompanied Connie to Manchester where she had an appointment with the family solicitor. Now that she had turned twenty-one Connie was able to sign the relevant papers and receive her share of the inheritance. The other shares were left to Margaret and Susannah in trust.

When Edison left the house Connie paid him forty pounds for the furniture, fixtures and fittings in the hope that this would break any connection he might have with the house. For two full months peace reigned within the Dixon Street household, the tension drained away and laughter returned. However, there was one fly in the ointment as far as the girls were concerned and that was the fact that Edison came up to the house almost every evening.

He only ever stayed long enough to let Sarah know how much he missed her and how their separation had made him realise just what he was missing. This cut no ice with the girls and Connie told Sarah that he was playing on her good nature. For a while Sarah resisted her husband's charm offensive. She was still adjusting to the novelty of having her life back, of being able to have a meal without the fear of being attacked for no good reason. Christmas was to be the happiest time that Sarah and the girls had enjoyed for many years and they all looked forward to a brighter future.

As the New Year of 1897 dawned the musical chimes of Saint Mary's bells in Nelson drifted along the valley on the midnight air. Bob Hargreaves blacked his face with coal dust and, humming continuously, entered Sarah's house to sweep in the New Year with a willow besom. Sarah gave Bob a silver three penny piece for luck and everyone agreed that the household deserved better fortune in the coming year.

"After all," said Connie, only half jokingly, "It couldn't get much worse!"

The sequence of events that would bring Connie's words back to haunt her began before the first month of the New Year was even half-way through.

The celebrations of the Christmas season passed, January brought the dark, cold mornings of mid-winter and Sarah began to feel sorry for Edison. He still came up to the house but his clothes had been getting shabbier and the hair surrounding his large bald patch had sprouted to the extent that he resembled a mad professor. He needed a shave and, all -in-all, he looked downright unkempt. Little did Sarah realise that he was actually cultivating this appearance of neglect to gain his wife's sympathy.

However, this pathetic attempt to inveigle himself back into the household did not impress Connie, she saw what her cousin was doing and tried to warn Sarah. But gradually Sarah fell soft, Edison was contrite and realised what he had done, he promised to behave if he could come home - he would be a model husband in fact. The novelty of living a single life had worn thin for Sarah, it had been two months since Edison had left and this had given her time to reflect. Absence makes the heart grow fonder and she was deeply conscious of the marriage vows she had made before God. She was prepared to give her husband another chance.

And so, on the second weekend in January, Edison lugged his belongings back up the hill. Things were better than they ever had been, Edison took Sarah on outings to the theatre and he accompanied her to her Sunday chapel services. This did not impress the girls, though, there was a distinct chill between them and their returned cousin; they had seen how upset Sarah had been when Edison hit her and they could not for the life of them see why she had taken him back. But they did not realise that deep down Sarah needed the security that

Edison offered to her; violence or no violence he kept a roof over her head.

This new face that Edison presented to the world had a shelf life of exactly two weeks. He had managed to maintain the sham of happiness to the end of January but Sarah was still taking her trips into Nelson with Sarah and he was sure that there was another man involved. It was time to put his cunning plan into operation.

On the first Saturday in February the Dixon Street household awoke to find a scattering of powdery snow on the windowsills. The sky was that brilliant blue that only winter days ever saw and the surrounding white hills shone in the bright morning sun. Sarah was glad of her heavy tweed overcoat in the sharp frost of the morning as she and Connie set out on their shopping trip to town.

As the pair walked along Market Street they stopped to look in the large, double-fronted window of John Bond and Company's drapery shop. Sarah was looking for a new dress and, while she was peering intently through the glass, Connie spotted an odd movement out of the corner of her eye. As she looked along the street a figure suddenly leaped from the pavement into a shop doorway. This struck Connie as a little odd but, then again, there were always odd people around.

She turned to inspect the dress that Sarah was ogling when her eye was once again drawn along the street. This time the figure had moved one shop closer to them and once again he dived into the doorway. This happened again and Connie gave Sarah a nudge.

"Don't look now but there's something strange about that man. He keeps watching us and ducking in and out of the doorways."

Sarah turned her gaze from the window display and caught sight of the dodger; and a strange sight it was. He wore a long, heavy coat that almost drowned him and on his head, pulled down around the ears, he sported a very peculiar onion-seller's bonnet. Protruding from the edges were huge, bushy sideburns whose shocking red colour was matched in intensity by a

291

bristling moustache. The two companions looked at each other and looked back at the apparition who had, by now, lunged back into yet another doorway. They watched the spot where he had disappeared and, sure enough, after a few seconds a whiskery head poked out from the edge of the window. Seeing the two women looking in his direction the head promptly disappeared again.

The shoppers moved on, turned the corner into Scotland Road and walked to the next drapery shop. The two were slightly unsettled by the odd behaviour of the man in Market Street and they looked nervously around them. And there he was again, just as he turned the corner he saw them looking in his direction and made his way across to the other side of the road. As he did so both Sarah and Connie noticed something very familiar about the loping gait as the man slouched across the street.

"That chap walks just like Edison,"

They had turned towards the window so as not to let the stranger know that they were watching him and Sarah spoke out of the side of her mouth.

"You're right Connie," they could see his reflection in the window and followed his movements along the opposite pavement.

"Must be coincidence though. Edison doesn't have whiskers like that."

They returned home later in the afternoon and found Edison sitting contentedly by the fire. He had splashed out on a newspaper and appeared to be absorbed by the weekly news.

"Hello, have you had a nice day at the shops you two?" Butter wouldn't melt in his mouth.

By now Sarah and Connie, their minds full of dress colours and materials, had all but forgotten the strange man who appeared to have been watching them.

On the following Saturday the congregation from the Higherford Wesleyan chapel were holding a fundraising fair and Sarah had baked a Dundee cake for the proceedings. Along with Connie and Susannah, Sarah had volunteered to run the cake stall and, at half-past ten, the three of them set off on the half-mile walk to the chapel. As usual the fair was very well supported and by one o'clock the cake stall had sold out. The girls sat down for a well earned cup of tea while Sarah cleared the cloth from the trestle table. She took the cloth to the outside door and began to shake the crumbs from it when out of the corner of her eye she saw someone disappear round the corner of the chapel building.

Thinking that it was probably some young lad looking to beg unsold buns she returned to the hall and joined the others for a cup of tea. She had just poured herself a cup from the large pot on the table when Connie nudged her sharply and nodded towards the door. Sarah looked up just in time to see a red, whiskery face, topped by a ridiculous beret, gurning through the glass panels of the inner doors.

"That's him from last week," Connie's horse-whisper made Susannah turn round.

"Who's that then?"

"Oh, nobody, just someone we thought we knew." Sarah did not want to alarm the lass. Just to be on the safe side Sarah and the girls made sure that they walked home in the company of one of the Dixon Street neighbours. When they were alone Sarah and Connie decided that it was probably a coincidence that the stranger had appeared a second time and they were being silly to assume otherwise.

On the next Saturday the shopping trip had hardly begun when Connie saw the shuffling of a great-coated figure with a whiskered red head perched on the top. They were walking up Scotland Road towards Nelson and Connie happened to look behind them. There he was again and as soon as he saw that Connie had seen him he ducked down the side of the Derby Arms. This game of cat and mouse carried on all the way to the town centre with the whiskered one running furtively backwards and forwards across the road, dodging in and out of shop doorways and peeping around corners at the two women.

"Right, that's it," Sarah had had enough of this, "I'm telling the Bobby."

In the very centre of town, where the four major roads crossed, a policeman was stationed on permanent duty and Sarah approached him.

"There's a very strange man following us and we don't feel safe."

Unable to leave his post the Constable summoned a colleague who walked back towards Barrowford with the two nervous women. Needless to say they were troubled no further by their pursuer and when they arrived home they again found Edison sitting by the fireside attentively reading his newspaper. Sarah told him of their escapade with the strange man and described him in full, lurid detail. She told him how ugly he was, how he was very short and walked with the loping gait of a chimpanzee and how he was definitely a strange and probably dangerous individual.

"You'll have to come with us in future, Edison. We're not going far on our own with that crackpot following us everywhere."

On the following Thursday Sarah was cleaning out the tallboy drawers in the front bedroom as they were due for new mothballs and brown paper linings. She did not usually bother with the drawer in which Edison kept his travel magazines and brochures but, for some reason, she decided to re-line that drawer too. As she removed the bottom layer of magazines she uncovered a large rat and almost jumped out of the window in fright. She retired to the doorway and stood waiting for the huge, red rodent to make a move. Of course, it never did because it turned out to be Edison's false whiskers.

Sarah sat on the edge of the bed, deep in thought; something was gnawing away at the back of her mind but wouldn't quite come into focus. Why on earth would her husband want to keep a set of false whiskers in his drawer? And then it clicked.

*"That chap walks just like Edison."*

She recalled Connie's words from the first time they had laid eyes on the stalker and here was the answer, staring her in the face. She dashed around the house, rummaging in cupboards and pulling clothes frantically out of the wardrobes. She knew exactly what she was looking for and she eventually found it in the outside shed. This was where the firewood and newspaper for starting the coal fires were stored and at the very bottom of the pile was a canvas bag. Sarah dragged the bag from beneath the pile and as she did so wood and paper flew across the stone flags of the yard. She knew what she would find before she opened it. Sure enough, the bag held a large, heavy overcoat and in the left-hand pocket was stuffed a navy-blue beret.

Connie was the first to arrive home from work and she found Sarah sitting at the kitchen table with an odd look about her. Sarah pointed at the coat folded neatly on the table and Connie saw the red whiskers on top. At that moment, only two minutes behind his cousin, Edison walked into the kitchen. Sarah's expression did not alter but there was no mistaking the anger in her voice,

"Right Connie. Meet the man who's been putting the fear of God into us!"

Connie was taken aback. She did not have a clue what Sarah was talking about, but Edison certainly did. His face took on the colour of freshly boiled beetroot and this spread rapidly to the top of his bald pate.

"So, this is what you do when I'm out is it," he thundered, "Can a man have no bloody privacy in his own home?"

"You don't deny it then?"

"No, I don't bloody-well deny it and if you weren't always gallivanting off with her," he jabbed a derisory thumb at Connie, "I wouldn't have to check on who you're knocking about with."

"Oh, so it's all my fault again."

Although she was outwardly calm the veins on Sarah's neck throbbed alarmingly as she rose to her feet. She looked her errant husband straight in the eye and spoke quietly but firmly.

"This is the end of the road for us. You've ruled my life with a rod of iron but you've never trusted me and you've certainly never appreciated me. The day we married I had such high hopes that we'd be settled and have a family but you never wanted that. Why did you marry me when you cunna love me? You're a freak and a brute Edison Nowell."

The tears welled in Connie's eyes, she knew that this was the final straw for Sarah but she still could not get to grips with the fact that her cousin could behave like a lunatic. Sarah maintained her composure.

"I can't even go shopping now without you spoiling it, where's it going to end? Anyway, I've made up my mind. You'll leave this house and this time you wunna get back in. Tomorrow I'm going to report you and that's that."

That night Edison slept on the sofa. The morning of Friday the twenty sixth brought with it a dense fog that seemed appropriate given the heavy atmosphere within the Dixon Street household.

"So you're going to report me today?"

Edison knew that once the matter was reported it would become public knowledge. The whole of the village would be aware that he had treated Sarah badly and he could expect a good deal of hostility from the community. This would be especially true at the mill where he was surrounded by women; the local people did not take kindly to men who hit their wives and some of the mill women were not to be messed with. They would make his life hell, just as he made Sarah's life hell.

"Yes, I am. I've made my mind up."

Edison leapt to his feet in anger and grabbed Sarah by the throat. She grasped his arms but was powerless to stop him, her breath rasped and she could feel her face beginning to swell. If Connie had not hit him hard on the back of his head with the brass ash-pan brush Edison would in all probability have strangled his wife.

This was a sinister turn of events, never before had Edison actually showed signs of wanting to cause his wife any real harm. But the ante had been increased now that he knew he was about to lose her, he did not care anymore. He knew that once he was permanently separated from Sarah there would be no life for him in Barrowford and she would be free to take up with another man.

After three sweet cups of tea Sarah felt able to face the day and she walked slowly up the village to the police house in Victoria Buildings. Sergeant Thomas Wilson listened sympathetically to her story and advised her that if she was going to press charges against her husband she should first consult a solicitor. It would also be wise for her to move out of the house and stay with friends until the matter came before the Police Court. Because she had nowhere to go, and being unsure as to whether Edison would leave the house a second time, Sarah decided to take Sergeant Wilson's advice and seek legal advice. Fortunately she was on speaking terms with James Atkins' family solicitor, Samuel Davies, who she had seen a number of times on his visits to Spring Hill. She knew that Davies would at least be fair with her and so she decided to pay him a visit at his Nelson office in the Station Buildings.

When Connie came home for her dinner she learned of the morning's events and insisted that she should support Sarah on her trip to see the solicitor. Edison arrived home shortly after Connie and, when he heard of Sarah's intentions, he demanded that she give him her house key. Fearful of another attack Sarah handed her key over and Edison stated that he would accompany the two women to Nelson.

"No you don't, you're not coming up town with us." Sarah looked back over her shoulder as she left the room.

"And don't follow us in your silly whiskers or we'll have you arrested!"

Sarah and Connie made themselves ready and at half-past one they left by the back door, accompanied by Edison. He followed the two companions to the Station Buildings, keeping a discreet distance between them, and stood at the end of the street as they disappeared inside.

Sarah and Connie spent forty minutes with Samuel Davies. He listened to the story of abuse with concern and advised Sarah to go along to the Colne Magistrate's Court where she should obtain a summons on the grounds of common assault against her abusive husband. Sarah thanked Davies and as they left his office she noticed that Edison was no longer there. Now he knew that she was serious he had left the Station Buildings to set about putting his final plan into action.

The pair crossed the station yard and walked up the tile-lined tunnel to the platform where they bought tickets for the next train to Colne. As Sarah waited on the platform her mind drifted back to the day almost fourteen years ago when she had arrived here with her small travel bag and little else. She considered the events that had brought her to this unhappy stage in her life and, once again, that familiar pit of dark loneliness opened up before her. Just as an earthquake rents the ground and swallows all before it Sarah was keenly aware that some invisible force was about to consume her and leave no trace of her life behind.

The Clerk at the Magistrate's Court was an officious little man. He sat with his hands clasped on a huge stomach that strained the buttons of his waistcoat and peered at the two women over a pair of pince-nez spectacles. After Sarah had explained her wish to summons her husband on a charge of assault he asked her haughtily if she really knew what she was doing. In a condescending manner he explained that it was not unusual for women to come into the office and ask for a summons to be taken out against their husbands. More often than not they would be back the next day, when everybody had sobered up, and demand that the summons be retracted.

"My advice to you, madam, is to go home and let things calm down."

"But I've been waiting for things to calm down for nearly ten years!"

Sarah's frustration was rising to the surface as Connie placed her hand on her friend's arm.

"Come on Sarah, we're wasting our time here."

Arm-in-arm they walked down the Court House steps.

"Bumptious little so-and-so."

# 32

# The Final Betrayal

Edison was in no doubt now that his wife intended to carry out her threat to summons him. His jealous rages and constant suspicion had drained his already limited mental resources and he was now at the end of his tether. In truth he really needed professional help to make sense of the overwhelming thoughts that raged within him. But there was no sign of help from any quarter as Edison Nowell set out on a collision course with fate.

Having watched Sarah and Connie enter the solicitor's office Edison turned on his heel. Within two minutes he stood before the oak-panelled counter of his bank and began the process of emptying the account that held every penny he and Sarah possessed. He left the bank clutching a small velvet bag tied at the neck with a thin leather draw-string and, as he waited on Manchester Road for the coach to Burnley, a work colleague stopped to pass the time of day with him.

"Look here Bill, bet you haven't seen this much brass for a while."

Edison opened the neck of the bag and his colleague's eyebrows rose at the sight of the gold coins.

"Bloody 'ell, 'ave you robbed a bank?"

"There's twenty sovereigns here, I like to carry a bit o' brass about with me."

Edison smirked and lovingly pulled the draw-string tight.

Sarah and Connie arrived home at half-past four but not until they reached the front door did they remember that

Edison had taken Sarah's key. They knocked on neighbour Isabella Hargreaves' door and she invited them to come in and wait until he arrived home. After a while Sarah had the idea of trying Isabella's door keys to see if they might fit her own locks. It turned out that the same latch-locks had been fitted to the back doors of all the houses when the street was built and Sarah was soon letting Connie into the house. The pair busied themselves making the evening meal and as they sat down to eat Sarah gave a sigh of frustration.

Buttering a slice of bread she sighed - "Well, I'm really no further forward am I?"

"Perhaps you should let the solicitor deal with it. I'll help you out with the money."

"Thanks Connie. I don't know what I'd do without you and the girls to support me. I'll have a think over the weekend. There's one thing for certain – things can't go on as they have been."

At that moment a key turned in the back door and Edison walked in. He put his coat on the hook behind the door, secured the mortice lock and slid the key slowly and deliberately into his pocket. He then went to the kitchen sink and poured himself a glass of water. Sarah and Connie exchanged puzzled glances; they were used to Edison's odd behaviour but he was too calm and collected now, he was obviously planning something.

Having taken a mouthful of water he quietly placed the glass in the sink, walked over to his coat and fumbled in the side pocket. He then calmly moved over to the table where Sarah remained seated and his voice rose slightly as he choked out the words, "You'll not get the better of me!"

Sarah never saw the flash of gunpowder, nor did she hear the sharp crack as the revolver spat a Kynoch .360 calibre bullet into her brain. She was only aware of her head being forced backward as the lead pierced the centre of her forehead. There was no pain, just a surreal sense that this was happening

300

in a dream; as her world became enveloped within a state of slow-motion Sarah sank to her knees.

For a split second there was an eerie, cordite-filled silence then Connie realised that her cousin was about to fire another shot. She ran to stop him and as she did so he wheeled around and aimed the revolver directly at her face; she raised a hand in protection and the bullet passed straight through the flesh and bone below her wrist before embedding itself in her jaw.

"No, Edison, don't. Please spare me. Don't shoot."

The power of the revolver in Edison's hand had raised him to an unknown level - no longer were people laughing at him, no longer was he the 'Little Squire.' He had been betrayed by the woman in his life and she was going to pay - nobody was going to stop him. His murderous actions did not even register in his clouded mind as the revolver cracked again and again – this was avenging power – the revenge of a social victim who had been forced to live a tiresome life through no fault of his own. The fate of those around him was in his hands now.

Connie's entreaties went unheeded. Another shot rang out and another bullet hit Connie's outstretched hand, this was swiftly followed by a third which entered her shoulder and spattered her blood in a perfect arc across the wall. The room quickly filled with the thick, cloying stench of gunsmoke.

While her husband played out his lethal fantasies upon Connie, Sarah had managed to crawl into the passageway leading to the front door. All sense of reality had deserted her now but survival instinct was screaming that she must get out of the house. Seeing this, Edison walked calmly along the passage to where Sarah lay face down, bleeding heavily and gasping for life. Still . . . somewhere deep within a force kept her scrabbling at the soft linoleum with her fingernails, desperate to get out of the hell that her home had now become.

Sarah was unaware of her husband as he strode over her comatose body; breathing deeply he puffed out his chest, aimed the revolver once more at his stricken wife and fired into the back of her neck.

In the meantime Connie was trapped; she could not get out of the house through the locked back door and the front exit was blocked by her gun-wielding cousin. In desperation she took the only other possible way out - through the kitchen window. With her fist clenched, and the adrenalin coursing through her body, Connie frantically swung her arm and was relieved to see the shattering glass spray fan-like across the concrete floor of the back yard.

Climbing out into the welcoming air she did notice the jagged fragments of glass jutting from the window frame like broken teeth - she did not feel any sensation as a large sliver sliced deep into her arm. Nor was she aware of the three bullets that she had taken; her body had closed down all perception of reality excepting the desperate need for survival. Leaving a trail of blood in her wake Connie ran into the back street and knocked frantically on Margaret Aston's door, two houses below.

"Quick, please come and help, Edison's shooting Sarah."

In a state of shock Margaret went out into the street just in time to see Edison stumble from his yard into the street. He was wearing neither coat nor cap and his eyes darted alarmingly from side to side. In his state of agitation he was certain that he should run . . . but in which direction? Glancing frantically up and down the street he finally made up his mind to run up the hill towards Wheatley Lane. He squeezed through the railings separating the top of Dixon Street from the surrounding fields and literally bolted for his life.

Isabella Hargreaves had heard the commotion and went to see if her neighbours were in need of help; she heard Sarah groaning in the passageway but the front door was locked. Making her way around to the back Isabella found Connie in the yard bleeding badly from her face, shoulder and arm.

"The passage – she's in the passage." Connie was trembling with shock.

Isabella sent her son to bring the police and when he breathlessly told Sergeant Wilson what had happened he immediately telephoned his superiors at the Nelson Police

Station. He had seen Sarah only that very morning and, knowing the situation, he feared the worst. He then telephoned Doctor Pim at his home higher up the village and asked him to attend as quickly as possible.

Isabella and Margaret found Sarah still alive in an ever-deepening pool of blood. They enlisted the help of two young men who were on their way home from work and they helped to carry the stricken Sarah through to the kitchen.

Doctor Pim's horse and gig drew up at five-forty and he found his patient sitting upright in a chair with a trembling Isabella mopping the streaming blood from her face. Sarah was still conscious and managed to get a few words out when she saw the doctor,

"It was my husband. My husband shot me – he did it."

By this time young Margaret had arrived home from work to find a scene of carnage. Her sister was bleeding profusely and Sarah was obviously seriously injured. There were policemen everywhere and a crowd had gathered outside.

Sergeant Wilson and his Constable, John Simpson, recovered the revolver from the kitchen floor where Edison had abandoned it along with spent bullet cases. There was a single cartridge left in the chamber and this meant that every shot that Edison had fired had hit its target. Doctor Pim finished examining Sarah and, having dressed her wounds, ordered that she be taken up to bed; she was far too fragile to be moved to the hospital. He turned to Superintendent Barnett and shook his head,

"No hope I'm afraid."

Connie was taken to the Burnley hospital and Doctor Pim enlisted the help of Doctor Crump who had access to the new x-ray equipment. Exposures of Connie's wounds showed that the two of the spent bullets found on the kitchen floor had entered her arm and shoulder but both had exited her body. The wound that was causing the most concern was in the jaw and the x-ray showed that a bullet had lodged in the bone. Because they had been able to accurately locate the bullet the doctors could now operate and remove it successfully.

Doctor Pim, however, was firmly of the opinion that Sarah's wound was inoperable. She had a bullet lodged deep within her brain and he considered that blood poisoning or haemorrhage would prove to be the logical outcome.

By the afternoon of the following day Sarah had lapsed into unconsciousness. As her coma deepened she was still able to hear the concerned voices of those around her bedside - but they belonged to another world.

The light in the house on The Lyndon was uncommonly bright as Sarah's mother and father came through the door. Sarah and Fran rushed in excited greeting and John lifted them each in turn, laughing and spinning around until they were dizzy.

Out on the street were all of Sarah and Fran's friends, playing happily, skipping, shouting, singing and chasing each other. When they saw the sisters they grouped together around them, smiling their greetings and inviting them to join in their play.

The summer was never-ending; the sky hovered close with a blue so intense that it almost hurt the eyes and occasional bursts of white cloud drifted serenely as if they were floating dreams. Beneath this wondrous sky Sarah ran side-by-side with Luke across a swaying hay meadow and upwards through the Hilly Fields. They kissed and danced beneath the huge oak tree that had stood sentinel over the Harborne township for a span of many forgotten lives. They swept down the hillside in a melee of waving arms and stumbling legs and Luke caught the love of his life in the safety of his powerful arms before she could come to any harm.

The Johnson family were delighted to see Sarah and there, in the kitchen where the range roared its glowing welcome, were the whole of Sarah's family. Every single relative that she had ever met was gathered there and she hugged each and every one of them. Ann Johnson was clearly happy as she sat and smiled at Sarah; Ann's husband stood proudly by her side, resting his hand on her shoulder.

The whole of the Atkins family stood at the door of Spring Hill and smiled at Sarah as she walked past, arm-in-arm with Luke. The children were dancing and shouting in their excitement at seeing Sarah again and everyone waved in greeting. Laughing, Sarah returned the waves and promised to call in to see them all on the way back from their walk. The pair strolled happily along the lane, Sarah chattering about this, that and nothing while Luke smiled contentedly by her side.

All the while, however, Sarah felt that something was wrong. Her mind did not attempt to clarify the doubt; it was just that somewhere a gear-wheel deep within this machine of happiness was not meshing as it should.

Things were becoming less clear now. Sarah and Luke stood on the waterside at the mouth of the Mile Tunnel and Sarah recalled how this place had made her so uneasy the last time she had been here. Now, however, things had changed; no longer did the maw of the tunnel entrance echo with dripping darkness and danger. Instead, the opening issued an ethereal multi-coloured shaft of light as if all the sunsets of Krakatoa had been bottled up within the bowels of the tunnel to be set free at this moment.

Luke's arm, clasped firmly around Sarah's shoulders, told her that she was safe here; the cares of the world were a million miles away and that is how things would stay.

A long time passed and yet it had been the blinking of an eye. The two lovers stood still as alabaster on the edge of the water and the outside voices were more certain now. Within those voices Sarah knew that there was concern but this quickly gave way to babbling, laughing whispers drifting on the radiant light.

The growing darkness was pierced by the brilliantly coloured shafts as Luke stood immovable and unspeaking. Sarah felt her weightless body slide gently down the banking, sensible now only to the voices gently echoing through the tunnel. She could clearly make out the individual tones of her mother and father while, pitched slightly higher, Fran's voice called to her over and over. Sarah now knew where she must go; she looked for Luke but, enveloped in the inky blackness that had crept steadily upon them, he was gone.

With a floating sense of forward movement Sarah entered the yawning void and became suddenly aware of the rushing light. Bright energy penetrated every fibre of her consciousness as if they were trying to force her back but a hidden, steely determination carried her onward. She knew that very soon she would meet again with her beloved Fran and would once more be safe within the protection of her family.

Six days had passed since Sarah had been shot by the very person who should have protected and cherished her. It was now two twenty-five in the afternoon of Thursday, the fourth of March. Time no longer existed for Sarah; her soul was consumed with an indescribable light that brought with it the promise of eternal love. She no longer heard the voices but she held a certainty that wherever the rushing light came from was the place where she should be, where she was expected and where she belonged. As her world faded she drifted ever more slowly until a final, still blackness quenched the light.

There, in the distance, a figure gestured and smiled, her flame-red hair glowing like a beacon of hope against the unknown distance. In a single heartbeat Sarah emerged from the heavy darkness and she knew that there were no limits here – there were no walls and no horizon. The air was filled with the unmistakeable aroma of Balkan Sobranie tobacco mingling with the scent of lavender and, for a moment, all was quiet. Without warning a wave of sound crashed into Sarah's senses as the thunder of a million wings rent the air; everywhere she looked the lids of countless wooden cages were opening as every skylark that had ever been caged broke free, rising joyously into the sky and beyond. As quickly as it had appeared the thunder ceased and Fran was taking Sarah gently by the arm, leading her onwards . . .

# 33

# The Letter

With his head bowed in sorrow James Atkins finished the prayer and slowly closed the covers of his book. Doctor Pim sighed and, looking around at the sisters, sadly shook his head. As he covered Sarah's face with the crisp linen sheet he was sure that he could detect a slight smile on her lips. He gently opened her hands and removed the object that had been clasped there and, laying Sarah's arms across her chest, he held out the jet-black rose to Susannah.

"That is a beautiful brooch. In the language of flowers the rose represents eternal love, you know."

Doctor Pim gave a short statement to the press gathered outside Dixon Street. He said that Sarah had passed away at two-thirty in the afternoon and that she had borne her torment with great fortitude. In fact Sarah had been the bravest patient that he had ever had the privilege of tending in the whole of his medical career. The neighbours also told the press that Sarah had been an upstanding member of the community; quiet and unassuming in her manner she had never given her husband the slightest reason to commit this hideous crime.

On the day following Sarah's shooting the West Cumberland Times carried the story but Luke did not see it; he always bought the Saturday edition of the newspaper but was in the habit of reading it in snatches. It had been Tuesday the second of March before he read the story and, at first, the reality did not register . . . this couldn't possibly be his Sarah . . . shot and left for dead by her husband? It was only after the third reading that the facts began to sink in.

The following morning saw Luke steaming his way southward; he could not rest without knowing the truth of the matter. The news story had said that Sarah was in a serious condition and he realised that there was probably nothing whatsoever that he could do but, nevertheless, he had to be there. Luke booked a room at the George and Dragon for the night and went straight across the road to Spring Hill where Ellen answered his knock.

"Hello. Can I help you?"

"Hello. You probably wunna remember me. I'm Luke – Sarah's friend."

The look of sorrow that overtook Ellen prompted Luke to quickly add;

"I know about the attack, I read of it in the paper and I have come down to see if I can be of any help."

"Yes. It is a terrible business. Poor Sarah."

Ellen wrote down Sarah's address for Luke and gave him directions. It was early evening when he arrived at Dixon Street and the downstairs gas lights were burning brightly in every house as he passed on his way up the hill. Edison's cousin, Percy Nowell, answered the door, he had taken time off from work to support his sisters in their time of need and was proving invaluable in fending off ghoulish questions from the many sightseers. Luke told Percy that he was a friend of Sarah's but, after enquiring of his sisters, Percy had to turn him away as they had never heard of him.

"Can I just ask . . . how is Sarah?"

"There's no change." Percy spoke through the half-closed door.

And that was that. After his long journey Luke was not going to see Sarah. He walked dejectedly back up the village and settled in the George and Dragon saloon for a jug or two of ale. Unsurprisingly the talk in the pub was all about the drama on Dixon Street and where had Edison Nowell got to? There were lurid and fantastic theories regarding Edison's whereabouts but the truth was that nobody, including the police, knew where he was.

Over breakfast Luke had an idea. At half-past nine he walked up to Spring Hill once more and told Ellen of his being turned away from Dixon Street. As he had hoped, Ellen knew of the situation between Luke and Sarah and she sympathised with his plight.

"Right, come on. I'll have a word with the girls and see if we can't at least let you see the poor lamb."

Within the hour Luke and Ellen were at Sarah's bedside. This was the first that Luke had seen of her for years and his heart sank; her head was heavily bandaged and she lay motionless.

"Sarah, it's Luke. I've come to see you." As he took her hand Luke was sure that he noticed a faint flicker of response cross Sarah's face but the others did not see any change whatsoever. After ten minutes or so Doctor Pim arrived and ushered everyone out of the room. She's still alive and at least that's something, Luke said to himself. As he sat in the George and Dragon that evening the news that he had been desperate not to hear filtered through the gossip network – Sarah had passed away at two-thirty in the afternoon.

On the following afternoon Luke was again at the door of Sarah's home. During yesterday's visit he had seen the jet brooch on her bedside table and he had a request to make. He told the sisters that he had bought Sarah the brooch many years ago and it would mean so much to him if it could be placed with her when she was interred. Margaret had known that Sarah cherished the object and assured Luke that she had intended for it to go with her. The sisters informed Luke that Sarah's funeral had been arranged for eleven o'clock on the following Saturday morning and he decided to stay until he had paid his last respects.

Standing at Sarah's now-deserted graveside Luke took the paper from his breast pocket and, taking one last look, let it slip from his fingers. As the very last leaf of autumn might flutter and dance in protest against the hard promise of a coming winter the paper settled on Sarah's polished mahogany casket. As it did so it divided to reveal the two separate hand-written sheets of a letter. Luke thought of the time that he had spent in writing that letter and the many times that he had almost had the strength to actually post it.

He had recovered very well since he had last seen Sarah, his nerves were no longer constantly on edge and his depression had lifted a great deal. He knew that he had lost Sarah the minute she showed him her engagement ring but he also knew that he would never stop loving her. He had decided that there was nothing left for him now in England; a number of his workmates had emigrated to the New World recently and they all seemed to be making good in their new lives.

Luke had been offered a job with a mining company in Western Australia and arrangements had been made for his departure at the end of March. He had explained this in the letter and intended to post it to Spring Hill from where he hoped the letter would find Sarah. He told her how he felt and how he deeply regretted not having kept in touch; when he was settled he would send his new Australian address and Sarah could write to him if she ever wanted to do. He walked to the Post Office with the letter in his pocket on many occasions but it somehow never found its way across the counter. Now fate had transpired for the letter to be delivered in person but it would remain forever unread.

# 34

# Escape

As Edison squeezed through the railings his heart was beating as if it would burst from his chest. He had but a single thought and that was to get as far away from Dixon Street as possible. He had no cap or coat but, jangling reassuringly in his pocket, was his bag of gold sovereigns. If anything could save him it would be his money!

Up the hill he ran, his lungs burning with the unaccustomed strain; he quickly crossed Wheatley Lane Road and on he ran, through the next field along the side of the deep Noggarth stone quarry. Finally he reached the heights of the ridgeway and turned his face eastwards. He knew that the mills were now emptying and the streets of Barrowford would be filled with the clatter of worker's clogs as they made their way homeward. He wanted to escape the village without detection and to this end he would keep to the paths and trackways where nobody was likely to see him.

He knew the ridgeway track like the back of his hand so the falling dusk held no fears for him; onward he went until he came to the steep drop down through Utherstone Woods to the Water Meetings. He had given up running now as he was out of condition and wanted to conserve his stamina. Down the path he stumbled and followed the Blacko Water stream to Blacko Foot; crossing the ford here he made his way up the steep Wheathead Lane near the top of which he turned onto the rough track leading to Highor Wheathead Farm

On the heights of Wheathead Hill the lights of the solitary Firber House Farm glowed in the dark valley below; there would be no welcome here for Edison and onwards he walked as the adrenalin raced in his system. Stumbling over the darkened moor the distant lights of Rimington bade a welcome to all solitary travellers and, seeing them, Edison paused for breath. His mind was still reeling from the excitement of the past hour and his heart was still trying to leap from his chest. As he stood atop the highest point of the moor his thoughts momentarily turned to his mother and he wished with all his heart that she was still waiting down there in the village for his return. Tears of self-pitying frustration stung his eyes as he forced himself to carry on along the desolate moorland track.

Finally, as he left the dark, quiet moor behind the lights of Gisburn were clearly visible below. Making his way down the deserted road he sat down on a large stone set in the embankment and gathered his thoughts. He knew that without a hat and coat he would stand out like a sore thumb in February so he would need to purchase new clothes. He decided to wait for an hour or so for the streets of Gisburn to quieten and then he would venture forth.

As he rested at the roadside Edison's heart-rate began to fall. The events of the day raced through his mind and he could not quite believe that this was actual reality; he was sure that he had killed Sarah, and probably Connie too, but had he gone one step further than he had planned?

He had not been sure what exactly he was going to do as he had walked home that afternoon but up to that point his intentions had been clear. As the omnibus rattled towards Burnley the bag of gold jingled reassuringly in his jacket pocket and he patted the bulge as a proud father might pat his child's head. At three-thirty Edison walked up to the counter of Frederick Stockdale's ironmongery on Saint James Street and asked to see a quality pistol. He was passed over to the firearms assistant who answered to the grand name of Mr Robert Henry John Fogg.

"Might I enquire as to the purpose for which you would require the firearm Sir?"

"Well . . . I'm emigrating to America soon and I'm told that I'll need some sort of gun for self-defence."

Fogg took a box down from the shelf and placed a shining six-chambered revolver on the counter.

"This is a good quality weapon Sir, it's especially easy to use if you have no experience."

The gun was a Kynock Improved Revolver, made by the Kynoch factory in Aston, near Birmingham. The design of the gun was such that it had a double trigger; one trigger cocked the weapon and the other fired it. Edison picked up the gun and waved it around while Mr Fogg looked distinctly uneasy.

"Feels alright, how much is it?"

"Two pounds and five shillings Sir."

"Right, can I pay you two pounds on account and take the gun? I'll have to show it to a friend of mine who is emigrating with me to see if it's suitable. If you can load it for me I'll buy more ammunition when I come back in a couple of days."

Fogg loaded the six chambers with Kynoch .360 calibre, round-nosed lead cartridges of 145 grains bullet weight and 5 grains powder weight.

"These are Number Fives cartridges capable of 1,030 feet per second. I trust that Sir will not wave the firearm around now that it is fully loaded?"

The specifications of the bullets meant nothing to Edison, he just wanted to make the purchase and be on his way. He filled out the firearms sales certificate in the name of Frederick Norcross of number sixteen Commercial Road, Nelson. Having paid the two pounds deposit he walked out of the shop knowing full-well that he would never return to pay the outstanding five shillings.

On the train journey back to Nelson, Edison was overcome by a strong feeling of elation; he was carrying a bag of gold in one pocket and a loaded revolver in the other and this made him feel powerful. He looked around at his fellow passengers, ordinary people going about their ordinary daily business, and wondered if they realised just how powerful and special a person he really was? Did they see beyond the balding pate, and the shuffling frame to the man who was now bursting with a new-found vigour – a man about to break out of a lifetime of victimhood?

This sense of power stayed with him as he walked the mile from the Nelson railway station into Barrowford. Climbing the Dixon Street hill his heart began to race but not because of the physical effort. Isabella Hargreaves came out of the Co-op butchers as Edison's loping but determined stride carried him homeward.

"Hello Edison. Finished for the weekend?"

Edison was too wrapped in his thoughts to even notice his neighbour. If he concentrated hard enough he knew that what he was doing was wrong and that he was playing with fire. From somewhere hidden, but deeply compelling, came a wave that rose through his body and numbed his mind; he was being driven by something far beyond his control.

And so it proved. When he confronted Sarah his actions were simply those of a man going through the motions of a deadly automaton. In the twinkling of an eye the foul deed was done and his only conscious thought was that he had to get out of the house and as far away as possible. Without spoiling the habit of a lifetime Edison Nowell was concentrating upon nothing other than saving his own skin.

Shortly after nine o'clock, beneath the dim light of a third-quarter moon, he walked into Gisburn and found to his relief that the Park View Post Office was still open. Ben Robinson ran the Post Office and general stores on one side of the shop and his wife, Nancy, ran a millinery and drapery department on the other. Edison told the Robinsons that he was a travelling salesman and was staying at the nearby New Inn; he had lost his travel bag and was in need of a few items of clothing to tide him over until he reached home.

Nancy Robinson served Edison with a combined collar and front and a pair of woollen stockings. When it came to finding a cap to fit things were not as simple; the largest one in stock was still too small but he bought it anyway. Back out on the street the fugitive pulled his new cap firmly on to his head in

314

an attempt to stretch it; at least, he thought, a tight cap is better than none.

A rickety outhouse served as shelter for the fugitive and as soon as dawn broke through the winter sky he set off to walk to Hellifield, the next village along the road to the Yorkshire Dales. As he passed through the hamlet of Nappa, where his Uncle Peter had once farmed, a head popped up from behind a limestone field wall.

"Narthen, young Nowell. What's thee doin' over 'ere?"

The farmer knew Edison from when he used to visit his uncle. Edison's heart leapt into his mouth, this was the last thing he wanted.

"Oh, er, just visiting someone Sam."

Within thirty minutes Edison found himself on the outskirts of Hellifield and, as he passed the railway station, he stopped and rubbed his chin, deep in thought. The hands of the station clock clunked over to eleven o'clock as he bought an express ticket for a northward journey to Carlisle.

Without realising it at the time Edison had only narrowly avoided capture in Gisburn. At the same time that he was stumbling over the moor Superintendent Barnett was calling on the help of all surrounding forces to look out for the escapee. Susannah had told the police that she and Edison had an uncle in Burnley and they immediately assumed that he would head in that direction. As somewhat of an afterthought Barnett telephoned the Gisburn Police House.

Constable George Firth's wife answered the call and informed the Superintendent that her husband was out on his rounds. Night had fallen by the time that the Constable had arrived home to Church View, clouds were obscuring the moon and the streets were black as pitch. Firth was under the impression that the fugitive was not expected to appear in his neck of the woods and had decided that a local search could wait until morning. By the time that Firth had walked around the village, armed with the description of Edison Nowell supplied by his Nelson colleagues, his quarry had slipped well and truly through the net.

The express train to the Scottish border town of Carlisle passed along one of the most scenic routes in the country. The journey from Hellifield took Edison along the outskirts of the market town of Settle and onwards through the Yorkshire Dales. Onwards over the high heathlands the train steamed while Edison caught up on the sleep he had lost on the previous night.

When he awoke the train was approaching Carlisle and he was overcome by a sense of excitement and fear. Would there be a police presence at his destination, ready to pounce and drag him off to an appointment with the gallows? If not, would he manage to follow his plan and escape the country?

He had very little thought for the carnage he had left behind. He did not know it but the police had circulated a wanted poster with his description along with an artist's impression taken from a photograph. The national newspapers were also carrying the story of the fugitive along with his description. The trouble was that the artist's impression showed Edison before he had shaved off his moustache, and without a cap. This meant that the sketch was not accurate; without his moustache, and with his new grey cap covering his bald head, Edison did not closely resemble the police description.

If the Law was on the lookout for him at Carlisle Station he was unaware of it; without hindrance he purchased a ticket for the West Coast Express to Glasgow and by late afternoon he was on his way. His first priority on arrival in the city was to find a decent place to stay; he would then need to purchase a suitcase and a change of clothes.

The next day saw Edison wandering the Glasgow docks where he enquired at a number of shipping line offices; he was looking for a ship out to Australia as soon as possible. It was Saturday the twenty seventh of February and he was out of luck for the moment; there were sailings to America and Canada within a few days but he had set his heart on a new life in Australia. The next available ship was to be the Ben Nevis and she would sail on the thirty first of March and this meant that Edison could be treading the shores of the land of his dreams before the end of July. He duly fished a handful of sovereigns from the velvet bag and booked his second-class passage to a new beginning.

The month of March passed slowly; for the first few days Edison hardly strayed from the small hotel in which he was staying for fear of being recognised. However, as the days turned into weeks, he grew in confidence; this was a bustling city and he was but a very small fish in a very large pond. He walked around the shops, ate in small eating houses and kept well away from the many public houses. Finally the month was ready to turn and it was time to leave British shores forever.

He arrived at the dockside early on the morning of departure, too early in fact as the ship was not due to start boarding for another hour. To pass the time Edison sat at a window table in a small dockside coffee house nestling beneath the sign; *Neptune's Cabin*.

"Can I join ye?" Edison looked up from his coffee to see a man struggling to balance his cup while wrestling with the straps of two large hold-alls, one on each arm.

"Yes, yes. Here let me help you with that." Taking the man's cup and placing it safely on the table Edison guessed rightly that his new companion was a seaman.

"Ah, English eh? I bet you're away out today?"

"Yes, Australia - on the Ben Nevis."

"Ye're goin' with the Loch Line then."

"That's the one, just waiting for her to start boarding."

"Ach, weel. I wish ye luck."

Something about the sailor's tone unsettled Edison.

"Why, is there a problem with the ship or something?"

"Nay, nay, a fine ship. It's just that some say she shouldna have carried her name, that's all."

He went on to inform Edison that there had been other ships named Ben Nevis but they had all suffered some misfortune or other.

"So ye see – there are people aroond here who say the name shouldna have been used . . . not so quick after the disaster, at any rate!"

This did nothing for the emigrant's nerves but little did he know that it was the habit of seamen to put the wind up landlubbers. Edison had absolutely no experience of the sea and any small knowledge of ships that he might have had been gleaned from the pages of his large travelogue collection. He took his leave of the jolly sailor and thought to himself that he was now in possession of facts that he would rather not have known.

The Ben Nevis made good progress and by the twenty third day of April was cutting through the seas of the South Atlantic. The weather had been predictable for the Atlantic crossing and storms tossed the ship for endless hours before leaving her to sail onwards in calmer periods.

The journey south had taken them to within a day's sail of Inaccessible Island but there was nothing on the horizon now but the edge of the heaving ocean. From the first day at sea many of the passengers and crew began to suffer from sea-sickness and Edison was thankful that he had escaped the dreadful affliction. As he leaned on the ship's rail a fellow passenger appeared at his side.

"Sea's not too bad today. Wunna want to be like them though."

The stranger turned his head in the direction of two rows of canvas chairs occupied by green-faced passengers, their blankets flapping wildly in the sea breeze.

Edison was startled from his thoughts and his knees almost buckled - this man spoke with exactly the same accent as Sarah! He gathered his composure and looked around at the stranger. He saw a man of around thirty whose coral-green eyes carried a weight of life far beyond his years. The pleasant features were marred only by a blue-black scar above his right eye.

"Yes," Edison looked back out to sea, "It's been a bit rough for us that aren't used to it. I've not been too bad though."

Curling wave-tops spattered a salty drizzle against the ship's hard metal bow and the rainbow droplets were thrown high over the ship to maintain the wet sheen of the maple decking. Edison turned his face into the ozone-laden breeze and breathed deeply. The shock of hearing the West Bromwich accent brought home to him the reason why he was here and, with an inward sigh of relief, he realised that nobody was going to stop him from achieving his dream now.

As the ship hissed through the foam it was followed by a school of joyful dolphins leaping through a miniature rainbow that flitted among the trailing spume - but the two strangers did not see them. They remained lost, each deep in his own thoughts.

Side-by-side, with gun-metal skies closing around them, they held fast to the rail as they rode the pitch and swell of the deck. The improbability of fate is one of the few certainties in life and the two lonely figures, adrift in a new world, would never forget this.

As Edison Nowell journeyed south towards a new life Eddie Pollard sat at the heavy, worn old kitchen table at Blacko Top Farm and stared into his rapidly cooling mug of tea. On the heavy stone mantelpiece, propped up by an old chipped Worcester vase, was the raffia Easter cross that Eddie's young niece had made for him in the previous year - he threw nothing away without very good reason and there was every possibility that the cross would be gathering dust this time next year. In a corner of the large room the single hand of an ancient grandfather clock showed the hours as the worn brass movement solemnly ticked away Eddie's day.

The last time that he had seen Edison had been the day that he had found him staring wistfully down the lane at Flax Moor Farm. When he had heard of Sarah Ann's tragic shooting Eddie had been deeply affected and now that he had learned that Sarah had died he could not concentrate, he was not sleeping and he snapped uncharacteristically at his farm hands for making the slightest of mistakes.

319

As he watched the last of the tendrils of steam escape from his tea Eddie's mind drifted back to a day over thirty years ago when he and Susannah Nowell had celebrated her twenty-first birthday in a momentary flurry of passion. When Susannah had found herself to be with child she reluctantly told Eddie of the fact but swore him to secrecy. Quite rightly she pointed out to him that if her father and brothers found out that he was to blame then the errant father would be forced to marry her or face the consequences – and she made no secret of the fact that Eddie was not on her list of possible husbands.

Susannah never asked for any quarter from Eddie following the birth of their child, in fact the only acknowledgement she ever made towards the father was in naming the child Edison. Eddie was not expected to be involved in the lad's upbringing, neither was he asked for maintenance, but as he watched the child grow up the pain that he felt in not being able to relate to the lad was at times almost unbearable.

Susannah had been Eddie's only consort with the opposite sex in the whole of his life and he was a lonely man; true, he had his farm and he had money but 'brass and land' cannot lead to true happiness without someone to share it with - and Eddie did, in truth, have someone to share his wealth with. But that someone was now heading rapidly to the opposite side of the globe, never to return.

And so Eddie sat and ruminated upon a fate that had, against all odds, seen him father a son only to have that son blocked from his life. Now, after watching the boy from a distance - after standing, half hidden, outside the church gates on the day that he was Christened, and again when he married Sarah, after more than thirty lonely years, Eddie knew that he would never have the chance to tell Edison the truth.

When Susannah had died it seemed like an opportunity for Eddie to approach Edison with the facts, to tell him that he did indeed have a father and that he would have the security of the farm for the rest of his life. Above that, Edison would have the love of the father that he had craved throughout his life; the nights that he had spent dreaming on the grassy banks of Old

Ebby's lake while his real father was living but yards away could be placed firmly in the past. As was the nature of these things, though, Eddie never actually plucked up the courage to approach his son – and he now regretted his failure with all his heart.

Eddie poured his cold, stewed tea down the stone sink and looked sadly out upon his domain. The farm bustled with animals and people but this brought little comfort to him as he wished with all his heart that things had turned out differently. If only Susannah had allowed the lad to know who his father was, even if only in later life, then Edison's life would almost certainly have followed a different track. There was every chance that he would not have taken the murderous route that he had; Sarah would still be alive and Connie would not be maimed for life.

As the ocean-bound Edison leaned against the rails of the ship and considered his future Eddie leaned against the front door of Top Farm and thought how Susannah's simple refusal to acknowledge the father of her child had brought havoc, destruction and heartache to so many people. Wearily, Eddie closed the heavy farmhouse door behind him and, in his loping fashion, trudged aimlessly across the farmyard to where the only living beings in this world that needed him awaited their evening milking.

# Epilogue

The extended Nowell family were devastated by the actions of their nephew and cousin. All Edison's uncles attended Sarah's funeral, along with many of their children, and the hearse was filled with their floral contributions.

Edison's step-father, alone once more following the death of his wife, Susannah, moved to Nelson where he lived out his life. He was one of the chief mourners at Sarah's funeral.

Joseph and Martha Atkins organised a number of concerts to raise money for the stricken Connie Nowell. At one of these the Reedyford Prize Choir performed to over four hundred people in the newly-opened hall of the Central Board School. In all, well over £100 was raised as a mark of the respect and sorrow felt towards Sarah and the Nowell sisters by their fellow villagers.

Connie slowly recovered from her wounds but would carry the mental and physical scars for the rest of her life. The healed tissue on her hands and arm could be covered by long sleeves and gloves but the operation to remove the bullet from her jaw had left a severe facial disfigurement.

Nobody in the village saw anything in Connie other than a brave person who had dealt with a situation that no young woman should ever have to endure. It is true that young children would point at Connie and ask their mothers why that lady had a funny mouth but they soon came to see past the surface to the stoical character beneath.

Understandably the Nowell girls did not wish to remain in the Dixon Street home that Sarah had hoped against hope would provide a new start for them all. Connie, Susannah and Margaret moved into number two May Street, just around the corner from Joseph Street. Brothers Percy and John moved from their Nelson home and joined their sisters. Connie never worked outside of the house again and her sisters carried on weaving at Lower Clough Mill.

The Nowell family purchased the grave plot in which Sarah was laid to rest, but the grave carries no memorial - no headstone now tells the living of the events of that fateful February evening in 1897.

In the spring of 1902 Margaret Nowell, the youngest of the three sisters, married a Barrowford joiner.

On the ninth of January, 1922, Susannah Nowell died, at the age of forty-one, and was interred along with Sarah. She was followed by Connie who died on the third of March, 1929, at the age of fifty-three.

And so, in a quiet corner of a country graveyard in the Pendle Forest, lie three women who paid the price for the insane jealousy of one man; they now stand silent witness to an increasingly violent situation of domestic violence that reached a tragic conclusion.


In the July of 1897 a whirlwind passed over Colne. Richard Storr, a farm worker at Alkincoats Farm, was one of a number of men making hay when the twister passed overhead. The wind sent the worker's caps toppling across the meadow and, as they ran for shelter, they saw their cut grass being whisked into the air and carried away. Some half-a-ton of hay was transported on the wind until it blew itself out over Barrowford.

Spring Hill was at the centre of the fall-out and, where the flying hay had been abandoned, the house had all the appearance of having been thatched. Bill Greaves rushed out of the neighbouring farm and began to rake the unexpected windfall into a stack; this was indeed manna from Heaven and he was not going to let it blow away again.

Next door at Spring Hill all was not well. James Atkins had not been himself for quite a while now; Sarah's death had affected him, as had the tragic death of young Manfred Halstead. The pressures of business played increasingly upon

James' mind and his depression deepened, as a result he had not slept for a full month and became increasingly despondent.

James and Martha were sleeping in separate rooms because of his severe insomnia and, on the morning of Monday the ninth of August 1897, just four months following Sarah's tragic demise, Martha went into James' room to open the curtains and greet her husband for the new day. The sight that met her eyes stunned Martha and she stood stock-still, shocked and disbelieving. James lay on the bed surrounded by pools of drying blood that had turned the crisp white bed sheets a dark crimson; unable to bear his dreadful depressive affliction any longer James had taken his razor and opened the main artery in his throat. At the age of fifty-three the man whose ministrations had brought comfort to so many had left his widow and six children to grieve their tragic loss.

The streets of Barrowford no longer echo to the clip-clop of the mill worker's clogs. At the time of writing the last of the village weaving sheds is in the process of weaving-out to be replaced by a supermarket and this will be the final sweep of change to overtake a village whose very soul has been nurtured by the clatter of weaving looms for over two full centuries.

Dixon Street is still a quiet street but the open fields around have been built over. Spring Hill remains very much the same as when the Atkins family lived within its solid stone walls, only the name has changed. The farm next door is no longer a working farm but old William Greaves' descendants still cling on to the old ways elsewhere within the village.

The town of Nelson never did annex its little brother of Barrowford although they are both now an integral part of the larger Borough of Pendle.

The Higherford Methodist church building that Sarah was so proud to attend, and in which James Atkins was so happy to preach, has been replaced by a modern building. In the later twentieth century the building was dismantled brick-by-brick and transported to Japan. The church now stands in a foreign city where no one cares to listen to the hymns and prayers of a Lancashire village as they echo still within its stone walls.

And what of Edison Nowell?

The reports of his whereabouts on the day following the shooting are quite clear. However, the evidence begins to cloud from the point of his buying an express train ticket at Hellifield Station. Some reports say that the fugitive caught the train to Carlisle while others state that the ticket was never handed in at any onward station and was, therefore, never used.

There is no hard evidence to show that Edison Nowell ever left the shores of Britain; he certainly would not have used his own name when registering with an outbound ship. However, the fact that he was obsessed with the New World, especially Australia, would suggest that emigration would be his intention. If he had indeed used his ticket to Carlisle then it would be a simple matter for him to take the connecting train to Glasgow where a great number of vessels plied their trade with the southern hemisphere.

Neither would it have been a difficult matter for him to have taken a ship out of Liverpool or London. As a matter of interest, a ship by the name of the 'Austral' left London for Australia in the autumn of 1897 and one of her passengers was registered as Mr Tom Nowell. He was exactly the same age as Edison Nowell and carried the name of his deceased uncle. This is food for thought but is offered as nothing other than an illustration of the possibilities open to a fugitive with money in his pocket.

It is also possible that Nowell made a new life for himself much closer to home as his skills as a clothlooker would stand him in good stead in any district of textile production. Certainly, the cities of Leeds, Bradford and Halifax were no more than a one-hour journey from his last known sighting at Hellifield.

With a pocket full of gold sovereigns Nowell could easily have rented a house, or at least a room, and taken work in any one of the cities in Britain where textiles were woven. Given the massive turnover of immigrants and emigrants within these districts he could have settled chameleon-like into a new life with little fear of detection.

Some twenty years after his disappearance Edison Nowell's family applied for him to be officially recognised as deceased in order for his properties to be sold. The judge refused this request on the grounds that Nowell, if he were still alive, had every reason not to make himself known.

The fugitive was never seen or heard of in Barrowford again; but there is always the question, given his predilection for disguise, did a red-whiskered, slouching figure ever again tread the streets of his native village? Did he ever return, perhaps many years later, to stand and stare at his marital home - the scene of his dreadful actions - and feel at least a twinge of remorse?

*Photograph from around 1894: Nowell (left) with friends*

*Sarah Ann Nowell; a sketch from 1897*